D1546721

The
Secret Life
of Insects

The Secret Life of Insects

P. Passarin d'Entrèves
and M. Zunino

CHARTWELL BOOKS INC.

8314

This book is based on the television series *Les insects, un monde étrange et méconnu,* produced by Gérald Calderon. Jean-Marie Baufle of the Natural History Museum, Paris, was director of photography.

The photographs used in the book were either specially taken by Claude Huyghens or appeared in the television films, with the exception of those on the following pages: 52 W. A. Sands; 216, 235, 287 C. Bevilacqua; 218 S. Lombardi; 227, 269, 279 I. Bucciarelli; 237, 239 IGDA Archive; 240, 245 D. Giussani; 330, 332 Centre for Overseas Pest Research, London.
Drawings by Studio Due Punti and Ottavio Cencig.

Translation by AGET (language services) Ltd.

The authors wish to thank the following for their help: the Natural History Museum (Paris) and Professor Balachowsky; the Station of Zoology and Biological Control (Antibes); Professor Jourdheuil (Mali); the Bee and Social Insects Research Station (Bures sur Yvettes), Professor Lecomte and Messrs Louveaux, Pouvreau and Theurkauff; the Ecological Laboratory (Mount Ventoux) and Mr Demolin; and the Orsay Faculty of Sciences and Mr Lespinasse.

Title page: Fighting stag beetles (Björn-Eyvird Swahn/Naturfotograferna)

Endpapers: Worker bees and queen (Colin G. Butler/Bruce Coleman Limited)

Contents

Introduction

The word 'insect' tends to conjure up a rather unpleasant image of a creature that either creeps, bites or stings or is undesirable in some other way—and this is in spite of the beauty of butterflies and the usefulness of bees. To an entomologist, however, this attitude is incomprehensible. After all, there are at present more than 800,000 known kinds of insects, which is about three-quarters of all known species in the animal kingdom. When all species are found, the final total may well be doubled. This means that most animals are in fact insects. The majority of this vast horde live their own lives in their own way, not impinging upon man in the very least. One of the functions of this book, therefore, is to cast a ray of light on a somewhat unknown way of life.

Insects are a highly successful form of life, as their numbers demonstrate. One of the reasons for this is their great adaptability. They are to be found in every kind of land and freshwater habitat from polar regions to the Equator. They feed on all sorts of plants, on other insects and on decomposing animal and plant remains. The numbers of individuals, as well as of species, is also immense. For example, there may be 50,000 bees in a hive, whilst a swarm of locusts may contain 40,000 million individuals, covering hundreds of square miles, weighing perhaps 70,000 tons and eating twice as much food in a day as the population of Greater London or New York City.

Being so numerous, insects frequently come into conflict with other animals, and to us this is important when they eat crops or carry disease from person to person. Chapters are devoted to these aspects of insect life and also to another fascinating subject, that of 'biological control'. By this is meant pitting one insect against another by encouraging the natural enemies of a pest species. The natural enemies of insects do include birds and other vertebrates but their main enemies are undoubtedly other insects, for there are not only many predatory species but also the so-called parasitic ones. Females of the latter lay eggs in or on the bodies of other insects, generally choosing the larvae. Their own larva hatches and feeds on the tissues of the host larva eventually killing it.

Aquatic life is another important aspect. Most people will have seen water insects at some time or other, be they water beetles that spend most of their life beneath the surface of ponds, or dragonflies and others that only spend their larval or nymphal stages in the water. These make a good introductory study to insect life. When insects took to water as a home various obstacles had to be overcome, one being air supply. Some of the ways in which these difficulties are surmounted are demonstrated in the photographs, which are an impressive feature of this book.

A final topic that must be touched upon is the coloration of insects. Here we are confronted by an extraordinary display of camouflage on the one hand, with creatures melting into their surroundings, and on the other a confusing array of seemingly similar forms which on close examination are seen to be simply mimicking each other for protection. This phenomenon, though found in other animals, is particularly prevalent in insects.

All in all, the study of insects is one of the most rewarding in natural history and one that can be carried out very easily in a confined area. It is to be hoped that many people's interest in the subject will be stimulated by this book.

Paul Freeman,
Keeper of Entomology,
British Museum (Natural History)

Pond life

A pond, by definition, is a body of water that is limited in area and depth, factors which favour the multiplication of water plants, which may be confined to the edges of the pond but which also often tend to spread more or less evenly over its whole surface. This environment may, at first glance, appear to be poor in animal life, but in fact it is extremely rich, both in numbers of animal species and in individual animals. Even leaving aside the more conspicuous forms of animal life such as amphibians, reptiles and fish, the pond generally harbours endless small or middle-sized organisms, which are active both by day and night. Among insects, which are the main concern here, important groups include the Coleoptera, Odonata, Ephemeroptera, Hemiptera, Trichoptera and Diptera. The members of this last group—at least in point of numbers—are true masters of the pond.

Water beetles

Two groups of water beetles are particularly well known: the dytiscids and the hydrophilids. The commonest dytiscid, *Dytiscus marginalis*, is an elegant insect that may attain a length of 3.5 centimetres (1.37 inches). It has a black body with a yellow border to the pronotum (the rear of the thorax) and the elytra (hardened fore-

Left: A tree-frog and a damselfly on the same stem. Before reaching their adult form, both these creatures spend a considerable time as wholly aquatic larvae

wings that cover the membranous hind wings). In this species, the sexes can be distinguished by the front legs. In the male, the front tarsi show widening of the first three segments and the edges of these are lined with a thick set of bristles, while the under side bears a large number of hairs, the ends of which then widen to form a funnel. This whole arrangement (which is absent in the female) functions as an adhesive pad, and among other things is used by the male for holding on to the back of his mate during copulation. In addition, the male elytra differ from that of the female, being smooth while, on the other hand, the female's are heavily grooved.

The hind legs of both sexes are equipped with long dense hairs, which make dytiscids excellent swimmers. They are very agile in water, but are able to leave it for long periods and even to fly long distances. When in the water, the dytiscid breathes with the aid of a unique mechanism. It carries a bubble of air imprisoned between the elytra and its back, in the region of the spiracles or openings of the tracheae (the tubes that convey air to the interior of the insect's body). When the oxygen in the air-bubble is exhausted, the beetle must come up for more air; at such times it is capable of breathing atmospheric air directly.

After mating, the female will lay her eggs individually in the stalks of water plants. The larvae, which are long and also tapered in shape, are relentless predators, no less ferocious than the adults. They will attack any water creature that is not too large—adult insects and insect larvae, crustaceans, amphibians such as salamanders, newts or young frogs, and even fish.

The mouth parts of the larva are of the piercing and sucking type, and the large mandibles have a hollow channel along their whole length. A unique feature is that the mouth is closed in front and open only at the sides, where it communicates with the channels in the mandibles when these have pierced the insect's prey. As soon as the victim is grasped by the dytiscid's mandibles, it is paralysed by a poisonous liquid. At the same time, the dytiscid injects it with a secretion rich in digestive enzymes, which dissolve the victim's tissues, turning them into a mushy fluid that can be absorbed through the mandibular channels. Before long the dytiscid will have sucked out all the digestible matter in its prey, which it then abandons as an empty husk. When dytiscid larvae have grown to maturity and are ready for metamorphosis,

they leave the water and dig themselves a chamber by the waterside, where they then undergo their transformation.

The largest member of the Hydrophilidae family is *Hydrous piceus*—shiny, pitch-black and a giant among water beetles, at times reaching a length of 5 centimetres (almost 2 inches). Unlike the dytiscids, only the larval form of the hydrophilids is carnivorous. The adults live mainly on plants, though they will not disdain the occasional dead or wounded small animal.

Left: In ponds such as this, the large and voracious Great Diving water beetle Dytiscus (above) swims with its powerful hind legs and feeds on other smaller water creatures, including small fish and tadpoles

Hydrophilids both swim and walk on the bottom of the pond, on plants and other underwater objects, and come up more or less regularly for air. They breathe through the covering of the thorax, which is constantly in contact with the layer of air that is held in place partly by the elytra and partly by the unwettable hairs on their ventral surface. Every so often, an insect that has exhausted its oxygen supplies will surface to refill its remarkable 'tanks'.

In spring, the fertilized female lays her eggs in a sort of foamy cocoon, known as the oötheca—a very conspicuous floating object. The oötheca of a hydrophilid is shaped like a flattened sac, about 2 centimetres (0.75 inches) in diameter and straw-coloured. One end sweeps upward in a long curve and is pointed. The way the female makes this cocoon has been described by A. E. Brehm, and his account cannot be bettered.

'When the insect is ready to lay its eggs, it stretches out on its back on the surface of

Above: Different kinds of water beetles. Top left: The female of the common Great Diving water beetle, *Dytiscus marginalis.* Centre: The male of *Dytiscus latissimus* moves by means of its powerful, fringed swimming legs. Above left: The Great Silver beetle, *Hydrous piceus.* Above right: A larva of Dytiscus captures a tadpole

Below: Aquatic larvae of Diptera float at the surface of the water Right: A friendly-looking frog perhaps, but a carnivorous monster as far as tiny pond-dwellers are concerned

the water, underneath a floating leaf of some water plant, which it presses against its abdomen with its front legs. Out of four tubes—two long and two short—that project from its abdomen, it extrudes a series of whitish threads, and with the end of its tail it weaves these together by waving the tail ceaselessly from side to side, so as to cover the whole of the abdomen. The female insect then turns over and makes a second covering, joined to the first along its edges. By this means, the abdomen is enclosed in a pouch that is open at the front and which is filled with long strings of eggs arranged neatly in parallel lines. When the eggs are mature, the tail end of the abdomen is pushed out of the sac. When the right time comes, the insect grasps the mouth of the sac with its hind legs, and adds further threads to it, gradually narrowing the opening and thickening its edges. Then it stretches a number of threads across the opening and closes it with a sort of lid, which is finished off with a point. Threads

Above: A dragonfly and a damselfly (right) execute skilful and delicate landings on twigs. These insects, which date back some 250 million years, combine both advanced and primitive structural features. Their visual powers, for instance, are better than those of any other insect

Below: A dragonfly of the species *Anax imperator* (left) fights a member of a different species

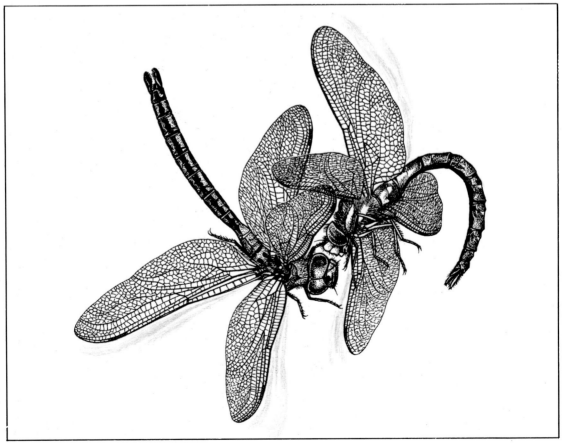

run from the base to the tip and back again, each longer than the last, and the point gradually becomes sharper and slightly curved, like a horn. In four or five hours, the bag is ready, incorporating all the improvements suggested by long experience; and off it floats over the water, among the water plants, like an odd-shaped boat. If a sudden wave submerges it, it immediately reappears on the surface, pointed end first, obeying the law of gravity, since the eggs are in the rear part while the front is full of air. These oval-shaped cocoons are sometimes distorted in shape by bits of vegetable matter that stick to them.'

Hydrophilid larvae, like those of the dytiscids, are carnivorous; they feed on insects, crustaceans and small gastropods, crushing these creatures' shells with their powerful jaws. Because of the way they eat, they do not have an inner channel in their jaws as the dytiscids do. Hydrophilids can open their mouths in front to take in the food that has been finely chopped by their mandibles, and have no need of liquefying it first like the dytiscids. When hydrophilid larvae reach maturity, they leave the pond

Left: The elegant form of a damselfly, which is similar to a dragonfly but smaller
Above: The aquatic nymph of a damselfly (right) has three gills at the tail end. Before mating, the male grips the female by the neck (left). The couple remain in this position for a long time, even during egg-laying which may take place under water
Below: *Aeshna cyanea* prepares to leave its nymphal skin. The wing rudiments can be seen

and dig themselves a cell in the damp earth of the bank, and here they pupate.

Observation of the surface of a pond in the heat of the day may well reveal some tiny shining insects, alone or more usually in groups, whose swimming movements take the form of broad gyrations. These insects are a type of water beetle, commonly called whirligig beetles, whose Latin name, *Gyrinus*, is derived from the way they move. This type of movement is brought about by their hind legs, which are flattened like paddles and also edged with bristles. If a stone is thrown into a pond, the whirligig beetles will quickly dive for the bottom, but they reappear just as quickly on the surface. As they dive, they take a supply of air with them under their elytra. If one of these beetles wants to stay on the bottom, it is obliged to hold on to some underwater object with its legs; and when it wants to surface, it merely has to let go.

Adult whirligig beetles or gyrinids are carnivorous, attacking any convenient prey, especially weak or wounded small creatures. They do not scorn dead meat; indeed, according to some naturalists, they actually prefer it. When food is scarce, they may also attack and eat one another.

The females lay their eggs on underwater plants or stones, sticking them in place with a viscous secretion. The larvae are as carnivorous as the adults. They have hollow jaws like dytiscid larvae, and similarly digest their prey outside their own bodies, draining the liquid nourishment into their mouths through the channels in their jaws. When mature, the larvae leave the water and construct a cocoon either on the earth or on a water plant, using some sand or earth, tiny shells, fragments of wood and leaves, seeds and similar items. The shape of the cocoon, however, varies from species to species.

The graceful dragonfly

The dragonfly, a member of the order Odonata, is beyond doubt the queen of all water insects. The largest species may have a wingspan of some 20 centimetres (7.85 inches); they are a marvellous sight as they dart hither and thither over the smooth surface of the water. But what can be observed and admired today is nothing to what a human being might have seen millions of years ago when huge dragonflies flew as modern species do now. These insects have existed since the Carboniferous Age, about 300 million years ago, and at that time were represented by species of enormous size, like the famous Meganeura, which had a wingspan of 65 centimetres (more than 25 inches).

Dragonflies of whatever kind, can be recognized by their elongated bodies, great protuberant eyes, and two pairs of well-developed wings. The eyes are their chief organs of sense, allowing them to perceive shapes up to 5 or 6 metres (16 or 19 feet) away and movement up to 15 or 20 metres (50 or 65 feet). Their wings are elongated and are held firm by five principal veins which are joined together by a maze of secondary veins. Some species have transparent, colourless wings; others have brilliantly coloured ones—blue, green, purple or bronze. Not only the dragonflies' wings, but their bodies, too, may be brightly coloured, and often there is variation in colour between the sexes. The males are generally more vivid in colour than the females. For example, the male of the species *Agrion virgo* is blue with a metallic sheen on his wings, while the female is green with dull brown wings. In another species of the same genus, the male is violet while the female is greenish-bronze. Besides this variation between the sexes, which is not at all uncommon among insects, there is the more unusual phenomenon of variation among females only. In some species, the males are of a single colour, while the females have two different colorations. The more widespread of these two types of coloration is described as 'normal' and the other as 'aberrant'. In *Ischnura elegans*, for instance, the normal females are marked with blue patches, as are the males, while the aberrant females have patches of orange. In another species of the same genus, the normal female is bronze and blue while the aberrant is orange and black.

It is rare to see a dragonfly motionless for more than a few seconds at a time. The flight of these marvellous insects is quick, light and varied. They are capable of hovering motionless in the air, climbing, diving, swerving to right or left, and moving forward or backward. They are capable of covering distances of hundreds of kilometres or miles at speed in order to reach a favourable environment. However, they are highly active only in warm temperatures and sunlight.

Dragonflies are essentially carnivorous insects, and they never stop hunting for food. They prey on all kinds of insects, and as soon as they catch a victim with their legs, they devour it, crushing it to pulp or chopping it to pieces with their jaws.

An extraordinary feature of dragonfly life is their sexual behaviour and the events

Above: Dragonfly nymphs of the family Aeshnidae are voracious creatures. They are armed with a death-dealing weapon that they carry folded away below the head, like a flick-knife blade. They lie in wait in the tangle of weeds on the bottom, ready to leap into attack and tear their prey apart with their powerful, pincer-like jaws. The red Chironomus fly larva (left) will find it difficult to escape if attacked

19

that lead up to copulation. The male's copulatory organs are not situated close to the genital opening, which is at the hind end of the body, but at the level of the second abdominal segment, near the thorax. They consist of a penis and a sac for holding sperm. Before or during mating, the male bends his long, flexible abdomen, so as to bring the genital opening into contact with the copulatory organs, and transfers a supply of sperm to them.

Copulation sometimes occurs in flight. The male takes hold of a female and grips her with his legs, as if catching her for food. He then also grasps her with a pincer-like organ at the very end of his abdomen, made of two movable jointed structures known as 'cerci'. Often a lengthy period elapses before the female completes the sexual act by bending her own abdomen downward and forward in a circle so as to bring her genital opening into contact with the male's copulatory organ. The spermatozoa are thus introduced into the female's genital passages. When the sexual act is completed—usually after approximately 15 minutes—the two insects separate and go their own ways.

As soon as she has been fertilized, the female seeks a suitable place to lay her eggs, either on the water's edge or in the water itself. Those species that have tough ovipositors lay their eggs either singly or in small batches in the leaves of water plants, or the stems of irises, rushes or reeds. Other species merely drop their eggs into the water or on to water plants.

The dragonfly larva that emerges from the egg is a small creature equipped with legs, eyes and extremely tough jaws, which enable it to hunt for the most varied kinds of prey in the water. For capturing their prey these predacious larvae use a sort of jointed chin, known as a 'mask'. This is actually the labium or lower lip, the final two segments of which are elongated and bear a pincer-like structure at the end. The labium is folded under the head when not in use, but when used for capturing prey, it is thrust forward. This simple and perfect mechanism enables the dragonfly larvae to capture small crustaceans, insect larvae, tadpoles and even small fish. They catch hold of their prey with their mask, and chew it to pieces with their mandibles.

Dragonfly larvae breathe by means of gills, but these are situated in an unusual place—the last segment of the alimentary canal (that is, in the rectum). The rectum is lined on the inside with circular ridges and projections, and the tracheae branch and divide among them. When a dragonfly larva breathes, it dilates the rectum and draws in water through the anus. Then the rectum contracts and the water is expelled, a process that ensures a continuous supply of oxygenated water to the rectum. In addition, in some species at least, this expulsion of water from the anus provides the larva with a type of 'jet propulsion'. The larval stage among dragonflies lasts several years, and the final metamorphosis, preceding the appearance of the adult, takes place on the stem of a water plant or on land, away from the watery environment that has been the insect's home for so long.

Less well known than the dragonflies, partly because they are small and inconspicuous, are the mayflies or Ephemeroptera, so called because of the shortness of their adult life. Most of their life is spent in the larval stage, in the water. The larvae, mainly herbivores or scavengers, have mouth parts of the chewing type. On their heads are antennae and eyes. Characteristic features of the abdomen are the three long, slender tails, which are also found in the adult insect. Some larvae spend their lives in underground tunnels that they dig in the slimy bed of the pond, using their jaws as a hoe and raking through the earth with their front legs. Others swim freely in the water, sometimes at great speed. Species that are found in rivers and streams are not often seen in ponds. Living where currents are sometimes quite strong, they move by crawling over the river-bed, clinging on to it so strongly that it may require a knife-blade to detach them from a stone or some other underwater object.

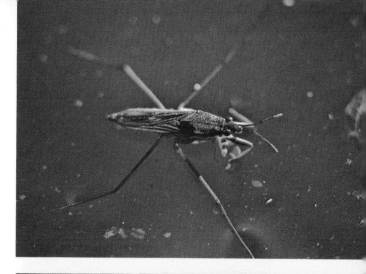

After two or three years in the pond, mayfly larvae come to the surface to complete their final metamorphosis. This takes place during the hottest months of the year, and at this time millions of adult insects take wing and invade nearby houses, particularly at night when they are lit up. Mating takes place during swarming, when the males fly in a 'dancing' swarm which attracts the females, and this is the adult insect's only important act before dying. (The adults are not even able to feed, since their mouth parts are closed and unusable.) And so these graceful little creatures take to the air for just an instant of their lives—all that nature allows them in order to reproduce, to enable each species to carry on its existence in pond or stream.

Water-scorpions

The order Hemiptera contains species with very specialized piercing and sucking mouth parts. Typical aquatic species one might expect to find in a pond include the back-swimmer Notonecta, the water-scorpions Nepa and Ranatra, and the water-striders of the family Gerridae.

Back-swimmers may grow to a length of 16 millimetres (0.62 inches). Their elliptical bodies have a convex back, and unlike other insects, they swim upside down. They can swim very fast, using their long, flattened hind legs, edged with long bristles, as 'oars'. When seen on the surface of the water, back-swimmers appear to be silver in colour. This is because the body, practically waterproof, is covered with water-repellent hairs which maintain a layer of air of varying thickness around it. This layer reflects the rays of light and gives the insects their silvery sheen.

Back-swimmers often leave the water

Right: The top and bottom two photographs show pond-skaters (Gerridae), which move in a rowing-type action over the water. *Ranatra linearis* (second from top) is a stick-like water-scorpion that lives under water, periodically replacing its supply of air through a tube or siphon at the end of its body

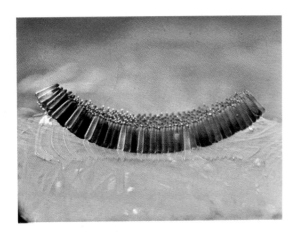

Above: A 'raft' of eggs of the mosquito
Culex pipiens
Below: A microscopic view of the segments
of a larva
Centre top: Mosquito larvae hang from the
water's surface. They feed by continuously
filtering the water that is wafted towards the
mouth by the 'feeding brushes' beside it.
Centre bottom: After four moults the larvae
become pupae. These are also lighter than
water and float gently just below the surface
Far right top and bottom: The mosquito pupa
is completely transparent, and the wings of
the future adult can already be seen

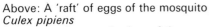

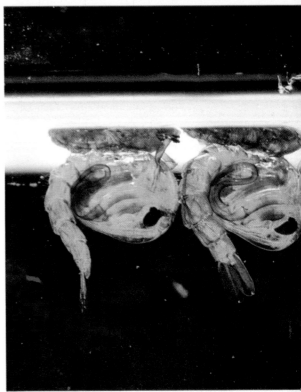

Overleaf: The most critical moment in the
life of a mosquito occurs as the winged adult
emerges from the pupa. During this process,
performed very slowly, almost laboriously,
the insect is practically defenceless

during the hours of darkness and move from one pond to another in search of new homes. They are essentially carnivorous creatures, living on any kind of animal that is not too large. They will take small vertebrates, for instance, such as amphibian larvae and young fish fry, and because of this fondness for fish they sometimes constitute a pest.

The Nepidae or water-scorpion family include the genera Nepa and Ranatra. Water-scorpions are characterized by their raptorial (snatching) front legs, and by the fact that their abdomen ends in two segments which vary in length between species and lie against one another to form a breathing tube. The front legs are formed, like those of the Praying Mantis, from two segments that can be raised or lowered like the blade of a penknife. The breathing tube supplies the insects with air on their regular visits to the surface.

Unlike the back-swimmers, water-scorpions do not move over the surface of the water, nor are they agile swimmers. Their legs are particularly suited to walking over the mud, debris and plants at the bottom of the pond. Although they are able to swim up to the surface, they prefer to climb the stems of underwater plants.

The genus Nepa may exceed 20 millimetres (0.78 inches) in length. Like Ranatra, they are known as water-scorpions because of their broad and flattened shape, their front legs and their breathing tubes— these last two features resembling the scorpion's claws and tail. Nepa species are carnivorous, and will lie motionless for hours waiting for a victim to pass by within reach of their rapacious claws. They live on insects, crustaceans and small aquatic vertebrates such as tadpoles and young fish fry.

The females lay their eggs in heaps of decomposing plant matter, or insert them into the stems of live plants. The larvae, like the adults, are poor swimmers. Moreover, they lack the breathing tube at the end of the abdomen. They get their oxygen supply by periodically coming up to the surface and imprisoning air among the water-repellent hairs on the underside of their bodies. The genus Ranatra is quite different from Nepa in appearance. The body is long and delicate, almost cylindrical, and equipped with a very long, slender breathing tube. Its way of life, however, is practically identical to that of Nepa.

Insects that walk on water
The family Gerridae contains species of insects that can move over the surface of the water with great agility, like expert skaters. They are able to do this because of the water-resistant hairs that cover the ends of their legs and the underside of their bodies. The surface of the water is 'indented' by the leg segments as they rest on it, but surface tension prevents the insect from drowning and enables it to skate around at great speed and even to make leaps of considerable distance—up to 60 centimetres (almost 2 feet). Gerrids (or water-striders) have long, mobile legs, and usually live in large groups in areas of the pond that are particularly rich in plant life.

Water-striders are carnivorous, living mainly on insects, live or dead. They are also not averse to eating small molluscs. They take their prey with their front legs and immobilize it by injecting a poison. Then they suck out all the nutrients with their piercing and sucking mouth parts.

Water-striders lay their eggs in groups on water plants or other floating objects, to which the eggs will adhere because of a sticky liquid in which they are enclosed. As the larvae emerge from the eggs, they make their way to the surface of the water and then take up their parents' way of life.

The family Hydrometridae (water-measurers or marsh-treaders) includes the genus Hydrometra, which is Greek for 'water measurer'. These insects have long, thin bodies, with very long and slender legs. They like quiet ponds with lush, overgrown banks. Like water-striders, they move on the surface of the water, but more slowly, and they, too, live on dead or dying small creatures.

Underwater net-fishers

Still, quiet pond waters harbour another group of insects that are well known to fishermen, who prize the larvae as bait. These are the caddisflies, whose scientific name is Trichoptera—a term derived from the hair that covers the wings of the adults.

Many caddisfly larvae live in cases which they build themselves by sticking together various materials with a thick network of silken strands. They are equipped with silk-glands, just like silkworms. Pond-living species mainly use scraps of wood and leaves; those that live in rivers and fast-running streams make their cases with tiny pebbles, grains of sand and minute snail-shells in order to make the case heavy enough to cling to the river-bed. The case is generally wider at the front than the back. This comes about because, as the larva grows, it does not build itself a new case but expands the existing one. The larva holds on to its case with two little hooks, which are modified bristles, located at the hind end of its body. When it wants to move about, it will protrude the front of its body from the case and then go forward on its agile legs, dragging its 'house' behind.

Some forms of Trichoptera that live in streams do not build cases, but have quite a different mechanism for catching the animals on which they prey. They construct traps for this purpose which are master-pieces of ingenuity even for the amazing insect world. Some make funnel-shaped nets out of silk, attaching these to under-water plants or stones. The larva then lies in wait at the far end of the net. The slightest current will carry minute water creatures such as crustaceans, larvae and insects into the net where they are immediately seized.

In some species, these nets are astonishingly specialized and form perfect animal traps. This type of net is typically found in fast-running streams. It is formed from a funnel-shaped antechamber, the mouth of which faces upstream. This part is woven, not out of widely spaced silk threads but from a thick layer of silk reinforced by a tough frame around the edge. To one side

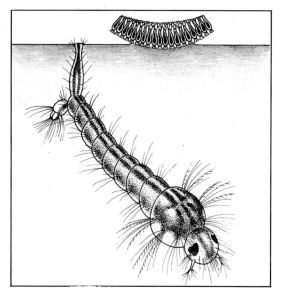

Above: Unlike Anopheles, which lies horizontally below the surface of the water, Culex larvae hang downwards. They breathe through a respiratory siphon or breathing tube situated at the tip of the abdomen. An egg-raft is shown on the surface

of the antechamber, and downstream from the violent current that swirls into it, is placed a wide-meshed net, behind which the larva lies in wait for its victims that are carried towards it in a never-ending stream.

When the caddisfly larva reaches maturity, it shuts itself into its case or spins a cocoon amongst stones and then transforms into an adult. Once it reaches this stage, it lives only long enough to mate and reproduce itself.

Mosquitoes

At sunset on a fine summer's evening, the edge of a pond is a place best avoided. An idle bystander may resist the onslaughts of mosquitoes for a minute or two, but eventually he will be forced to yield to these insects, which hold undisputed sway over such areas all night long. They are Diptera of the suborder Nematocera and the family Culicidae; one of the commonest species is *Culex pipiens*, an insect that feeds mainly on birds. Mosquitoes are far too well-known for a description of their naked-eye appearance to be necessary, but their microscopic features are certainly worth description.

The moderately well-developed head bears a pair of clearly visible compound eyes, and a pair of antennae which are of different shapes in the two sexes. The male's antennae are covered with groups of hairs, much longer and more numerous than those of the female. Both sexes have piercing and sucking mouth parts, composed of a suction canal and a number of stylets, which have the function of piercing the vegetable or animal organisms they feed upon. The males live on plant juices, sugary saps and liquids arising from decomposition. The females, in contrast, require a meal of vertebrate blood before they can bring their eggs to maturity. It is therefore the females that constitute a nuisance to humans.

A mosquito bite generally causes only slight irritation, but some people may react more dramatically, particularly if they have multiple bites, and may suffer skin eruptions with widespread reddening, and sometimes nausea, vomiting and abdominal pain. Why these violent reactions occur is still not clear, but the most probable cause is the saliva injected by the insect while biting.

Mating among mosquitoes is preceded by a nuptial dance by the males, who use this display to attract members of the opposite sex. After mating, which takes place only once in a mosquito's life, the female lays her eggs. She takes up a position on a plant or a floating object in such a way that she can remain dry while holding the rear of her abdomen under water. The elliptical eggs float in the water and stick together with their tacky surfaces so that they come to form a sort of raft. One raft might consist of 200 to 300 eggs. Considering the number of eggs present in a raft, and the fact that they can develop into sexually mature adults in a few weeks, it is easy to see how vast numbers of mosquitoes arise in swarms that can rapidly take over areas of land where stagnant water is plentiful.

As it emerges from the egg, the larva is tiny—scarcely 1 millimetre (0.03 inches) long—and legless like all dipterous larvae. It is equipped with a sideways-mounted breathing tube, which is brought to the surface of the water to take up oxygen. These larvae are capable of rapid movement, and although they normally stay at the surface in order to breathe, the slightest movement sends them diving for the bottom. They live on microscopic plankton-like organisms, particles of vegetable and animal matter, and apparently also on dissolved organic and inorganic matter.

These larvae have to undergo three moults before reaching maturity. Three times in succession their cuticle splits open, releasing each time a larger creature than its predecessor. A fourth moult produces the pupa which is an extraordinarily shaped creature. The head and thorax appear swollen; the abdomen is sharply curved, giving the whole creature the shape of a question mark; the breathing tube is replaced by two structures nearer the head and which fulfil the same function. The pupae are very active: they do not eat, but require much more oxygen than the larvae and therefore remain suspended from the water's surface with their breathing tubes constantly in contact with the atmosphere. The pupal stage does not last long. After three or four days, pupae change into adults which usually emerge at dusk or after nightfall and most frequently on the surface of the water, so that they can leave the pupal skin without becoming wet.

The carrier of malaria

Not many years ago, the stagnant waters of Italy harboured not only the common (culicine) mosquito but also another member of the Diptera, the anopheline mosquito, which has been responsible for millions of human deaths—for Anopheles is the mosquito that carried (and, in some areas, still does carry) the organism responsible for malaria.

There are a number of marked differences between the common and anopheline mosquitoes, though they might appear similar on superficial inspection. The main points of difference are the shape of the larvae and the resting position of the adults. When the common mosquito larva comes to the surface, it lies obliquely, owing to the fact that its breathing tube is at an angle to its body. But anopheline larvae, because they lack a breathing tube, lie parallel to the surface of the water. In the resting position, the common adult mosquito holds its body more or less parallel to the surface on which it is standing, while Anopheles tilts its body with its rear end raised. In addition, anopheline mosquitoes lay their eggs singly, not in rafts. These eggs give rise to larvae that live on minute water creatures and particles of suspended matter.

Among Anopheles, too, it is only the adult female which feeds on blood; in doing so, she transmits the organism that

Top: The adult mosquito has cast off its larval skin, and gradually its various parts dry out and become firmer
Above: A man-biting species procures an abundant supply of fresh food

causes malaria and is a member of the genus Plasmodium. When the adult female bites, she injects these parasites into the victim's bloodstream in the form known as 'sporozoites' (long, thin cells). These first head toward the cells lining the liver or other internal organs where they then reproduce to form 'daughter cells' which enter red blood corpuscles and start to grow again. At this stage they are known as 'trophozoites'. When they have completed their period of growth, they divide, leave the red blood cells and invade others, where they resume asexual reproduction. Throughout this process the parasites all divide and migrate to new blood cells at about the same time. The waste products that enter the bloodstream when the infected red blood cells burst open cause the periodic bouts of fever that are typical of malaria.

At a certain stage of the parasite's life cycle in its human host, a number of parasites transform themselves into sexual forms, which are then sucked up by a mosquito during a 'blood meal' and reach the insect's stomach. Here, after undergoing further changes, the sexual forms fuse together and give rise to a type of capsule known as an 'oöcyst'. Within the oöcyst, several thousand new organisms, known as 'sporozoites', take shape and migrate throughout the insect's body by way of its blood. Most of them reach the salivary glands, ready to be injected into another human victim.

Malaria has had terrible consequences for mankind, carrying off millions of dead and causing severe economic damage. The presence of Anopheles has led to the depopulation of vast territories and prevented the colonization of others. In many parts of the world the disease has been banished by various means: drainage of marshes, the use of insecticides, and the introduction of organisms such as Gambusia (a small South American fish) into infested waters, where they feed on Anopheles larvae. Nevertheless, there still remain enormous areas of land where malaria is endemic.

Besides Anopheles, another mosquito has earned notoriety for causing human disease. This is the genus Aedes, of which the species *Aedes aegypti* transmits yellow fever, an infectious and contagious disease that is endemic in tropical regions of America. Caused by a virus that the mosquito injects into its victim, yellow fever usually runs a rapid course. The onset is marked by shivering and fever, pains in various areas but particularly the back, headache and extreme congestion of the skin and mucous membranes. Although occasionally a patient may survive, overcoming the crisis quite rapidly, death at an early stage is much more usual.

The termite colony

Termites are land-dwelling insects that generally lack wings and eyes. They live in colonies, which may reach a considerable size, within nests that are generally dug out of the soil. Their common name of termites is derived from the Latin *tarmes*, a word that was used in ancient times to indicate any small creature, such as termites, woodworm beetles, the larvae of many kinds of small butterflies, and other creatures that bored holes in various materials, especially dead wood.

Today, the name 'termite' is applied to a well-defined group of insects, comprising more than 2,000 known species (though experts calculate that the number of still undiscovered species must amount to at least three times this figure). Termites form an order of their own—the Isoptera. This particular grouping is considered far closer to cockroaches and mantises than to the ants, although they have been often confused with ants in the past, and in many languages their common name is indeed 'white ants'.

Termites are found all round the world, but chiefly in the tropics: in Africa, South and East Asia, Australia and throughout the American continent, except for Canada. Though they are lovers of warm climates, some species have moved to cooler latitudes or altitudes. Southern Europe, for instance, including Italy, has

two species of termite, though they are not particularly striking members of the order. An instance of how termite species can abandon tropical climes and penetrate into cold mountain regions is afforded by some American species that have been discovered in the Rocky Mountains, where they have adapted to conditions at an altitude of more than 2,000 metres (6,550 feet).

The resemblance to ants

On first consideration, there appears to be many points of similarity between ants and termites, quite enough to have led early naturalists astray, since they had neither present-day optical equipment—microscopes and the like—nor the modern systematic criteria of classification. Both termites and ants behave as social insects. They live in communities, often very large ones, within which they show a more or less marked tendency to divide among themselves the tasks to be done. Both groups tend to live in nests which may be large or small, depending on the degree of evolution of the species inhabiting them, and they are built by the community itself. In both groups, again, most members of a community are incapable of reproduction, though they cannot properly be considered asexual since they are equipped with reproductive organs, but these may not be fully developed and the insects are therefore sterile. In the general management of the community, such insects provide food,

Left: Hectic activity in a termite nest that has been recently opened

build and repair nests, care for the young, and carry out specific functions— but never that of reproduction, which is reserved for individuals known as 'kings' and 'queens' (the 'reproductives'), the only sexually mature and active members.

Despite all these formal points of resemblance, it is generally recognized that the Isoptera come from a totally different stock than the order Hymenoptera, which includes the ants. The termites' long evolutionary history (some of their fossils date back to the Oligocene, others to the Eocene and others again to the Miocene periods, that is, some 50 million years ago) has led to a type of organization and a pattern of behaviour that bears a marked resemblance to that of the ants, though the two groups have developed quite independently. This is an example of what is known as 'convergent evolution'. Another example of the phenomenon would be the way in which fish on the one hand, and mammals such as the dolphin and the whale on the other, although belonging to groups which are taxonomically remote from one another,

Above: An impressive nest of
Bellicositermes bellicosus
Below: A large hole has been made in the side of this nest to examine the internal structure

have both colonized the same environments and adopted similar solutions to their environmental problems. Their final forms are therefore similar both in appearance and in behaviour.

Close examination shows the termites to be easily distinguishable from ants, even on a few external features. Their body covering is colourless, which makes most termites look white. They have no eyes, while ants have well-developed ones; and whereas ants have a thorax that is sharply divided from the abdomen by a narrow feature known as the 'petiole' (present in all Hymenoptera), the Isoptera lack this feature. Furthermore, ants belong to the higher insects and undergo a complete transformation, with a number of larval stages leading to an immobile pupal stage, followed by the emergence of an adult which is very different in appearance from the preceding stages. This type of development is not found in the Isoptera.

The termite community

As already noted, a termite community usually comprises a couple of fertile members, the reproductives, and in most cases a very large number of sterile individuals, workers and soldiers, as well as all the insects undergoing development. In the so-called lower insects, these immature individuals cannot be strictly defined as larvae or pupae, and are known as nymphs.

The adults are subdivided into types or 'castes' according to their functions in the general running of the community, and different castes will vary markedly both in appearance and development. The queen is usually the only fertile female in the community. She will have given birth to every member of it, continually supplying it with new members. Striking features of the queen include her extraordinary size, and

Top right: Following damage to the nest, Cubitermes soldiers and workers transport nymphs to safety deep inside
Centre right: A worker grooms a soldier
Bottom right: Two workers exchange food

Top: The presence of wing rudiments on the nymph in the foreground indicates that it belongs to the fertile caste, unlike the nymph on the left which is wingless. The large head of a soldier guarding an entrance to the nest may also be seen
Above: A group of asexual nymphs

Right: The castes of the Natal termite *Bellicositermes natalensis.* The tiny nymphs (bottom left) give rise, after five stages of development, to winged individuals which go on to swarm, lose their wings and mate. The sterile caste of large workers is derived, after two intermediate stages, from asexual male nymphs. The somewhat smaller asexual females may give rise to small workers, which can undergo a further transformation into large soldiers, or to small soldiers (far right)

especially her enormously developed abdomen.

In adult insects, the front part of the body is the only part that bears legs. The gross disproportion between this part and the enormous abdomen of the queen renders her incapable of doing anything on her own, except laying eggs. Indeed, she is always surrounded by a nucleus of workers who feed her, watched over by a number of soldier guards, with a liquid they secrete themselves. They also clean her, frequently move her, and carry away the eggs she continually produces.

The king, the only fertile male in the community, always lives at the queen's side. He can be distinguished from her at a glance by his size, for though he is generally larger than the workers and soldiers, he is always considerably smaller than the queen. His head and thorax may be more or less as big as hers, but his abdomen is normal in size or at most slightly enlarged; his abdomen is never as great as hers.

Members of the sterile caste

Apart from the immature insects, the rest of the colony's population is made up of the sterile caste. Its members are permanently wingless and completely blind. (The reproductives, by contrast, have more or less rudimentary eyes and also develop wings when it is time to swarm, though these break off immediately after the nuptial flight.)

The sterile caste consists of at least one type of worker, and in almost all species at least one type of soldier as well. Unlike the ants and the bees—that is, the social Hymenoptera, among whom the sterile caste consists entirely of females—the sterile termite caste consists of both males and females. As a result the Isoptera reproduce in all cases through fertilization—unlike the Hymenoptera, whose eggs that are to develop into females (workers or queens) are fertilized, while those that are to develop into males are unfertilized.

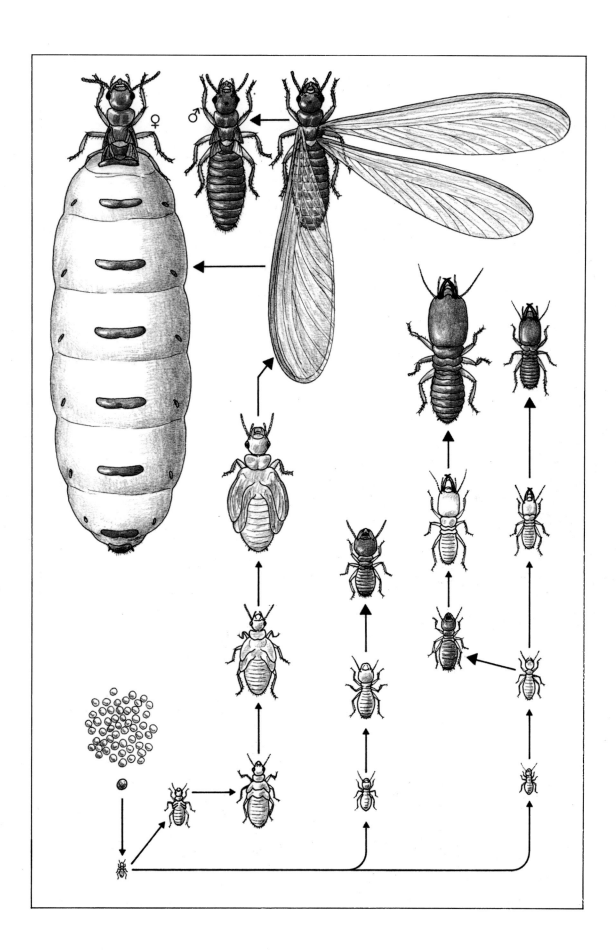

The members of the sterile caste of termites do possess sexual organs, but these show an arrested state of development. From this point of view, therefore, they are immature. Their development has taken an 'abnormal' course—different, that is, from the 'normal' (or rather 'complete') development that leads to the formation of kings and queens.

The workers can be considered as the least specialized members of the community, since they may carry out any number of functions such as the care of the young, from egg to independent adult life; the care and mouth-to-mouth feeding of both reproductives and soldiers; and the building and maintenance of the nest. Even among the workers, however, there is frequently sub-division of labour, often accompanied by differences in outer appearance. Many species have at least two classes of workers, 'large workers' and 'small workers', which are distinguished from one another both by their size and by a number of detailed features, particularly the mouth parts and the limbs, which are adapted for different functions in the two classes.

The soldiers' job is to defend not only the king and queen but also the food stocks, the nest itself—especially its entrances—and the columns of workers proceeding to or from the sources of food. Soldiers are usually larger than workers, and are immediately recognizable by their exceptionally large heads. These are also much darker than the rest of their bodies, because of their thicker and harder covering layer. The well-developed head generally goes with enormously powerful jaw muscles, though this is not always the case. The soldiers' jaws, much larger than those of the workers, are formidable weapons—indeed, the only weapons that termites have, for, unlike the Hymenoptera, they do not have a poisonous sting. Some species of termites, particularly in Malaysia, have soldiers whose jaws are asymmetrically developed. The right jaw is short and straight while the left is longer, bent in the

Above and right: Close-ups of a soldier. Note the strong jaws and the antennae

Top left: The king termite (Cubitermes species) shows the various parts of the body fairly equally developed. By comparison, the head of the soldier is disproportionately large
Centre left: When a nest is broken open, the workers hurry to repair the damage
Left: A soldier on guard at a breach in the nest senses danger and assumes a threatening posture with jaws outstretched

Left: When danger threatens, every termite runs to his post in a perfectly organized distribution of labour. This worker carries a nymph to safety

Top right: Two nests of Cubitermes from Africa show the sloping cap-like roof which lets water run off in heavy rainfall
Bottom right: Detail of the structure of a nest wall

middle and straight again at its tip. The soldiers' jaws close with a snap, and are so sharp that the insect can literally chop an intruding enemy into pieces.

The most curious soldiers of all, however, are the so-called 'nasuti' who have given their name to a subfamily, the Nasutitermitinae. The nasuti are practically jawless, and their head is pear-shaped, prolonged at the front and downwards into a long conical protuberance. This protuberance—the 'snout' or 'nose' that gives them their name—is merely a modification of the front of the head. At its tip is the opening of a duct that leads from a special gland known as the frontal gland. This gland is extremely well-developed in the nasuti, occupying most of the head and responsible for its large size. It secretes a sticky liquid that the nasuti can squirt out of the tip of their snout for quite a distance in the direction of attackers (generally ants) in order to envelop them in a glue-like substance and render them unable to move. Evolution has thus conferred on the nasuti an original type of weapon, quite unlike the jaws of ordinary termite soldiers. Another difference between the nasuti and other soldiers is their size. The nasuti are much smaller than the soldiers armed with jaws, but as defenders of their community they are every bit as effective since they are far more numerous.

All soldiers of whatever type share one common feature, however. They do not feed themselves, but are fed mouth-to-mouth by the workers, who give them regurgitated food. It is not that the soldiers are unable to feed themselves: they simply do not know how to do so, even though their mouth parts are theoretically capable of taking food independently.

The termite nest

A large proportion of all termites inhabit the subsoil, though some groups populate the most varied environments. All species, however, live in communities with the type of organization already described. No solitary species are known. Apart from the few termite species that make use of nests made by insects of another species, termites live in communal nests that they build themselves. These nests vary greatly in size and shape and material between different species. Some rather primitive species merely have a more or less complex labyrinth of tunnels hollowed out of dead wood by the workers. This is the case with the termite *Calotermes flavicollis*, which is widespread in Italy and other Mediterranean countries. It often sets up house in the beams of old dwellings and completely guts them from inside, without showing any outward sign of depredation until too late. A higher level of complication, perfection, and therefore of evolution too, is

seen in another species, *Reticulitermes luci-fugus*, which is also found in Italy, southern France and other Mediterranean regions. Like the preceding species, it builds its nest in dead trees or structural wood, but it is able to divide up its tunnels with walls made of chewed wood and excrement, all cemented together with secretions of saliva.

There is also a group of termites of the genus Anoplotermes, among whom there are no soldiers. They live in South America and build their nests underground, extending them above the surface of the soil into tower-like structures made of earth. The African members of the same genus also build the main part of their nest underground. In addition, however, they build an open-air annexe to the main nest—a sort of pouch made of compacted earth, about the size of a large apple, which hangs on a bush over the nest. This is where the young kings and queens gather to wait for the moment when they will leave the colony to found new ones elsewhere.

Another group of termites build their nests out of material like cardboard. These

Right, top left: A Eutermes nest with its sloping roof. Top right: *Bellicositermes bellicosus* nest. Centre right: The spherical subterranean nest of Apicotermes. Bottom right: Diagram of a typical termite nest. It is constructed of dense and tough material, which is pierced by ventilating tunnels. This structure serves to protect the royal chamber, which lies in its depths. Underground tunnels, and occasionally tunnels on the surface, lead to distant food reserves such as dead trees

Below: On the exposed surface of the opened nest, workers attend to their tasks, soldiers keep watch and nymphs seek shelter

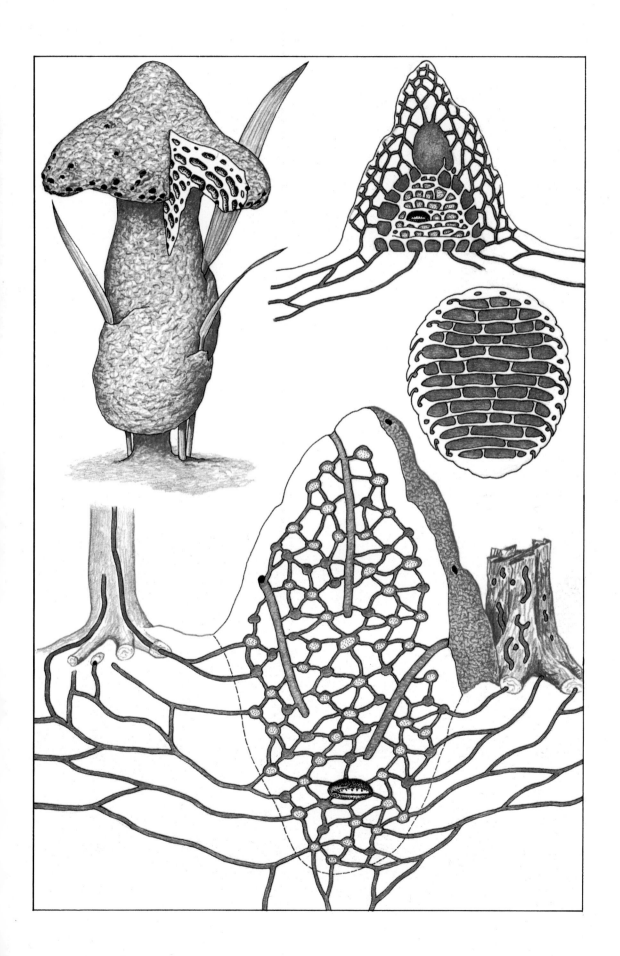

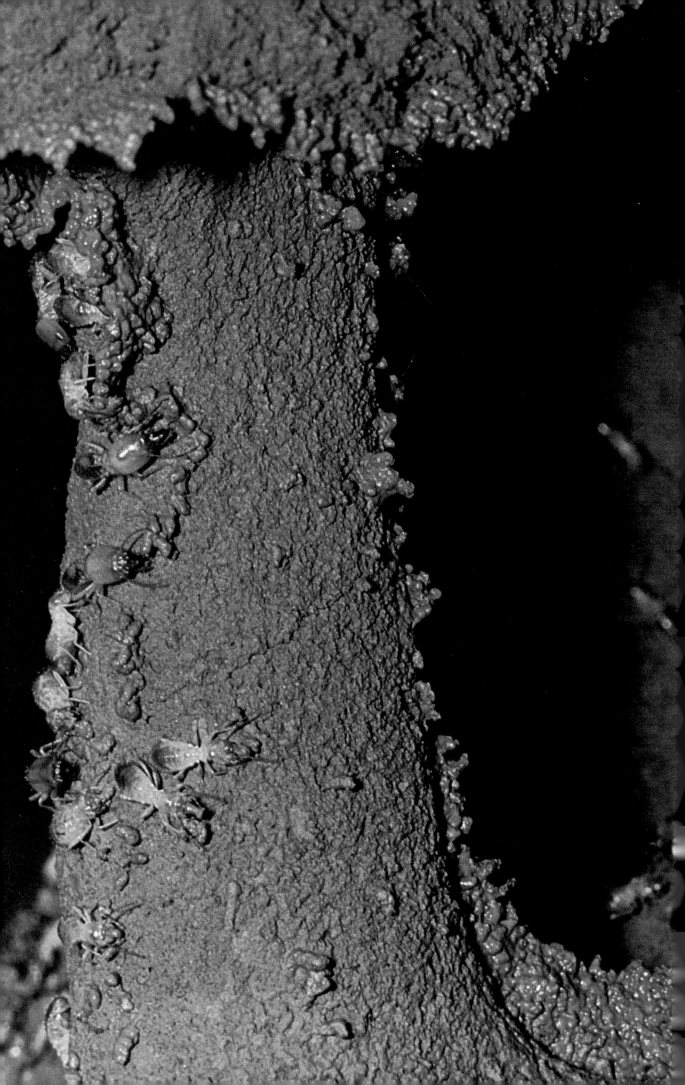

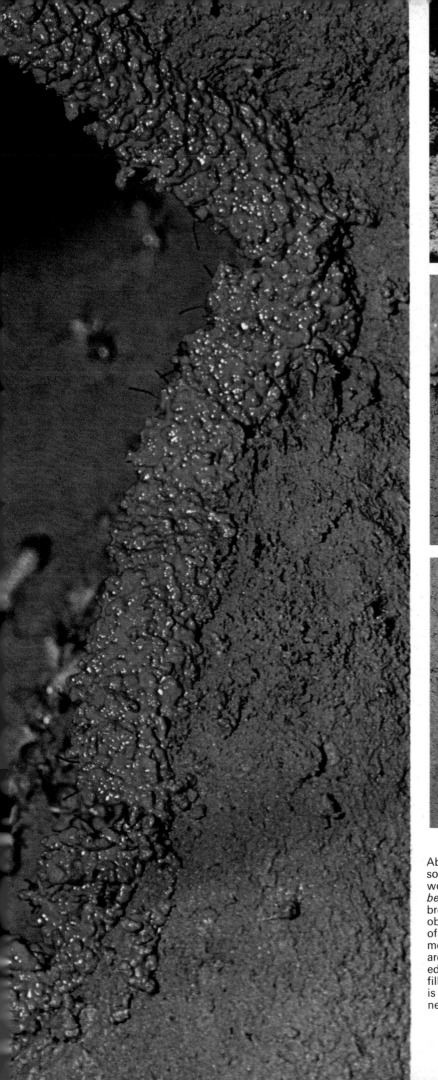

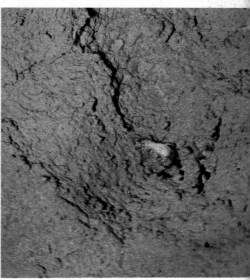

Above and left: While
soldiers keep watch, the
workers of a *Bellicositermes
bellicosus* nest repair the
breach made by a human
observer. Some prepare lumps
of earth or wood-dust
moistened with saliva which
are then cemented to the
edges of the hole until it is
filled. After the breach
is repaired, the life of the
nest returns to normal

termites chop up dead wood with their jaws and cement it with saliva until it turns into smooth wood-paste, which dries in the air and comes to look exactly like cardboard. They build round or oval nests either underground or in the open air, where they hang on the branches of trees.

One Australian species of termite, known as the 'compass termite', builds a very curious nest. It is pyramid-shaped, with a long, thin triangular base, and reaches a height of up to 3.6 metres (12 feet) above ground. The nest is made of soil and bits of wood, and the long axis of its base invariably lies in a north–south direction— hence the insect's popular name.

Another group of termites builds its nests, largely above ground, out of clay. The inside of the nest is on a number of levels, and the workers connect these levels together with complicated systems of sloping ramps, sometimes arranged in a spiral—exactly like a spiral staircase, but without steps.

Some termites living in the African rain forests have found clever solutions to the problem of rain and of the water that runs down the tree-trunks to which the nest is attached. The part of the bark that lies just above the nest is covered with a herring-bone pattern of leaves that deflects the water to either side of the nest.

The structure of the nest

So far, we have been looking in a general way at the different appearances of termite nests, depending on the species that builds them and the type of climate. Far more interesting, however, is the internal organization of a nest. P. P. Grassé, one of the greatest living experts on termites, claims that they never live in contact with the open air. They require a closed environment in which the air is always still and has a high humidity, where light cannot penetrate, and where there is a high concentration of carbon dioxide. This sort of microclimate can only be maintained inside the nest, and often the workers are able to help to maintain it by, for instance, wetting parts of the nest with their saliva, which then evaporates and humidifies the air.

The nest and its various annexes form a closed environment, insulated from the outside world. Those species that do not use tunnels to reach their sources of food, but have workers go in and out through openings in the nest, take care to seal up these openings the moment they are no longer in use.

The system of tunnels and interconnecting chambers in a termite nest can be inspected by removing the outside wall, or part of it. In certain large African termite species, such as *Bellicositermes natalensis*, this is made of a fairly compact surface layer that may be more than 40 centimetres (16 inches) thick. The raw material used here as in the remainder of the nest (in both its buried and raised portions) is composed of firmly packed grains of sand, which the workers bring up from the subsoil, carefully cleaning them and cementing them together with salivary secretions and excrement. This material hardens quite quickly when exposed to the air, and becomes almost as hard as stone, so that the great African termites' nests, some of which are over 5.5 metres (18 feet) high, can stand up unharmed to the fall of a large tree or a stampeding herd of buffalo. But they can sometimes cause men a great deal of trouble. In Katanga, Zaire, dynamite had to be used to clear the path for a railway under construction after bulldozers had failed to shift the termites' nests that lay in the way.

Within the outer wall, there often lies a system of tunnels known as the 'exoecia', which open to the outside world but not to the inhabited areas of the nest. The exoecia can therefore be regarded as a structure external to the nest proper. Not all species

Top left: The workers arrange little balls of chewed wood mixed with saliva, like bricklayers laying bricks, to build the walls of their home
Left: Close-up of a wall built in this way

build them. The term 'endoecia' refers to the inner complex of inhabited chambers, including the reproductives' cell where the young are reared, the spacious storehouses in which many species store their food reserves, and frequently the special rooms in which certain species of fungus are cultivated.

Also in communication with the endoecia is the network of tunnels known as the 'perioecia'. This term applies to the system of passages hollowed out of the ground or in dead wood and spreading out from the base of the nest, which enables the workers to go further afield, often for quite a distance from the nest in all directions, in order to search for food, without coming out into the open. It is rare for a termite species to have workers who venture out into unprotected areas of their own accord. A further part of this system is found in the artificial tunnels which start from the body of the nest and run over the surface of the soil, and sometimes ascend the trunks of nearby trees, in order to connect the endoecia with the sources of food. This sub-division into exoecia, endoecia and

perioecia is not a universal feature of all termite species but it is seen in its fully developed form only in the most highly evolved groups.

How termites feed

The food of most known termite species is of vegetable origin, and particularly dead wood. Some groups, on the other hand, while still vegetarian, do not feed on wood, but on leaves—rotten or fresh—or plant secretions or other matter. Other groups, again, have ceased to be vegetarian and eat a wide variety of substances. This is seen in the very well-known Australian species *Mastotermes darwinensis*, which can eat all kinds of human foodstuffs, as well as skins and textiles, and is even able to wreak havoc with the telephone system by destroying part of the lead-lined protective covering of telephone cables.

Most commonly, however, the termites' diet consists of wood in some form or other, more or less decomposed but in any case dead. The actual wood is eaten only by the workers, and they then see to the

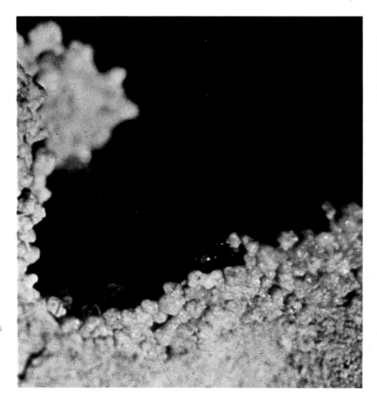

Left: The pattern of constructing a termite nest seems haphazard, but in fact the heaps of earth pellets held together by saliva are combined to form columns and other structures typical of the species

Right: The distinctively shaped fungus gardens within the nest play an important part in the nourishment of termites by breaking down the indigestible wood and making it available as curious small white spheres to form part of the food of workers and nymphs

feeding of the other members of the community. This may take place in a number of ways. The simplest is for the worker merely to pass on his food to another individual without processing it in any way. Often, however, the workers actually swallow the food. It is then partly broken down in the digestive tract and turned into an opalescent liquid containing only minute fragments of vegetable matter. This is then distributed to other members of the community by the process of oral regurgitation (or, more accurately, 'stomodaeal regurgitation', since the first segment of an insect's digestive tract is known as the 'stomodaeum'). There are in fact two quite distinct kinds of stomodaeal feeding. While the food often consists of predigested matter, there are also many groups of termites whose young, reproductives and occasionally even soldiers, are fed exclusively on the salivary secretions of the workers.

This kind of food exchange, in which all the termites in the nest take part, also enables the substances known as 'pheromones' to circulate throughout the community. These complex substances, whose functions are not yet fully understood, have been described as 'ecto-hormones' or 'social hormones'. They act in the context of the community in the same way that hormones act within the body of the creature that secretes them. From this point of view (and not this point of view alone), the termite community can be regarded as a 'social organism'. Just as the individual body cells of one of the higher animals are incapable of independent life if they are removed from its body, so too, an individual termite, if removed from the society to which it naturally belongs, would be unable to survive.

This explains why pheromones are described as social hormones, since they are responsible for the passage of all kinds of information within the community, and for the harmonious regulation of its activities. Even the fate of new-born termites, destined to grow into workers or soldiers or reproductives, is decided by reference to the community's needs, and the decision is arrived at largely through the direct or indirect action of pheromones.

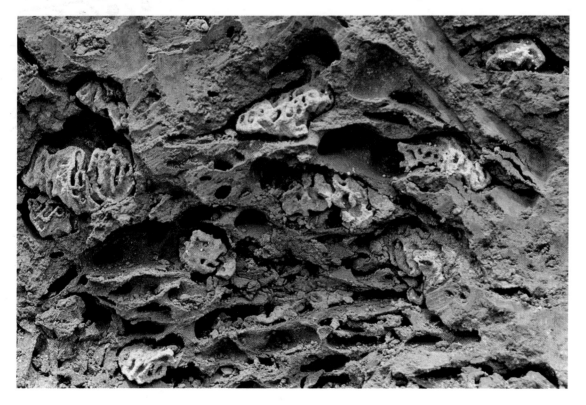

Above: One of the spongy masses within which termites of the species *Macrotermes subhyalinus* cultivate fungi

Left: A cross-section of one of these masses showing its internal structure. It is made of chewed wood, on which the fungus Termitomyces is easily grown

Although the vast majority of termites are wood-eaters, their digestive enzymes are not capable of breaking down the main component of their food, namely cellulose. In order to be absorbed, this has to be split into smaller molecules (sugars). Very many groups of termites have overcome this difficulty by adopting a similar system to that found in certain cockroaches: a system that represents an astonishing feat of evolutionary adaptation. The first stage in the breakdown of the cellulose molecules is carried out by microbes that live in the termite's alimentary canal. These permanent guests, which live in a state of complete mutual dependence with their termite hosts, are protozoa belonging to the flagellate group known as Hypermastiginae. They are single-celled organisms equipped with a very large number of movable whip-like appendages called 'flagella'; and (perhaps with the help of bacteria) they bring about the first stage in the digestion of cellulose, converting it into simpler molecules that the termite can absorb.

The degree of co-operation between these very different organisms is extremely close. The termite gives its protozoa an environment with ideal conditions of temperature and humidity and a permanent and effortless supply of food, and in return the protozoa enable the termite to digest a food that it would otherwise be unable to use. The termite groups that have adopted this system of symbiosis invariably have the protozoa in their gut, the organisms being transmitted from one termite generation to the next through secretions from the alimentary canal that are fed to young termites by the workers.

The importance of the symbiotic protozoa to their hosts has been demonstrated experimentally. Special techniques exist by which termites can be deprived of their resident protozoa without physical harm. It turns out that when they are removed the termites soon die, in spite of taking their normal dietary requirement of wood. If, however, they are fed with a solution of sugars such as are normally obtained by protozoal digestion of the wood they eat, then they survive and do very well.

Some groups of termites prefer to feed not merely on dead wood, but on wood in a more or less advanced stage of decomposition. The process of decomposition, which takes place particularly rapidly in tropical climates, is due to fungi and bacteria, and these termites take in woody material which has already been made digestible. They also ingest a considerable quantity of fungal material. It appears that this latter component of their diet supplies them with their vitamin requirements. A similar phenomenon is seen in those termite species that specialize in feeding on humus—the dark brown earth that is particularly abundant in undergrowth, and is produced by bacterial and fungal disintegration of wood, leaves and any other vegetable matter that falls to the ground.

Fungus gardens

The highest degree of adaptation to this sort of feeding habit is seen in the fungus-cultivating termites of the group Macrotermitinae. When the earliest naturalists, towards the end of the eighteenth century, looked inside the great termites' nests of Africa, they were struck not only by the queen's enormous size and the large numbers and varied appearance of the insect population, but also by some curious brown or brownish-yellow structures, spongy in appearance and consistency, housed in special chambers and emitting a characteristic fungus-like smell. Much later it was shown that these strange hoards were 'fungus gardens', made up of lumps of woody matter which the workers chew to the consistency of a fine wood paste and form into round balls. These are then joined together into bunches which may reach a considerable size, sometimes as big as a melon. The sponge-like structures provide a very favourable environment for the growth of certain species of fungi, some of which, such as the genus Termitomyces

51

Left: Although termites are threatened by bats, nightjars, pangolins and toads, their worst foes are undoubtedly ants. *Megaponera foetens* are shown taking captive termites back to their nest

(a member of the family Agaricaceae, like the common field mushroom), have never been found in any other environment.

The fine fungal threads or filaments that botanists call the 'mycelium' form a dense network throughout the whole spongy lump, and cover it with a velvety surface. Sometimes the mycelium bears fruiting bodies—like the caps of mushrooms and toadstools—which penetrate through the outer wall of the nest and sprout on its surface. The termites cultivate these fungi with extreme care. Their importance, however, is not so much as a food in themselves (the termites seem to eat a negligible amount of fungus, and in practice could only be getting their requirement of vitamins from this source) but as a means of breaking down the cellulose in the fungus beds on which they grow, thus making it digestible for these termites which lack symbiotic protozoa in their gut.

Enemies of termites

Although, in general, termites have little to do with the outside world, nonetheless

Above and right: Scenes in a battle between *Megaponera foetens* and termite soldiers. The blind termites are rarely a match for the ants, which have jaws that are both sharp and strong

(and despite the fact that most termites' nests are veritable fortresses) they have many enemies. Some mammals such as the aardvark (chiefly found in southern Africa) have made termites into their staple diet. The aardvark has powerful digging feet, strong claws, and is capable of breaching the outer wall of a termite nest. It can then slide its long tongue into the endoccia and wreak havoc among the workers, being completely impervious to attack by the soldiers. Certain ant-eaters do much the same, and so do some pangolins—strange mammals with bodies covered by horny scales. In the swarming season, when the young winged males and females leave the nest and pair off before founding new colonies, they fall victims by the hundred to the ready beaks of insectivorous birds such as the nightjar, or to the many species of bats that attack them at dusk. When they land, many more are taken by reptiles or amphibians such as the African regular toad, *Bufo regularis*.

But the termites' most formidable enemies are other social insects: the terrible army ants and the chirping ants. The former name is given to a large number of ant species, particularly of the subfamily Dorylinae, and the latter to some species of the subfamily Ponerinae and particularly to *Megaponera foetens*. Both are groups of social Hymenoptera that live a nomadic life without a permanent nest. The army ants move in family units of up to 1,500,000 individuals and at a speed of some 20 metres (65 feet) an hour, destroying whatever they meet and putting even large animals to flight. Even man himself is hard put to avoid being overrun.

Not surprisingly, therefore, termites suffer heavily if a horde of these ants passes by. The ants attack the upper parts of the

Above: Shrieking ants attack a termite colony while a single, large-headed soldier termite stands guard

termites' nest, where the building material has not had time to dry completely, and they almost always succeed in penetrating into the endoecia. The workers at the heart of the nest hurriedly erect barriers to protect at least the royal cell and some of the chambers where the nymphs are reared, while the main body of workers and soldiers occupies the outer tunnels and attempts to stem the invading tide. The ants, with their perfectly functioning eyes and greater agility, generally come off best, and the battle ends in wholesale slaughter. The corpses of the dead termites are carried off in hundreds and eaten by the victorious ants. It is unusual for a termite colony to be annihilated by invading ants, however. It may be greatly reduced in size, but once the danger is past the surviving members of the community can generally muster their strength and repair the damage to the nest. The queen then calmly starts laying eggs again, and before long the community is prospering as it did before.

Queen
of the termites

In proportion to their size, the termites build larger structures than any other living being; in this respect they leave even the human race far behind. The biggest nests are found mainly in Africa and the largest size is considered to be about 9 metres (30 feet) in height and more than 18 metres (60 feet) in diameter. The most astonishing fact of all, in this context, is that apart from the mature egg-laying queens, termites are generally less than 1 centimetre (0.39 inches) long.

The termites' cathedral-like nest has a number of functions, which can be summarized under three main headings: it affords protection of the chamber inhabited by the founding king and queen; acts as a refuge and defence for the colony itself; and is an efficient sun-screen, preventing the sun's rays from penetrating and from upsetting the activities of the workers. Neither the structural materials nor the shape of the nest are characteristic for any individual group of termites. The outer walls of every nest are not only an impressive piece of architecture: they also represent a highly homogeneous and very tough structure. These fortress walls are practically indestructible by outside forces, and even with the most modern techniques it is quite difficult to find a way into the nest.

Left: Termites show a highly developed pattern of social behaviour. A soldier is groomed by workers (top) while the queen is attended by workers and soldiers (bottom)

Exploring the nest

In order to learn all there is to know about a termites' nest, in all its parts without damaging the inner chambers, it is essential to work with extreme delicacy and care, doing everything possible to preserve the dense maze of tunnels and passageways throughout the structure. When it is not considered important to preserve the part of the nest above ground level, however, dynamite may be used in small amounts to open a nest.

But the best simple approach is to use large two-handed saws, various types of axe, chisels and tools of a similar kind. While working on the nest the investigator will be opposed by the frenzied efforts of the workers, who throng to the unexpected breach and do what they can to repair it. The soldiers, too, are alerted by a special alarm signal and rush to the place where the wall has been damaged, prepared to repulse the enemy's attack.

Immediately within the walls of the nest is an environment where the proper degree of warmth and humidity, essential for the colony's survival, can be easily maintained. Termites' nests do not have ventilation systems such as are found in bees' or wasps' nests. Instead, gas exchanges take place by diffusion through the walls of the nest; and the termites achieve control of humidity by wetting the walls of the nest with saliva. They get water by digging down deep into the subsoil, often as far as the water-table.

Penetrating deeper into the nest, after

removing part of it and most of the fungus crop—real gardens, full of valuable reserves of food—the investigator reaches the royal apartment. As already noted, this is the original chamber round which the whole nest was built; it is instructive to see the extent to which the whole life of the community revolves around this chamber.

The royal apartment

The most interesting feature of a termites' nest, for those who wish to penetrate its secrets, is the royal apartment. This is a sort of home within a home, inhabited by the king and queen, the workers responsible for cleaning and feeding the queen, and the soldiers responsible for defending the royal couple. Among the more highly evolved termites, the royal apartment is provided with openings that are too small for the reproductives to pass through, while the walls of the chamber are often extremely thick. In the course of its development, the

Right: The compact walls of a termite nest (top) serve as a 'fortress' for the defence of the royal chamber (bottom) in which the queen lives

Below: A naturalist opens a termite nest in order to extract the royal chamber

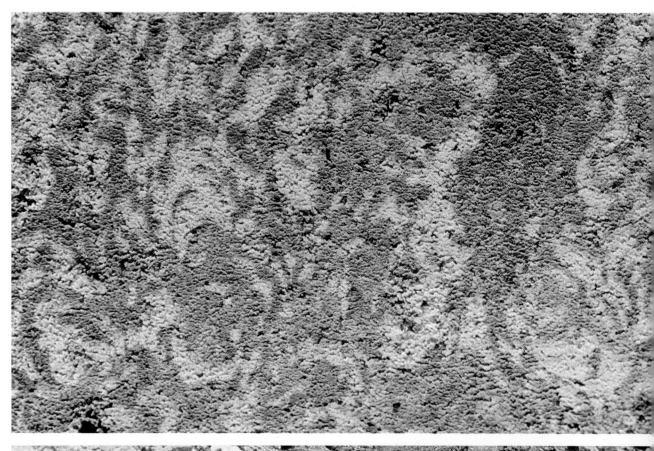

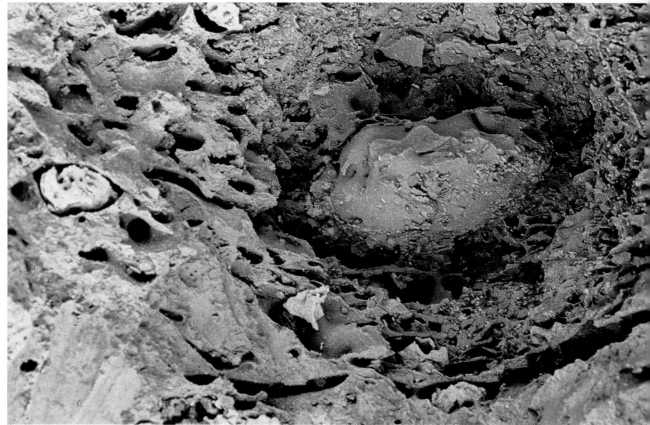

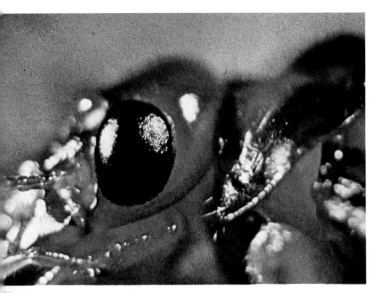

Above and top: Close-ups of the queen's head. All termites of the sterile caste are blind; only the reproductives possess eyes. Living in total darkness, these insects obey highly developed social instincts which govern the provision of food, cleanliness and defence, particularly where the queen is concerned. The queen herself acts as an enormous egg-factory to guarantee the colony's future

queen's abdomen grows to a monstrous size, and the royal apartment may be too small to hold her and her court. If this happens, the workers will enlarge the cell until the queen can rest comfortably within it. Indeed, cases have been observed where, in the interests of safety or following irreparable damage to the old royal apartment, the workers have actually built a new chamber elsewhere, and then carried their queen bodily into her new home.

The reproductives do not always have an apartment to themselves. Among termites at a lower stage of evolution, the females are smaller and more active, and in these cases, the reproductives may be found in one of the recesses of the nest, depending on the season. Sometimes the royal couple are even to be found in a fungus garden, specially converted into a 'bridal suite'. After her nuptial flight with the king, the queen will begin the task of founding a new colony.

How the queen lives

The queen has a tougher body-covering than the workers, she is dark in colour and, unlike the workers, has a normal pair of compound eyes. In addition, to begin with, she is equipped with two pairs of wings, which are large and membraneous. The base of the wing, almost at the point where it arises from the thorax, is marked by a fracture line, and the wings break off here after the nuptial flight. At rest, the wings are held horizontally along the abdomen, overlapping to such an extent that only one of the front pair is visible.

The queens possess fully-developed and functional gonads, and they alone bear the responsibility for laying eggs. In general, each nest has a single queen. As the queen grows older, her abdomen is capable of increasing in size and eventually reaches immense proportions. This phenomenon is known as physogastry, and the enlarged abdomen is known as a physogastric abdomen. Such a queen, for instance an adult queen of the African termite species

Bellicositermes natalensis, whose colonies are among the largest of all termite communities, may reach a length of 16 centimetres (6 inches) and a diameter of 4 centimetres (1.57 inches), while her abdomen may increase 200 to 300 times its original size. With such a disproportionately huge abdomen, an old queen is obviously incapable of moving on her own. All her needs must therefore be provided for by other members of the community.

The process whereby the abdomen develops to such great size results from the enormous growth of the ovaries, which increase both in size and in the number of eggs they contain. The process is facilitated, too, by the elastic nature of the

Above: A dense crowd of workers and soldiers is always to be found around the queen

Below: Detail of the queen's abdomen
Bottom: A worker busily grooms the abdomen
of the queen

membranes that join together the different segments of the abdomen. The hardened or sclerotized segments of the back of the abdomen (the tergites) and of the front (the sternites) appear as small brown or black patches lying along the insect's body. Besides the ovaries, the other internal organs also grow abnormally large so as to keep up with the tasks they have to perform. The tracheae for instance become wider, and their walls thicker.

The enormous queen is incapable of finding food for herself, and so she is continuously fed by a crowd of highly specialized insects. Her chief food is, in fact, none other than pure, protein-rich saliva, which is just what she needs in order to produce egg after egg in endless series. At the same time, the queen supplies the workers in her entourage with a clear liquid secretion that is greatly to their liking. This fluid issues continuously from her anus and is also mixed with an abundant secretion from her genital passages to cover the eggs as they are laid.

The queen's abdominal wall continually moves in rhythmic contraction waves, which have been explained in all kinds of ways. The most likely explanation is that these contractions assist in moving the blood through the abdomen, thus helping the heart in its work. Certainly, once the abdomen swells to an enormous size, the heart is no longer able to handle its work unaided. The contraction waves are known as peristaltic waves, and the phenomenon in general is similar to a type of movement seen in the human intestine.

As already noted, eggs are produced continuously and in enormous numbers. The rate at which they are laid varies widely between species, but it is always an amazing feat. The queens of a common African termite species, *Bellicositermes bellicosus*, can lay up to 36,000 eggs a day. In round numbers, therefore, she would produce over 13 million eggs a year. As soon as they are laid, the eggs are taken over by the workers, who hastily remove them from under the queen and shift them to a safe

Above: Diagram of the interior of a *Bellicositermes bellicosus* nest. This 'fortified castle' is a symbol of the social organization within it. Here, the individual is of no importance except in so far as he carries out a particular function for the efficient organization of the community as a whole

place. They are not always removed singly, but are sometimes picked up in great bunches. The workers carefully lick each egg as it is laid and also continually lick the queen. Mutual licking is a very important feature of termite life. It is quite common to see workers lying on one side having themselves licked by another worker, or several at a time. The main function of this procedure is probably to keep all the members of the community clean.

Swelling of the abdomen is not confined to termite queens. Some species of ant show the same phenomenon. Both the termites and these ants undergo swelling as part of the reproductive process; but in other ants it has a different purpose. The so-called 'honey ants' of Australia and Mexico have worker-ants that are fed by the foraging members of the community until their abdomen is so full of food that it swells to a monstrous size, many times greater than normal. These ants, incapable of moving themselves about, are then removed to underground chambers where their honey-stores are put to use by the ant colony.

The termite queen exerts a powerful attraction upon the other inhabitants of the nest. In some African species, enormous numbers of workers are detailed for duty in the royal apartment. Among Bellicosi-termes, there may be over 100 termites standing under the queen's enormous abdomen, supporting it. Sometimes, as they stand pressed one against the other, they form what amounts to a living wall around their queen. When there is great agitation in the nest—usually for some external reason, such as an enemy attack or the forcible opening of the royal apartment—the queen is the focus of a feverish activity. All the termites from the remainder of the nest are severely shaken by any event of this kind.

The fact that the queen is the only reproductive member of the termite community has led many experts to suppose she might regulate the production of recruits for all the other castes. But even today it is not known for certain how this comes about. Some authors consider that the process is regulated by particular hormones secreted by the queen—the so-called pheromones—that act on the sex glands of other members of the community and prevent them from developing. As yet, however, there are no hard facts available.

The king of the termites

Just as the queen is the only sexually active female member of the termite community, so the king is the only male capable of fertilizing her. In appearance, the king closely resembles the queen—at least before her abdomen expands to its enormous size.

The exclusive role of the king in the nest is to provide the queen with the sperms that she needs to fertilize her eggs. Copulation may take place only once in the couple's life, or several times, depending on the species. If copulation only occurs once, then the king will have completed his duties and so can spend the rest of his days in total idleness, waited on hand and foot by his attendants. In other cases, he may have to fertilize his queen as often as once a month. Such a degree of activity may well be necessary when the queen is laying vast numbers of eggs every day and needing vast numbers of sperms to fertilize them. The king lives his whole life in the royal apartment, by the queen's side, and is fed on the same food as her, though in much smaller amounts.

Like the queen, the king originally has two pairs of wings of approximately equal size. But the wings are lost during swarming, which immediately precedes copulation.

New termite colonies can be founded in various ways. By far the most important is based on swarming by reproductive members of an existing community. In general terms, swarming is the process in which a number of winged individuals leave the nest and take wing: among them will be the royal couples that will found new colonies. This would seem to be a simple activity, and yet it is one of the most complex and tense moments in the community's life.

The swarm

There is a distinctly marked season of the year during which the nymphs belonging to a nest that already has a large number of inhabitants reach their final stage of development and transform into winged individuals. Before developing into adults, these nymphs gather together and move to the outskirts of the nest. Here, they take no more food, and empty the last part of their alimentary canal of its content of faecal matter. With great effort they then transform themselves into winged insects. The so-called exuvial liquid that covers the young adults when they cast off their nymphal skin is greedily licked up by the larvae that surround the nymphs during their last transformation.

Above and right: The queen's 'maids-in-waiting' are rewarded with delicious food for the services they perform. This sequence shows how greedily a worker receives the sugary liquid that issues from the queen's abdomen: not a drop is allowed to fall to the ground

When the winged termite casts off its last larval skin, its wings—like those of many other insects—are folded and contracted. Different species take different periods of time to stretch their wings. It is a process that depends on forcing air into the tracheae, thus distending these ducts that run in the wing veins and so stretching the wings. The newly-formed adults then spend a certain time within the nest. During this period their body-covering becomes harder and quite dark in colour.

Shortly before swarming takes place, an atmosphere of chaos prevails in the nest. In the midst of this, the larvae (or, in some species, the workers) quickly cut openings in the walls of the nest so that the winged termites can get out. The creation of an exit for the swarm is an astonishing sight. The workers seem positively demented as they attack the hard walls with unrelenting vigour. As if under the orders of an invisible commander, detachments of soldiers stand ready to attack any and every foe, ferociously opening and closing their powerful jaws. Everyone carries out his precisely defined task in a marvellous display of ordered activity.

Among some species of termites, the workers make exits a long way from the nest's centre. They do this by excavating long tunnels towards the edges of the nest, often in the direction of its warmest part, and in the process they quite often find themselves obliged to tunnel in rock-hard material. This does not worry them in the slightest, however, and they soon get the better of even the hardest terrain. Outside a termite nest, specially raised areas rather like walkways or pavements are sometimes visible. One explanation for these, almost certainly the right one, is that they serve as launching pads for winged termites that are about to swarm.

During swarming there are approximately equal numbers of males and females present. The manner of flight during swarming is rather curious. Termites are not accomplished fliers, so their flight is a rather ungainly, undulating

Above: A worker carefully grooms a soldier

Left: The workers take particular care of the eggs that the queen lays in a never-ending stream. Once they are laid, the eggs are immediately carried off to the parts of the nest reserved for rearing

motion in an apparently random direction.

Swarming itself may last a considerable time, on average between two and two and a half hours. Throughout this period, the workers and soldiers are continuously engaged in helping and protecting the swarm. But although swarming may take quite a long time, the swarm does not cover a great distance. In general, the termites do not fly much more than 15 metres (48 feet), but many are capable of covering distances of several kilometres or miles. The altitudes reached by the Isoptera during their flight also vary considerably. In some relatively large-winged African species, the males and females may start off at a height of 15 or 30 metres (48 or 100

feet), dropping later to 4 or 5 metres (13 or 16 feet) which is the height at which they normally fly.

The shortness of the nuptial flight has led some experts to suggest that it might have some precise purpose. By covering only a short distance, the termites that have landed can be sure of mating with other individuals quite closely related to themselves. This prevents dissipation of the hereditary characteristics acquired by one group among others that live nearby but have markedly different characteristics. The phenomenon can therefore be explained as an effective system of reproductive isolation, tending to differentiate each species into a number of varieties.

Above left: A sexual nymph, which will give rise to a king or queen
Above: Workers attend to the king

Founding a new nest
By far the most striking feature of termite life is the formation of the couples that will

later become royal couples and go on to found new colonies. Pairing among termites, like many other activities, varies between one species and another. In some, the insects choose their life partner on the ground. After landing, the members of the swarm are in a state of extreme agitation and are unable to keep still even for a moment. After a second or two, as if remembering what the process of swarming was all about, they begin to amputate their wings. It is not difficult to locate a termite engaged in this operation once their habits are known. They employ a number of tricks to amputate their wings, but the commonest and most efficient is to

Below: Eggs and nymphs of *Macrotermes subhyalinus*

fold the wings and then twist the body in all directions until the edge or the end of the wing meets an obstacle on the ground. The termite then pushes its wing against the obstacle until it breaks off. As a result of this, the wings are reduced to four tiny stumps.

It is at this point that the males start to seek out females for pairing. Usually, once he has picked on a female, a male touches her with his antennae and palps. It is the female, however, who decides whether she cares for a particular male or not. If she accepts him, she turns a half circle and immediately walks off, closely followed by the male, who does not lose sight of her for an instant. But if she refuses him, he has to find another female and try again.

In other species, pairing takes place during flight. Having chosen his female and been accepted by her, the male flies up and grasps her round the abdomen. He then holds on fast and amputates his wings. The female lands with the male on her back, and as soon as she has landed she, too, gets rid of her wings. The pair then immediately begin their nuptial walk, during which they hunt for a suitable place to found a new colony.

The nuptial walk generally lasts a few hours, but may at times continue for several days. It sometimes covers long distances, too. Eventually the female halts at a place she considers suitable for nest-building, generally a humid environment. Once she has done so, the male accepts her choice without question, and if the site is found to be suitable, the pair immediately begin to dig a royal chamber. The chamber may take several days to dig, depending on the terrain, and is linked with the outside by a tunnel kept sealed with rubble.

Finally, within the royal apartment, copulation takes place—usually preceded by complex preparatory rituals. Some time later, the fertilized queen begins to lay her first eggs, which are few in number. These will develop into the first generation of inhabitants of the new nest. The larvae that emerge from these first eggs are initially fed

Below: Close-up of a bunch of eggs still sticking to the queen's abdomen
Bottom: A very young nymph, lost and bewildered in an opened nest

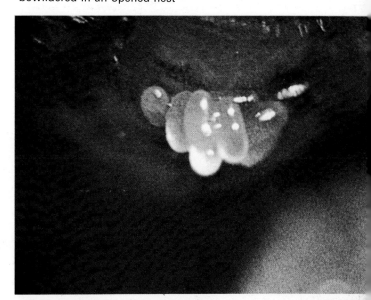

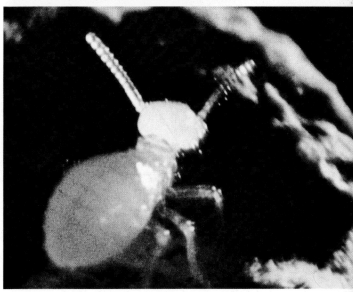

Left: In the royal cell, reproduction continues at a feverish pace even after the cell has been removed from the nest. On rare occasions, two queens may work as a team in the same cell. The photograph shows the royal cell of *Macrotermes subhyalinus*

Below. This royal cell is still intact after removal from the nest
Right: The king (below, next to the queen) remains by her side, sharing the care and attention of her suite; copulation occurs frequently

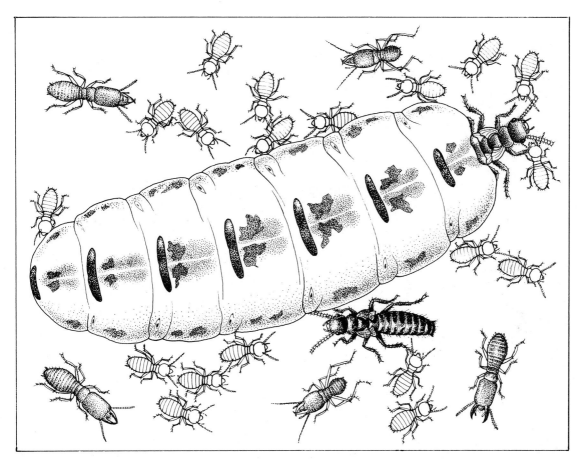

by their parents with substances that they secrete and regurgitate. Termites that build a nuptial chamber in wood draw their initial food supply for the larvae from the wood itself, while those termites that nest in the ground feed themselves and their young by digesting, as it were, their now useless wing muscles and the body-fat that they are provided with. Soon, however, the larvae become self-sufficient from the point of view of feeding.

The royal pair can now resume the reproductive activity which they were forced to suspend in order to raise their first brood. This initial brood consists almost exclusively of workers: very few members are of the soldier caste. The succeeding generations gradually complete the population of the nest, while the queen progressively grows to her final enormous size. But it takes many months for a new colony to reach full development and for the workers to be of real help to their parents and the rest of the termite family.

Not all termite species restrict themselves to one royal couple, however. Quite a few species regularly have several couples or at least several queens. Extensive studies have shown that in many cases such a situation is the rule rather than the exception. In other species it represents a transitory phase, being one of the systems for founding a new community. In such cases, supplementary reproductives are to be found near the outskirts of the nest. Eventually they are isolated by a closing of the communicating passageways and then proceed to form a separate community.

An important feature of termite society is the way the insects respond when the nest lacks a royal couple, or lacks a queen. The termites make good the loss by rearing new individuals who take over the functions of the missing king and queen. These individuals, known as substitute reproductives, arise from immature insects which, if suitably reared, can rapidly bring their sexual organs to maturity (although

73

they themselves continue to appear immature). When she reaches old age, a substitute queen may have an abdomen that is
only slightly smaller, if not actually larger,
than that of a true queen. If the nest is
deprived of a single member of the royal
couple, then either a replacement of the same
sex as the missing member is provided, or
more usually a new couple appears. This
will depend on a number of factors, but not
on the numerical size of the colony for
substitute reproductives only arise in a
community that has been deprived of its
true reproductives. This phenomenon
exemplifies the amazing degree of social
regulation of which the termite community is capable, thanks to the expenda-
bility of its members.

Above: Part of an opened colony of
Macrotermes subhyalinus. Workers and nymphs
are the smaller, paler specimens while the
large-headed soldiers are darker and have
big jaws

Diptera: the two-winged flies

When we think of an insect, we do not generally conjure up a mental picture of any particular species. Rather, we have a vague image of a small creature, and often, for various reasons, an unpleasant or unattractive one. But even the very briefest definition of an insect requires something more in the way of detail. So what are the fundamental characteristics of an insect? Firstly, its body is covered by an uninterrupted coat called the cuticula, a sort of external skeleton which is secreted by the cells of the epidermis. The body itself is divided into three regions—the head, which bears a pair of antennae and the organs of sight; the thorax, which bears three pairs of legs, and in a typical insect, two pairs of wings; and the abdomen, which differs in structure from species to species.

On the basis of this description, there can be no doubt at all that a fly is an insect, even though it differs in some respects from the generalized picture given above. The fly has, for instance, only one pair of well-developed wings—the front pair—while its rear pair has been reduced to so-called halteres, which are organs of balance. This is one of the many features that separates the flies into a well-differentiated group of insects known as the Diptera.

The name Diptera is Greek for 'two-winged' and is applied to insects that have only one pair of wings, the front pair, with which to fly. The rear wings have been reduced to halteres, little club-shaped organs that oscillate with extreme rapidity when the insect flies, just like its real wings. But instead of propelling the insect forward, they function as complex and important sense-organs for regulating flight. If both halteres are amputated, most species are rendered incapable of flight, while if only one is removed, the insect is still able to fly but will be far less agile.

Adult Diptera generally have a well-developed head, which is distinct from the thorax and joined to it by a narrow stalk. The antennae vary considerably in shape and in their degree of development. The organs of sight are compound eyes and ocelli, the latter being a much simpler type of eye. Compound eyes vary in their development from species to species, and may be absent altogether.

The mouth parts of Diptera can be of two kinds: they may be designed simply for sucking, or for piercing and then sucking. The majority of species feed on liquids that are found free—such as nectar, liquid plant or animal secretions, liquid excrement or portions of excrement—and these will have sucking mouth parts. Those species that feed on other forms of liquid, however—such as blood or haemolymph (insect blood)—which are contained within other creatures, have mouth parts designed for piercing and sucking.

Left: Many Diptera pay regular visits to the large flowers of the Umbelliferae in search of nectar and pollen. The photograph shows *Eristalis tenax*

Above and top: Some 75,000 species of flies are known and they may be found in all parts of the globe. These close-ups of a furry bee-fly (family Bombyliidae) show the compound eyes at the side of the head

Right: A bee-fly in search of food. The complex mouth parts of the Diptera enable them to scent their food, pierce and immobilize their prey before sucking out its juices, or drink other fluids as if through a straw

The sucking apparatus consists basically of a food channel, composed of separate structures that have been brought together, and of a widening in the end portion of the labium or lower lip. Piercing and sucking mouth parts consist, besides the food channel, of sharp, hardened structures rather like a needle. With both types of mouth parts, liquids are sucked up by the action of the pharynx, the front end of the alimentary canal, which dilates and contracts and literally pumps the liquid up.

There is wide variation in the mouth parts of the Diptera. As well as the best-known type, as seen on the common house fly, there are also, for example, long, hard structures capable of piercing a victim's body like a lance. It is sometimes hard to believe that a particular insect is a Dipteran, particularly if you see it sucking the nectar from a flower through a delicate proboscis. The Bombyliidae are a case in point. These graceful creatures have a body covered with long, thick fur, and their extensive mouth parts enable them to suck liquid from the deepest flowers. Another feature of the Bombyliidae is their rapid, darting flight. They often hover motionless in the air, like helicopters, and then suddenly dart to one side or the other.

In the Diptera, the three segments of the thorax are often fused together. Apart from the front wings and the halteres, the thorax also bears the three pairs of legs, which vary in shape from species to species. There is also considerable variation in the shape of the abdomen.

New-born and independent

For reproductive purposes, the Diptera can be divided into oviparous, ovoviviparous and viviparous species. Oviparous insects lay eggs in which development of the embryo has not yet started, or has only just begun. These eggs must therefore undergo a period of incubation outside the mother's body. Ovoviviparous species lay eggs from which the larvae emerge immediately, or after a very short time. Viviparous species

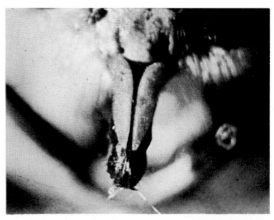

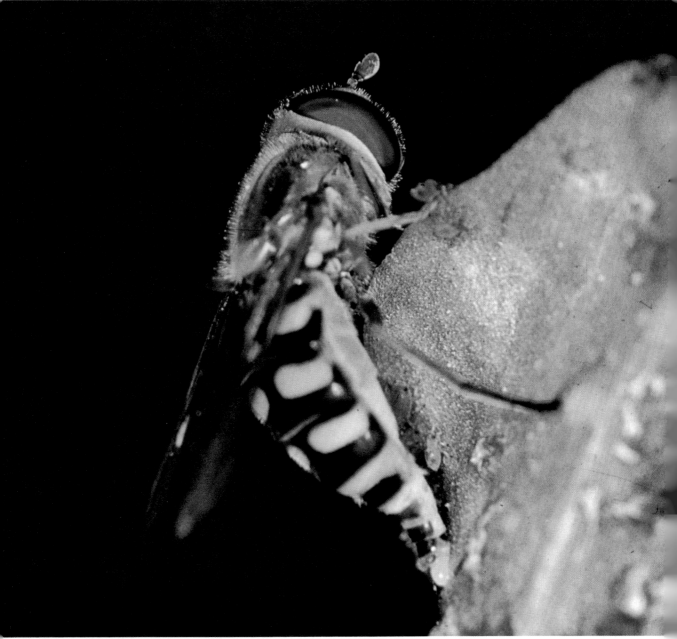

Far left: A carnivorous member of the Diptera attacks a large bee
Left: Close-up of the sucking mouth parts of the Diptera
Bottom left: A female syrphid lays eggs
Right: The paired large spiracles, placed at the end of the body of the larva, bring oxygen to the body's cells through a complex network of respiratory channels or tracheae

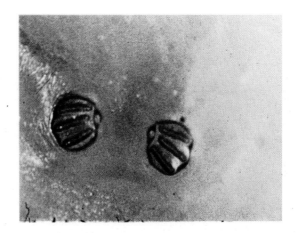

of Diptera have embryos that complete their development within the mother's body, and the larvae are deposited straight from the covering of the egg.

The larvae of Diptera (often called maggots) usually lack eyes and always lack legs. Very occasionally, they have little protuberances of various kinds on their bodies which they use to help them move about; and often they use their jaws for the same purpose. Their mouth parts typically consist of two tough, hardened hooks, which they use to fix themselves firmly in place. The more primitive forms, such as mosquitoes, have hard, firm heads with a complex chewing apparatus. More advanced species, meanwhile, show a strange form of involution, in which the outer covering of the head portion has been transformed into a soft, elastic cuticle, while the roof and walls of the pharynx have undergone an extreme degree of hardening. Together with a set of powerful muscles, this then converts them into an efficient suction-pump. At the same time, these larvae have strong hook-shaped jaws, capable of breaking off bits of tissue which the pharynx is able to absorb along with fluids. In the most highly evolved species of Diptera, therefore, the head of the maggot is soft, white, and as transparent as the rest of the body, looking nothing like a head at all. This has led people in the past to regard such larvae as headless creatures. A typical example is the blowfly larva or maggot, well known as fishermen's bait and sold at high prices during the fishing season.

The larvae of the more primitive Diptera need to live in water, or in conditions of extreme humidity. More highly evolved species, however, show progressively less dependence on a watery environment and more of a need for putrefying matter, excrement, various types of refuse, and finally for either live vegetable or animal tissue.

Larvae and pupae

Some aquatic larvae breathe through gills that take up oxygen dissolved in the water. Others use tracheae for gas exchange and must therefore come up to the surface for air every so often. Land-living larvae have a tracheal type of respiration. They take in air through spiracles, small openings through which the air passes to the tracheal system, a complex of air-tubes that spreads throughout the body.

In the pupa (the last stage of development before the adult) the body appendages such as the antennae, palpi and legs may be cemented down when there is no outer case or they may be free and unattached to the body when the pupa is enclosed in a case. The pupae of some Diptera are not enclosed in cocoons, but are merely buried in soil, float in water, or are attached to a submerged stone or plant. Other species have pupae that are wrapped in a protective cocoon of silk, or silk together with other agglutinated matter. In other species again, the last larval skin, which is discarded when the insect becomes

Above: A syrphid fly, whose markings mimic those of certain Hymenoptera, searches for food in a flower
Left: A robber-fly of the Asilidae family
Right: Another nectar-feeding syrphid fly
Far right: A fruit-eating fly. The drop of sugary liquid visible is produced by the fly itself

a pupa, is not actually cast off but becomes hardened and barrel-like, and within it the pupa finds refuge. This shell is known as a puparium, and has the same function as a cocoon. The adult insect escapes by cracking it open, or by pushing open a 'lid' at one end of the case. In each instance, the puparium opens along a predetermined set of fissure-lines—a process that results from the fact that the developing insect's body becomes swollen when it is finally due to hatch.

The importance of Diptera

Diptera may be divided into two sub-orders, Nematocera and Brachycera. The former consists of species with long, delicate antennae (mosquitoes, for example) while the latter, including common flies, consists of species with short antennae. About 100,000 species of Diptera have been described and they are found in practically all regions of the globe, from the lowest plains to the highest mountains, from equatorial regions to the frozen polar lands. They are of enormous scientific and economic importance.

From the scientific point of view, great strides were made by classical genetics using as a basis that splendid experimental model, Drosophila, the common fruit fly, which has the advantage of a very short reproductive cycle and a large number of potential mutations that can be found in a given population. It is also worth remembering that it was through a common fly that

Francesco Redi, a celebrated physician and poet from the Italian town of Arezzo, exploded in the late seventeenth century the theory of spontaneous generation (according to which certain creatures arose spontaneously from the substances in which they were commonly found). It is interesting, and somewhat surprising, to read his most lucid account of two of the simplest and most decisive experiments he performed.

'I began to wonder whether perhaps all the worms in the meat might not arise from the seed of the flies alone, and not from the rotten meat itself; and I was all the more confirmed in suspecting this, because with all the generations of flies that I had caused to hatch, I had always observed that the meat, before it became verminous, was visited by flies of the same sort that later were born from it. But my suspicions would have been in vain, had an experiment not confirmed it. Therefore in the middle of July I placed into four wide-mouthed flasks a serpent, some fish from the river, four eels from the Arno, and a piece of veal; and then sealed the mouths of the flasks well with paper and string, and with sealing-wax; and into four other flasks I put as many of the same things again, and left the mouths of the flasks open. Little time passed before the fish and the meat in the second set of flasks became verminous; and I saw flies entering and leaving these flasks at will. But I never saw a single maggot hatch in the closed flasks, even many months after the dead fish and

meat were put into them. But sometimes I found, on the outside of the paper, a maggot or worm that was trying by every means in its power to find some crack through which it could enter the flask and feed on the contents, which were all by then stinking, rotten and putrefied.'

Redi's experiments are remarkable, considering they were recorded in 1668. They were repeated by other European naturalists, and were the beginning of a series of researches into the life and structure of insects which gave rise to a new branch of zoology, namely entomology—all thanks to a humble fly.

Undoubtedly the Diptera are, in terms of human economy, the most important order of insects. The suborder Brachycera, for instance, includes many species that inflict severe and often irreparable damage on many types of cultivated plants, attacking leaves, roots and fruit. Then there are flies whose larvae produce severe injuries in both man and animals. Diseases due to infestation with these larvae are known as myiasis, and the family Oestridae are particularly important in this respect. Finally, there are flies that do no harm in the larval stage, but on reaching adult life become blood-suckers, particularly the females of the species. The common house fly, that well-known and unwelcome guest, is found wherever human beings settle. It does not suck blood, but is no less dangerous for that, being a carrier of a number of serious diseases.

But not all flies are enemies of the human race. Some of them are natural and true friends of man in his struggle against other, harmful, insects. A number of species of Syrphidae, for instance, live on aphids (common plant-lice) and are often responsible for keeping their numbers drastically down. The carnivorous larvae of the Tachinidae destroy vast numbers of other insects. In some cases, indeed, these insects have been successfully used by man as a biological weapon against other types of insects that cause severe damage to a wide range of crops.

Vegetarian flies

The species of fly that attacks the leaves of cultivated crops includes the sugar-beet fly. This is a small insect, about 6 millimetres (0.25 inches) long, having a yellow abdomen marked with a light brown line along the back. The adults appear at the same time as young sugar-beets, towards the end of April or the beginning of May, and lay their eggs at the base of tender young leaves. The larvae then burrow into the leaves and devour them from within. Damaged areas of the leaves stand out as pale areas against the green of the parts that are still healthy. As one leaf can harbour as many as 10 larvae, any damage done can be extensive, perhaps involving the complete destruction of infected leaves and the death of the plant. Obviously, more damage is done when young leaves are attacked; but even when the larvae invade the broad, well-developed leaves of the fully-grown plant, damage can still be severe involving a reduction both in the size of the roots and in the amount of sugar obtained.

Other Diptera invade the shoots of cultivated plants and also cause irreparable damage. An example is the asparagus fly, an insect the same size as the house fly but with an elegant black zig-zag pattern on its wings. The adults of this species become active in spring when the asparagus-shoots are beginning to develop into the heads that are later used in numerous delicious recipes. The female asparagus fly climbs to the tip of the shoot, plunges its ovipositor into the delicate tissues of the plant, and deposits some 50 eggs. These hatch out into whitish maggots which burrow into the shoot, eating the tender plant tissues, until they reach the part of the plant below the soil. Here they leave the plant and become pupae. If many maggots are present, the asparagus-shoot, instead of growing into the succulent vegetable we know so well, turns into nothing but a dry, twisted stick.

The parsnip fly, in contrast, lives on the roots of the parsnip, celery, and other plants. The roots of infested plants can easily be identified by little holes on their surface, through which the larvae have left to undergo metamorphosis in the soil. When infestation is heavy, the roots tend to rot and the upper part of the plant looks far from healthy.

A fly causing severe damage to fruit is the olive fruit fly, which bears a considerable resemblance to the house fly, but is smaller and brownish-yellow in colour. The female lays her eggs within the olive fruit. A few days later the whitish maggots hatch out and begin feeding on the flesh of the olive, making a winding tunnel that extends through most of the fruit and ends in a chamber where the insect spends the last few days of its life as a larva before pupating. Sometimes, however, pupation takes place outside the fruit.

The olive fruit fly has been known since ancient times, and the classical Latin writer Pliny noted that on some occasions it caused the loss of the whole year's crop. Even if the fruit is not completely destroyed, the maggot's presence invariably

Three views of *Ceratitis capitata*
Above: The fly takes a careful look at the fruit in which it intends to lay its eggs
Below: Attending to personal cleanliness
Right: The wings have delicate tracery

causes a fall in both the quantity and quality of oil produced, which is then hard to market. Economic damage is therefore always considerable, and since the eighteenth century all kinds of measures have been tried against the pest, some of them, fortunately, with encouraging results.

The Mediterranean fruit fly, *Ceratitis capitata*, although beautiful, is by no means appreciated by farmers, who often suffer enormous losses because of it. This insect has always been found in Africa, Australia, South America, Hawaii and Bermuda, and during the last century it appeared in the Mediterranean basin, too. It is now found in central Europe as well, in spite of strict control measures imposed by health administrations on fruit imports from the Mediterranean. The adults of the species live on the sugary sap of plants, as well as nectar and the sugary excretions of other insects.

The females lay their eggs within various kinds of fruit, such as peaches, persimmons, figs, prickly pears, apricots, pears, plums, oranges and mandarins. Bergamot fruit and limes are not attacked. There may be as many as several dozen eggs in one fruit, since a number of females may lay their eggs in the same place. After a short while, the eggs hatch out into very active yellowish-white larvae, and these live on the flesh of the fruit, which quickly turns into a brown, mushy mess. At the end of their development, the maggots leave the fruit and make for the soil, where they transform into pupae.

The campaign against this pernicious fly has extended to the ever-wider use of biological warfare. The aim is to introduce and acclimatize its specific parasites in the regions where the fly occurs, and fortunately there are quite a number of such parasitic species. This approach has occasionally given moderately successful results, but a great deal still remains to be achieved. Another effective means of attack is to hang on the fruit trees special containers holding non-poisonous substances that the flies find attractive—such as the juice of unsale-able oranges or fermented bran-water. The flies are drawn to the liquid and drown in it.

Parasitic larvae and blood-sucking flies

The name 'myiasis' is applied to diseases caused by the larvae of Diptera which behave as parasites and develop in the skin or body orifices of their host. Myiasis may be caused, quite accidentally, by the larvae of the blowfly, the flesh fly and the screwworm fly. These insects usually lay their eggs on rotting organic matter, and therefore may lay them on the open sores of man or animals. In other cases, the eggs are laid in the nostrils, the ears, the mouth or the anus, as the insect is attracted both by dirt and by smell.

The Oestridae family, on the other hand, contains species whose larvae can live only as parasites. The sheep bot fly is found, during the summer months, in sheep pastures. The fertile female fly lays her eggs in little clumps on the sheep's nostrils, and from here the larvae crawl up to the internal nasal cavities and then on into the sheep's frontal and maxillary sinuses, where they complete their growth before re-emerging to pupate in the soil. This causes a very serious sinusitis. Affected sheep stagger about and fall to the ground, have convulsions, dribble profusely, and in severest cases eventually die.

The female ox warble fly, *Hypoderma bovis*, lives in cattle pastures and lays her eggs on the cattle, choosing a place which the animal can easily reach with its tongue. The flies show an impressive instinctiveness in choosing where to lay the eggs, for in order to come to full development, the larvae must be swallowed by the cow, reaching its alimentary canal and eventually penetrating to just below its skin, where they gather in groups, forming a characteristic lump or 'warble'. When mature, they will crawl out, fall to the ground, and then pupate. Quite apart from any other harm they do, if there are many larvae and warbles, the animal's skin will be punctured with a large number of small

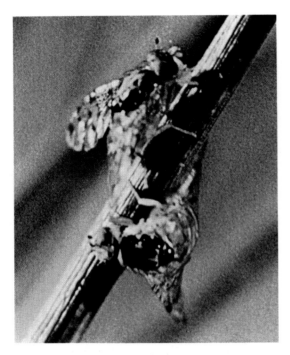

Below and left: Before mating, the male of *Ceratitis capitata* performs a dance of courtship, circling about the female with wings lowered (left)

holes, making it useless for the leather trade.

Horseflies are Diptera with a broad body and a flattened head. Their wings are large and powerful, and at rest they lie slightly apart. Their eyes are large, and in the male are very close together. Their mouth parts are of the piercing and sucking kind. The females live on blood, but the males feed on the sweet nectar of flowers. The eggs of horseflies are laid on the earth or on grass. The larvae, which have a pair of eyes and two powerful jaws, are vegetarian or carnivorous. They live in wet places, usually in the wet mud at the margins of ponds, streams and rivers though sometimes simply in damp soil.

Found throughout the world, horseflies are often a serious pest both for domestic animals and for man. They generally live in woods and pastures, and they carry out their annoying and painful attacks in the heat of the day. Their mouth parts are amazingly hard and can penetrate the thickest of animal skins and even heavy clothing. Their greed for blood is such that they hurl themselves at their prey at great speed, and, no matter how their victim reacts, they hold on until they have drunk their fill. Their bite is always painful, and

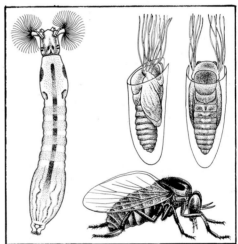

Above: The Simulium gnat. On the left of the diagram is an aquatic larva; on the right is shown the pupa in its case, seen from the side and from above. Vast swarms of Simulium adults (lower right) may attack both men and grazing livestock near watercourses. Their bite is extremely painful

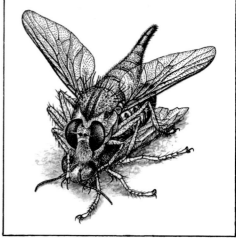

Left: A blowfly (*Calliphora erythocephala*) laying eggs that are almost ready to hatch
Above: An asilid attacks a hunting wasp

when they fly off, they leave behind a trickle of blood.

If horseflies were merely a nuisance, particularly on hot sultry days or just before a thunderstorm, this might not matter too much. But heavy attacks on grazing stock can reduce milk yield and weight increase, and they can infect any animal with various diseases. In addition, horseflies can transmit the larvae of parasitic worms.

Among blood-sucking flies, there are three genera of direct or indirect importance to man: Stomoxys, Haematobia and Glossina. *Stomoxys calcitrans*, the stable fly, is an impudent little fly that is very similar to the house fly in size and appearance. It is immediately distinguishable, however, because when at rest, and particularly when seen from the side, it shows a small but very obvious horizontal sting-like proboscis on the front of its head. This is only lowered when it is preparing to bite. This insect is very common in the summer months, especially near stables where horses are kept. Both males and females feed on blood. The stable fly does not confine its attentions to horses, however, and regularly attacks human beings, showing a particular liking for the ankles even when they are protected by thick socks. Its bite is extremely painful, but it rarely succeeds in plunging in its proboscis to the full extent, since the moment it starts to bite, the victim immediately reacts by driving it off. The stable fly is capable of transmitting poliomyelitis to humans and nematode (roundworm) larvae to horses.

While Stomoxys is particularly common near horse stables, the genus Haematobia is found in large numbers both in fields and near watercourses. It also lives on blood, as its generic name tells us, and will attack human beings as well as cattle.

The tsetse fly

Glossina species, well-known by the name of tsetse flies, are easily distinguishable from all other flies. Their mouth parts form a long and delicate but rigid tube, which is held horizontal at rest, as with Stomoxys. All the suborder Brachycera have antennae divided into three segments connected by joints. The third is clearly different from the first two, having a large number of fine bristles that make it look rather like a comb. The wings (unlike those of Stomoxys, for instance), though they are longer than the abdomen, overlap one another at rest like the blades of a pair of scissors so that the two outer edges are almost parallel. Tsetse flies in general are dark in colour: the thorax is grey with brown spots, and the abdomen is brown with pale tawny-coloured spots and stripes.

Tsetse flies do not lay eggs, but are viviparous. The eggs, on leaving the ovary, pass into the oviducts, and here the larvae hatch out. They then move on into a form of large womb in which they find both a suitable environment and the food they need for their further development. At the front end of the womb is a duct through which two specialized glands secrete a milky liquid so rich in nutrients that the young larvae grow at great speed. At intervals of 10 to 12 days, they are expelled from the womb. As soon as they are born, the larvae look for a hiding-place, taking refuge in the soil. Here they very soon pupate, and about a month later, the adult emerges from the puparium. Then, at the age of a mere three weeks, the female is ready in turn to give birth to new larvae.

Both males and females of the genus Glossina feed on blood; they show a preference for the blood of warm-blooded vertebrates and mammals in particular. Their greed for blood is remarkable. If left undisturbed, they can very quickly suck up twice their own weight of blood, completely changing their appearance in the process owing to the grotesque bulging of their abdomen. The tsetse flies are not only a general nuisance; they can also transmit very serious diseases, particularly sleeping sickness—a disease which can affect not only man but also wild and domestic animals, with similar symptoms.

Tsetse flies live in the humid tropical and sub-tropical regions of Africa. Two species are particularly important, *Glossina morsitans* and *Glossina palpalis*. These transmit the parasites *Trypanosoma rhodesiense* and *Trypanosoma gambiense*, respectively—both being causative organisms of sleeping sickness.

Glossina morsitans is an insect of gregarious habits that tends to live in large colonies. It survives well even in dry conditions. Flies of this species sometimes collect in large numbers in well-defined areas, and the natives take good care to keep well away. But at night, unless the moon is bright, men may safely walk across the flies' territory, for the flies are then completely inactive and merely rest on the ground or on bushes.

Glossina palpalis lives by the side of watercourses and in the very humid areas nearby. It has an absolute requirement for a high degree of humidity, without which it cannot survive. Unlike the previous species, these flies tend to scatter over a wide area without forming swarms when—as usually happens—the animals they feed on are widely dispersed. If animals are scarce or crowded into herds, however, the flies will then gather along the paths that both animals and men have to take to reach their sources of drinking water.

While piercing the skin in order to suck blood, the flies introduce the trypanosomes into their hosts. Trypanosomes are single-celled creatures, with an elliptical body equipped with a long flagellum (a whip-like appendage) that is connected to the body by an undulating membrane. The parasites invade the host's blood and multiply rapidly in it. At this stage, they cause an intermittent fever with a more or less regular cycle, as well as other non-specific upsets such as loss of weight, rashes and localized tissue-swelling in various parts of the body. They then spread into the cerebro-spinal fluid that fills the cerebral ventricles (cavities within the brain) and the central canal of the spinal cord, giving rise to severe upsets of the nervous system, with an extreme state of general depression resembling sleep (hence the name 'sleeping sickness'), progressing to coma and death. Negroes are particularly liable to this severe illness, since the tsetse flies are especially attracted to black skin.

Tsetse flies attack not only man but other mammals too, such as a number of domesticated equine and ruminant species. These animals do not suffer in the slightest degree from the trypanosomes that cause disease in man, but they constitute a highly dangerous living reservoir for these parasitic protozoa that are readily accessible for the tsetse flies to take on their death-dealing cargo.

There is also another trypanosome, *Trypanosoma brucei*, that is widespread among horses and other mammals in Africa. This organism is a harmful parasite that causes the disease known as 'nagana', in which the infected animal becomes extremely weak, emaciated, develops intermittent fever and internal haemorrhages, and generally dies. The disease causes great economic damage, and has hindered the development of agriculture and livestock breeding in many East African countries.

The house fly

The house fly is generally regarded as a very annoying insect, perhaps the commonest insect of all, and one to which we have become accustomed. We meet it everywhere, we drive it away—or try to—by every means in our power, before coming to the conclusion that it cannot really be banished for good. But if the house fly was really only an unwanted and annoying guest in our houses, we should be lucky indeed. Unfortunately this is far from the case.

The house fly lays its eggs, 100 to 150 at a time, especially on fresh horse-dung, but it will also place them on other types of excrement, rotting organic matter, meat and carcasses. Here the maggots can find food in plenty. The adults hunt for food, settling wherever organic matter is to be found. Obviously, then, this fly is one of the most terrible vectors of disease-causing bacteria, including those that trigger typhoid fever, cholera and plague. The germs stick to the insect's legs, its mouth parts, and other parts of its body. They are then deposited on solid and liquid food. The fly's digestive system can also harbour bacteria, which are deposited with its excrement and regurgitated food droplets on the surface of foods, plates and cups.

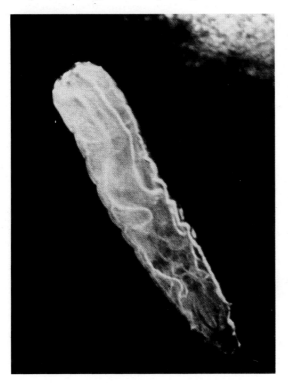

Far left: The tsetse fly (genus Glossina) is one of man's most dangerous insect enemies. The bite of the tsetse fly spreads sleeping sickness, which has brought death to hundreds of thousands of victims
Left: A syrphid larva photographed immediately after hatching from the egg
Above: Tsetse flies mating

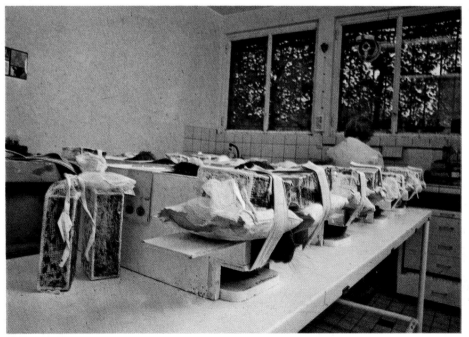

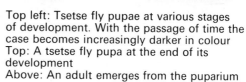

Top left: Tsetse fly pupae at various stages of development. With the passage of time the case becomes increasingly darker in colour
Top: A tsetse fly pupa at the end of its development
Above: An adult emerges from the puparium

Left and far left: Large numbers of tsetse flies are reared in the laboratory. The males are exposed to X-rays and become sterile and are then despatched to areas where sleeping sickness is endemic. Their sterile matings help to stem the growth of the species and the spread of the disease. They live on the fresh blood of rabbits, which they obtain by biting the animals' ears (an insensitive part of their bodies) through the mesh of the cages in which they are reared

93

Above: A fine example of a syrphid fly, a species of Diptera that is useful to man as its larvae feed on aphids
Left: Syrphid eggs which have been laid amongst an aphid colony

Right: An aphid-eating syrphid larva at its meal. By feeding on such pests, these larvae perform a useful service for gardeners

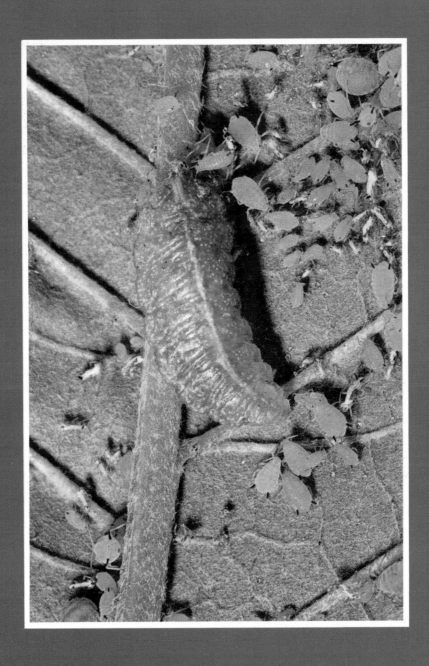

It is no easy matter to protect oneself against the house fly, and its total elimination can be ruled out for the present. Some relief can be obtained by keeping rooms dark, storing food in closed cupboards or covering it with fine wire gauze. This only succeeds in keeping insects away as much as possible, however. The most important thing is to stop them from developing. Flies would disappear if the deposits of organic matter available to them, such as excrement and refuse, were eliminated or drastically reduced. Only in this way can the house fly be finally beaten. So far, all forms of chemical warfare have failed to control it.

Flies that are useful to man

The Syrphidae are a family that contain middle-sized and large dipterous flies whose bodies often bear a strange resemblance to those of bees and wasps, being decorated in a pattern of yellow and black. The syrphid family includes insects that are neither harmful to man nor a nuisance to him, but are even to some extent useful. Adult syrphids are sun-lovers and visit flowers which provide them with plentiful supplies of the pollen and nectar on which they live. This feeding-habit makes them very important in the cross-fertilization of plants. The larvae of many known species live on a wide variety of foods—fungi, rotting vegetables and sap, for example. Others are very specialized and live on aphids (plant-lice). They can in fact wipe out large numbers of aphids, which makes them very useful to man.

The larvae of the aphid-eating syrphid, unlike other maggots, are brightly coloured in green and yellow. If you are ever fortunate enough to see one of these maggots on an aphid-infested rose-twig, you will notice it move confidently forwards, like a little leech, towards its prey. The maggots do not usually have to go far to seek their food, for their mother has the foresight to lay her eggs close to the aphid colonies on which they will come to feed. The maggot approaches its victim and impales it with lightning speed on its mouth parts. The aphid is then lifted up, and the front end of the maggot's body is retracted inside the thorax. This forms a sort of pouch in which the victim is imprisoned, unable to move, while its body fluid is sucked up by the maggot. As soon as it has finished, the maggot attacks a second victim, which suffers the same fate as the first. Aphid colonies stand up quite well to these syrphid assaults, for their reproductive powers are very great. But the syrphids are sometimes able to stem the tide a little, since a single maggot may well devour more than 40 aphids in a day.

The behaviour of ants

The ants—those 10,000 species of Hymenoptera that make up the family Formicidae—arose from the same branch as the Vespidae in tropical areas throughout the world. From these regions, they have spread to populate every continent and every environment. They have also shown an extraordinary degree of adaptability. For instance, there are marked differences between the mandibles of different genera, depending on the available food resources to which a particular genus has become adapted.

Ants may be anything from 1 millimetre to 4 centimetres (0.03 to 1.57 inches) in length. Their social organization is among the most perfect in the world; truly remarkable, in fact, considering that some communities may number up to 1 million individuals, every one active, each allotted to his own special task and all living together in harmony. The bulk of a colony consists of workers—sterile females with atrophied wings. The older ones leave the nest and forage for food for the whole colony, while the younger ones feed the larvae and the queens, who may number more than one. The males and the fertile females destined to become queens initially have wings. During the mating flight, the queen is fertilized. After this, the now

socially useless males die, while the fertilized queens shed their wings and deposit the eggs in a nest which they build themselves, and in which they will rear their first brood of workers, thus starting a new colony. As with bees, it is the workers who leave the nest and hunt for food. They store as much as possible in their stomachs, which then serve in effect as a communal stomach. Whatever they do not require for their own sustenance will be passed on to the other members of the colony.

Ants have an excellent sense of direction, and with the features of the landscape and the position of the sun to guide them, they can usually find their way back to a good source of food when they want to lay in stores. However, a crucial function such as the provision of food is generally not left to the memory of an individual ant. The workers use the odorous secretions of special glands to 'mark out' their path back to the nest, and these secretions then serve to guide others in the colony. Other scent signals serve to warn the colony of an enemy's approach—though in this situation many species prefer to sound an audible alarm by rubbing together two segments of the petiole, which is appropriately shaped for the purpose.

Unlike most social insects, ants welcome insects of other families, even invertebrates belonging to other groups such as spiders or millipedes, into their nests. Sometimes these are merely commensals: Acari, Coleoptera, or Lepidoptera in the larval or

Left: Cross-section of the nest of the Californian honey-ant. The central chamber houses the queen, the workers, the pupae and the larvae, while the lower chamber contains the repletes, which look like living wineskins

adult stage may settle in the ants' nest for shelter and warmth, feeding only on the ants' refuse. Cohabitation does not always follow this restricted pattern, however. It may take any form, even true parasitism. There are cases where the harm done by the parasite to its host is fairly mild—when, for example, the parasite mimics the ant larva in order to be fed by the workers, and waits patiently for the workers to let fall a drop of food during the process of trophallaxis. At the other end of the scale, there are situations where real harm is done to the ant colony. It is remorselessly exploited by the parasites and, being unable to provide sufficient food for the ant larvae, the visitors and the workers themselves, it eventually succumbs under the oppression of its unwanted guests.

From the point of view of classification the family Formicidae is divided into nine subfamilies, some of which are exclusively tropical while others have an almost world-wide distribution. Leaving aside the sub-family Myrmicinae, which is confined to Australia and which consists of aggressive ants, much feared for their painful stings, and also the Cerapachyinae and Leptaleinae, which are rather primitive and lead a nomadic life, two subfamilies are of parti-cular interest—the Dorylinae and the Pon-erinae. These are the well-known 'army ants' of the tropics, whose columns are continuously on the march in search of prey. Among the Ponerinae, expeditions are composed of workers, some of whom are wrongly termed soldiers. But some-times the queen herself takes part in the hunt, and on occasion the workers may even bring the larvae along with them if it is worth the trouble. This is the case with the genera Termitoponera and Megaponera, ruthless termite-hunters who set out fully armed, whenever one of their workers discovers a way into a termite nest.

The species belonging to the subfamily Dorylinae are even more ferocious than the Ponerinae. When they set off on a journey, an army of over 1 million ants marches in a close column at a speed of up to 30 kilometres (18 miles) an hour, devouring whatever lies in their path. The workers of this group show considerable biological diversity, including individuals with very large heads armed with powerful curved mandibles that can inflict sizeable skin wounds even on man. These nomad ants halt from time to time in temporary nests, but they never build a permanent one. They pause when the queen is ready to lay her eggs, and as soon as the grubs emerge they set off again, driven by their now-increased need for food. The fertilized queens are exceedingly fat, having (like the termite queens) an extended abdomen full of eggs.

The 3,000 known species of Myrmicinae

Below: A grain-gathering ant (left) and a leaf-cutting ant (right) bring home their booty

are far more highly evolved, with a far greater degree of social organization. They are found throughout the world, are usually small, and include some common European species. Among the most interesting species of this group are Tetramorium ants, harvester ants and leaf-cutting ants. Ants of the genus Tetramorium are the victims of a peculiar form of parasitism practised by Strongylognathus ants. These have over-developed, pincer-shaped mandibles, which make them unable to feed their own larvae. To this end, they 'enslave' the Tetramorium ants and compel them to play the role of nurses. Harvester ants, by contrast, are the prototypes of the thrifty 'industrious emmet' of legend. They store such large quantities of grain in their huge nests (up to 50 metres or 165 feet in diameter) that they make serious inroads on the harvest of any farmer whose land lies nearby. The leaf-cutting ants have an equally interesting practice. They are capable of completely denuding a tree in the course of a single night in order to provide their fungus-beds with a vegetable layer of finely-chopped leaves, flowers and shoots. These ants resemble the termites in that they cultivate in their nests one single species of fungus, the mycelium of which spreads out over the layer of rotting leaves and produces small spherical bodies which the ants use as food for the whole colony.

A fairly close relative of this group is the subfamily Pseudomyrminae, which is pre-dominantly found in tropical regions. These ants make their home in hollow branches and tree-trunks. They mainly feed on insects, and kill their prey by stinging. The sting is well developed in all species of this group.

Only two subfamilies now remain to be examined, the Dolichoderinae and the Formicinae. The first includes the genus Azteca, a particularly aggressive genus of South American tree ant, and consists of ants that have lost their sting and replaced it by glands that secrete a repellent fluid which is squirted at their enemies under pressure. The subfamily Formicinae includes 2,500 species that are scattered throughout the world and have adapted to the most varied habitats. Many of our common ant varieties belong to this group. These ants also lack a sting, and instead have poison-glands whose contents can be squirted, or more usually placed, in a wound produced with the mandibles. Their food consists mainly of small invertebrates and the 'honey' of aphids and similar insects, which enter into a true symbiosis with the ants. The ants relieve the aphids of their excess sugar, and protect their colonies from other parasites or predators; in return they receive the food they favour.

Slave-making is a common feature of this family, too. A colony will be taken

Below: A parasitic ant (left) rubs against its victim so as to take on its scent. It can then safely attack and kill the queen (right)

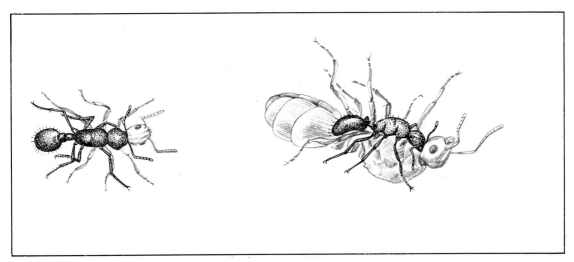

101

over by a queen from a different species who gradually steals the pupae of the host ant so that when they hatch out they will be faithful to her and her offspring and provide them with all the food they need. The sanguinea ant (*Raptiformica sanguinea*) and the amazon ant (*Polyergus rufescens*) provide examples of this practice, enslaving the workers of *Serviformica fusca*. Of equal fascination is the strange habit of the members of the genus Myrmecocystus. These 'desert ants' live a precarious life in their inhospitable surroundings, and they feed some of their workers vast amounts of food, inflating their abdomens till they are like balloons filled with sugary liquid. These 'repletes' are shut into special apartments with an opening that is too narrow for them to get through, and are then made use of in times of scarcity.

Below: Three parasitic ants ride on the back of the queen of their host species. Ants often take over an entire nest and kill the queen

Bees and wasps

Bees and wasps, together with flies, mosquitoes, butterflies, moths and beetles, are among the best-known insects. Indeed, they are among the very few organisms commonly recognized out of this vast zoological group comprising nearly 1 million known species and, in all probability, an incredible number of others which have yet to be described. Nearly everybody remembers vividly his first childhood encounter with a wasp or bee, made memorable by the insect's swift reaction and the sudden agonizing sting. A little ammonia applied with a piece of cotton wool soon eliminated the pain, but ever afterwards the child victim kept a wary eye on, and a respectful distance from, the many insects buzzing from flower to flower in their livery of yellow and black or light brown.

Most people's experience is limited to a healthy respect for the stings of such insects, to the smell of fresh mountain honey spread on a thick slice of buttered bread, and to moral tales about the discipline of the beehive and the industry of bees. In fact, wasps and bees, together with ants, are merely the best-known insects in the order of Hymenoptera, one of the most complex and highly evolved groups of insects.

Left: The bee and the flower depend on each other; neither can live independently. The bee feeds on the nectar and pollen produced by the flower and, whilst collecting them, transfers some of the pollen from one flower to another, thus effecting cross-fertilization

The biology of Hymenoptera

Hymenoptera range in size from the tiny Mymaridae (fairy-flies) 0.25 millimetres (0.01 inches) long, to the Pompilidae (spider-wasps) of Africa and South America which may be 6 centimetres (2.36 inches) long with a wingspan of 11 centimetres (4.33 inches). The very mobile head possesses two huge eyes which, as in most insects, are compound in structure: that is, each eye is made up of a large number of visual units called ommatidia. These lie closely together with no space between them, so that the surface of the compound eye appears to be made up of vast numbers of regular hexagonal segments which are, in fact, the corneas of the individual ommatidia. Minute, very fine hairs are often found on the surface of compound eyes and these have a sensory function.

Each ommatidium is a true eye, having a cornea, a crystalline cone underneath and a sensory structure known as a retinula, which has the same function as the retina in a human eye. All the separate images transmitted by the ommatidia collectively make up a panoramic view of the world surrounding the insect. However, the images seen by a bee are not the same as those seen by humans. Bees distinguish colours rather differently, and their perception of shapes is not the same as ours either. Generally, bees—the subject of much study in this field—have astigmatic vision, and objects appear more elongated vertically than they do to humans.

Also on the head, in the frontal region and between the compound eyes, there are usually three simple eyes, called ocelli, which are so placed to form a triangle. These are not used for actually seeing, but are sensitive to variations in the intensity of light. The compound eyes then act on the information thus gained, which is similar to that provided by an exposure meter.

The antennae are not normally conspicuous in Hymenoptera, although in some species they may be very elongated, comprising up to 70 segments. The antennae, as in other insects, are the site of very important structures, the sense organs, in particular those of mechanical sense (touch) and chemical senses (smell and taste).

Although Hymenoptera are provided, as part of the mouth apparatus, with well developed mandibles, these have sometimes lost their original function as organs for chewing food and have become adapted for other functions. The other mouth parts (that is, accessory jaws known as the first and second pairs of maxillae), often with the help of auxiliary structures, have developed to sometimes remarkable length and become modified so as to form the characteristic sucking or sucking/licking apparatus which allows these insects, mainly bees, to imbibe liquid food, generally composed of the sugary secretions of flowers but sometimes also of other substances.

The thorax normally carries two pairs of membraneous wings, usually transparent, sometimes coloured, but never covered with the scales which cause the amazing variety and vividness of colour in butterflies' wings. But Hymenoptera are generally good fliers and have various methods of ensuring that both fore and hind wings beat in unison. For instance, a mechanism allows the underside of the rear edge of the forewing to hook on to the upper side of the fore edge of the hind wing. The flight of these insects, often agile and rapid, is frequently accompanied by a characteristic buzz, the pitch of which changes according to the frequency of the wing-beat.

The thorax is directly joined to the abdomen without constriction in the more primitive groups, but in the higher Hymenoptera there is a characteristic narrow 'wasp waist' at the base of the abdomen, the second abdominal segment forming a petiole while the first segment is fused to the thorax and is known as the propodeum. In certain groups, the abdomen is actually pedunculate or 'stalked'—that is, joined to the thorax by a very thin tubular structure which may be more than a third as long as the total length of the insect.

Symphyta and Apocrita

As already stated, the order of Hymenoptera, although a natural or homogeneous group, comprising organisms genuinely 'related' to each other, is far from being uniform. Although the term 'bee' or 'wasp' may be used to indicate generally any winged member of the Hymenoptera, the order in fact includes numerous species which vary widely, both in their appearance and, particularly, in their habits. To understand this fully, it is worth looking at a few examples among the many different groups of Hymenoptera so as to demonstrate, not only the various forms of these insects, but also the degree to which they adapt to their surroundings, which are often extremely specialized. Indeed, they have adapted to such a marked degree that they are considered to be far more highly evolved than any other group of insects and, in short, one of the most highly evolved groups in the animal kingdom.

From the point of view of classification, Hymenoptera are divided into the two suborders of Symphyta (sawflies) and Apocrita, each of which contains a considerable number of families, some of which will be touched on in this brief account of a few of the better-known species.

The suborder Symphyta comprises medium-sized to large insects. The body is cylindrical and elongated, without the clear-cut waist at the base of the abdomen which is characteristic of the Apocrita. The

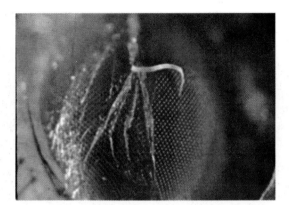

The head of a hymenopterous insect is a highly
sophisticated structure: every part, from
the myriad eyes to the tiniest tuft of hair,
has a specific task to perform
Left and above left: The heads of two bees,
showing the eyes
Above: An enlarged view of the head, showing
the eye segments
Below: The wasp uses its sensitive antennae
to pick up an endless variety of information
about its environment

larvae are generally plant-eating. They feed on living vegetable matter such as leaves, fruit, seeds and sometimes wood, in which they excavate long, winding tunnels, just like those made by the larvae of many Coleoptera and some Lepidoptera.

Some species are harmful to man, in the sense that they feed on cultivated plants or at any rate on plants useful to agriculture or forestry. Among the latter are many of the genera Acantholyda and Cephaleia which can cause a considerable amount of damage

to fir and pine forests, the needles of which they eat, particularly in central and southern Europe, in the Soviet Union and in Mongolia.

The larvae of the sawfly *Pamphilius inanitus* feed on the leaves of many different kinds of roses. They cut them into thin strips, overlap them like tiles and join their edges with threads of silk which they themselves produce. Then, they roll them up to form a sturdy cigar-shaped case a few centimetres long.

Above : This close-up of *Polistes gallicus,* a European wasp, clearly shows the segments of the legs, together with the mouth parts which are of the sucking type although they include mandibles designed for tearing food apart

Above: The wing veins (top) consist of narrow tubes which help to stiffen the wing. The two pairs of wings are connected by a coupling mechanism (centre) which enables them to beat in perfect time (above)

Above and left: The hymenopteran *Blastophaga psenes* lives in a state of symbiosis with the fig (above), on which it depends for survival. It inhabits the fruit of caprifigs (left and far left) in which it produces galls
Top right: Larvae develop within the galls
Bottom right: The insect's frequent journeys back and forth in the process of mating help to pollinate the fig-trees

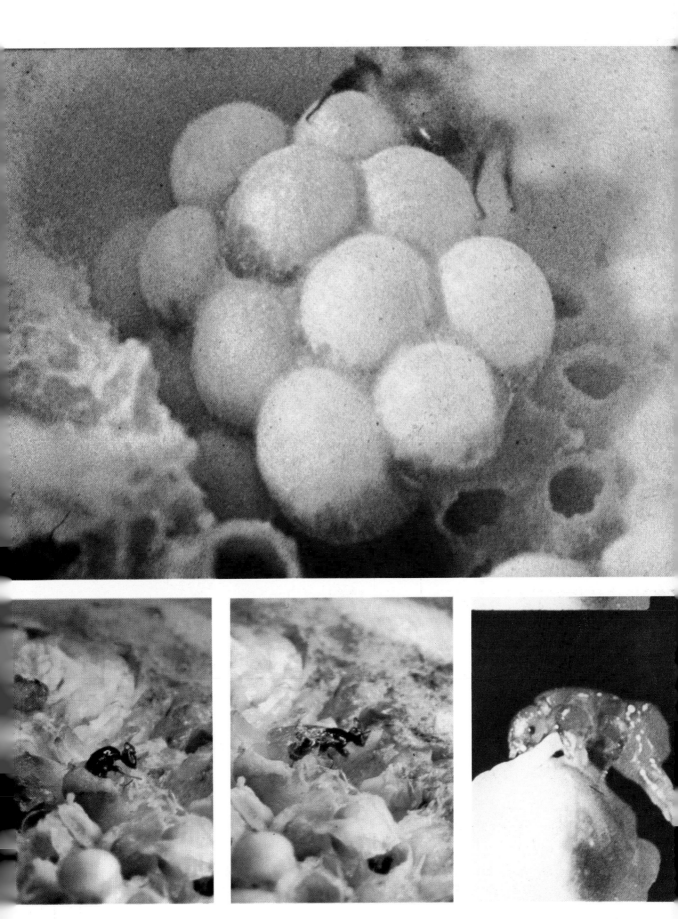

The superfamily Siricoidea includes some of the largest and most striking Hymenoptera, their bodies dazzling with metallic greens or dark blues so that they look like flying jewels. The adults show marked differences between the sexes. They may be different in coloration and in size (the female is often noticeably larger than the male), but the principal difference is that while the abdomen of the male is rounded, that of the female ends in a robust, complex, straight protrusion, part of which is the ovipositor. The larvae generally eat wood. They live inside the trunks of different kinds of trees and are constantly active, digging out long tunnels with their powerful jaws and ingesting large quantities of wood which are then expelled, after the insect's digestive tube has extracted the nutritious substances, through the anal aperture, thus obstructing the burrow immediately behind the larva.

This larva develops from an egg which has been introduced by the mother deep

Below: Many hymenopterous insects lead a life closely associated with flowers. The photograph shows a cargo of pollen on the hind leg of a bee

into the crevices of the bark of the host tree. Here it will live for from three to five or six years and then change into a nymph in a cell dug out for the purpose, from which the adult will later use its robust jaws to gnaw its way outside. Finally, after a long while in total darkness, the fully-formed insect is now free to fly out into the sunshine.

The spectacular giant wood-wasp

Within Siricoidea, the best-known European species is undoubtedly the giant wood-wasp *Urocerus gigas*, of the subfamily Siricinae, whose members frequent tall conifers, in particular the fir and larch. The adult of this fine species, the joy of young collectors, may reach a length of 30 millimetres (1.18 inches) if male, and 40 millimetres (1.57 inches), not counting the ovipositor, if female. Its colouring is mainly brownish-black and ochre yellow. The head, black with two large yellow patches behind the eyes, carries long, light brown antennae. The large wings are yellow; the whole surface of the abdomen is also yellow in the female, but reddish in the male, and the thorax and underside of the abdomen are brownish-black in both sexes. It is a sight worth seeing when, towards noon on summer days, these wood-wasps take to the air, often in large numbers, along the sunny glades of pinewoods in central Europe or the Italian mountains. The males fly in a cloud around the tree-tops, while the females flutter between fallen trees or over the bark of the conifers, exploring every crevice, ceaselessly feeling with their antennae, and seeking suitable places where, protected from enemies and with food at hand, they may deposit their precious cargo of eggs.

In spite of their appearance, which discourages non-entomologists from handling them, wood-wasps are completely harmless. The long, rigid appendage protruding from the female's abdomen is

Right: Flowers are far from being the helpless prey of plundering insects. The insects' flights from one flower to another are essential for cross-pollination

merely an inoffensive ovipositor. Thanks to this instrument, the female can deposit her eggs, singly or up to eight at a time, at a depth of some 10 millimetres (0.40 inches) below the surface of the wood. Egg-laying may last for up to a month, during which time one female may deposit as many as 1,000 eggs. The larvae which emerge from them will live in the wood for a period varying from three to five and even six years, depending on climate, the particular kind of tree in which they develop, and the age and physical condition of the tree (trees past their prime and which are not perfectly healthy are the ones usually chosen).

The family Cephidae (stem sawflies) includes some species which, in the larval stage, damage certain crops. *Cephus pygmaeus* (the European wheatstem borer) attacks grasses. This insect has in fact no particular preferences, and lives happily on wheat, rye or barley, as well as on various wild grasses little utilized by man. However, the presence of vast cultivated areas where the available grasses are those sown by man favour the development of the insect, and the resulting damage can be devastating, though this is rarely so in Britain.

The adult female wheatstem borer is a small insect which in late spring lays her eggs in the stems of the grasses when the ears have scarcely begun to develop. The larva begins to feed inside the stem, tunnelling downwards. At the completion of its fairly rapid development, it digs out a cell at the base of the stem, which is by now practically full of its own excretions. Here it undergoes metamorphosis. The affected cereals obviously produce either sterile ears or ears with a few half-empty grains; and neither hay-making nor reaping can hurt the insect, snug in its cell safely below the level of the scythe.

Caterpillar-like larvae

The more conspicuous and better-known larvae of the Symphyta are the larvae of the Tenthredinoidea, some of which live in groups on the leaves of plants, including cultivated ones such as currants and roses. These larvae are generally greenish or blackish, undistinguished in colouring but worthy of note because they are surprisingly similar to the caterpillars of butterflies or moths (Lepidoptera). Like caterpillars, these Tenthredinoidea larvae are described as 'eruciform' (caterpillar-like). They have elongated, cylindrical bodies with darker, rounded heads. Again, like caterpillars, they have three pairs of true legs on the thorax, one pair on each segment, and a varying number of false legs on the abdomen, each of which ends in a sucker. This resemblance must not be mistaken for evidence of family likeness between Hymenoptera and Lepidoptera, however. Rather, it is due to the phenomenon of 'convergence' by which organisms quite different from one another, but which colonize the same surroundings in similar ways, adopt similar solutions to similar problems and consequently come to appear alike.

Tenthredinoidea larvae of this type, however, are immediately distinguishable from those of Lepidoptera not only by certain structural details, such as the presence of false legs on the second abdominal segment (which in true caterpillars does not carry legs), but also by a curious defensive attitude. If you observe closely a leaf of, say, a rose, attacked by 10 or so of these larvae, probably you will not immediately realize what is happening, but see only the larvae, firmly hooked on to the edge of the leaf by means of their false legs, intent on chewing the leaf with an up-and-down movement of the head and thorax, just like caterpillars. But if you approach too closely, the larvae will interrupt their feeding and raise the upper part of their abdomen, curving it into an S shape and emitting at the same time a drop of yellowish liquid from the anal aperture. This behaviour, clearly defensive, is intended to frighten the adversary or potential predator, and is of a type that is fairly frequently found among many species of insects.

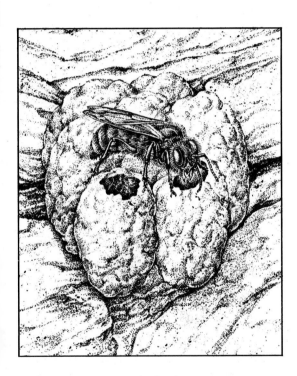

Above: A mason-bee (*Chalicodoma muraria*)
builds a nest of mud, skilfully shaping
it with its forelegs

Characteristics of Apocrita

Some examples of Hymenoptera suborder Symphyta have already been considered. The rest, by far and away the more numerous, belong to the suborder Apocrita (among them bees, wasps, ants and ichneumon-flies). They are distinguished by having a conspicuous separation between the thoracic and abdominal regions. But it is not strictly accurate to speak of thorax and abdomen when indicating the middle and terminal regions of Apocrita, since during the evolution of these insects some parts have shifted from their original position. This renders the general structure of this group very interesting, indeed unique in the whole insect class. It is generally accepted that the body of an insect comprises a series of rings, called segments or metameres, 20 in number, with some exceptions among the more primitive orders. These segments fall into three divisions, the head, thorax and abdomen, consisting re-spectively of six, three and eleven segments. Each of these has a dorsal part, or plate, the tergum or notum, and a ventral plate, the sternum, connected laterally by elastic structures known as pleura.

In the course of evolution of Apocrita, the sternum of the first abdominal segment has dwindled and disappeared. The corresponding tergum and pleura have migrated forward from their original position to the thoracic region, joining onto the third thoracic segment, where in the adult they form the structure, topographically thoracic but abdominal in origin, known as the propodeum or epinotum. This is followed in the simplest cases by a constriction separating the thoracic region (as already shown, more complex than a true thorax) from the remaining hind parts of the body, which are no longer known as the abdomen but as the gaster. The gaster may be further modified, too. While, for example, in bees it is separated from the thoracic region by a simple constriction, in other groups the first, or the first and second segments together of the gaster (that is, the second, or second and third segments of the abdomen) are much narrower. These form the characteristic peduncle or stalk, also called the petiole, which, whether rigid or articulated, means that the gaster of these Hymenoptera is very mobile. Such mobility plays an extremely important part in the life of these insects, since it enables them to manoeuvre the sting with which many species are provided, or the ovipositor, with great agility in various directions.

Feeding habits of Parasitica

The suborder Apocrita is further divided into two groups: the Parasitica and the Aculeata. The most obvious difference between them, though not the only one, is that female Parasitica carry at the tip of the abdomen a long tubular structure. In some cases, this can be retracted when at rest, and is thus invisible externally; but in others it is permanently extruded. It is used for depositing eggs and is called the ovipositor or terebra. The Aculeata, by contrast, carry in the same position a short retractable organ, the aculeus or sting itself, connected with the ducts of the poison glands. The function of these, as will be shown, is both defensive and offensive, and in many groups is extremely important during the building of structures destined for sheltering and feeding the larvae, such as the cells of the beehive.

More than 70,000 species have so far been ascribed to the Parasitica. They are modestly-sized insects, some very tiny like the already-mentioned fairy-flies, but so widely differing in appearance that it is impossible to give even a summary description which would be valid for all the groups. But from examination of the principal ones, certain salient characteristics emerge.

From the biologist's point of view, it is particularly interesting to find that in general the diet of the adults varies according to sex. Whereas the males, in order to fulfil their tasks, feed on sugary substances which they normally extract from flowers (for which they also act as pollinators), this diet is not always enough for the females, who must supplement it with proteins. Apart from sugary substances of vegetable origin, many females in the Parasitica also need to feed on liquids of animal origin, rich in proteins. To do this, they usually introduce their ovipositor into the chosen victim, generally an insect, either adult or larva. They then withdraw the ovipositor and lick up the liquids that have oozed out, sometimes also enlarging the wound with their jaws. In some groups, the female procures her animal nutrition by highly sophisticated methods.

Victims are larvae of wood-eating insects, buried in wood, or else nymphs or chrysalises wrapped in their cocoons. The insect pierces the wood or chrysalis with her ovipositor, reaches her quarry, drills through its skin into the main body cavity, and then slowly withdraws her ovipositor. Glands on the ovipositor now secrete a substance all around it which immediately solidifies, forming a rigid tube—the 'alimentary tube'—which, when completed, works much like a drinking straw. Through it, the insect peacefully sucks up its necessary animal proteins. Maturation of the eggs requires considerable expenditure of energy and materials by the female, and by thus seeking protein from the prey it does not need to use reserves accumulated in its larval stage.

Forms of parasitism

The most outstanding biological characteristic of Parasitica is undoubtedly the fact that their larvae are parasites. They live without exception either on plants or, in most cases, on animal organisms. However, the relationship between parasite and host is always very close, in the sense that either the Hymenoptera larva lives within the host's tissues, though without injuring its vital faculties (or at any rate not until the larva is almost fully developed), or an intimate and permanent contact is established between the two. There are in fact a number of exceptions to the condition of internal parasitism, some of the more relevant of which will be examined briefly later. In such cases, the mother prepares enough food reserves to last her offspring throughout its development.

Two enormously important evolutionary facts now stand out and represent an improvement on the mode of living of the Symphyta. Firstly, there is the structure of the Apocrita larva. This, no longer restricted by the demands of free-living, has lost its legs, false legs and eyes, and become transformed into a soft, defenceless worm-shaped organism, generally colourless. Secondly, in many cases, the adult insects have developed very sophisticated methods of constructing and provisioning the nests in which they shelter and nurture their offspring.

Parasitic Hymenoptera living in or on animal hosts usually attack other Arthropods, generally insects, with Lepidopterous larvae being especially chosen. They also attack spiders, larval ticks and, in one case, false scorpions. Parasitic Hymenoptera exploit insects at all stages of their life cycle. Some groups prefer eggs, others larvae or nymphs, while a few attack adults, even the toughest beetles. Successful experiments have been made in replacing chemical warfare against harmful insects— a method which is expensive as well as full of risks and unknown factors—by biological warfare based, to a great extent, on the use of parasites, but also by crop management involving changes in farming methods.

Hymenoptera have so many different ways of introducing parasites to their hosts that, before considering explanatory examples, they must first be classified. Ectoparasitism occurs when the larva does not live inside its host, but feeds on it from the outside. The host, which may remain alive for a long time, is usually incapable, for various reasons, of putting up any significant resistance.

More common is endoparasitism, where the mother injects the egg or eggs directly

Above and top: The wasp *Paravespula germanica* uses its sting to paralyse an egg-laden processionary moth (top). It then proceeds to eat the eggs (above)

into the host organism, where the larva will feed on the tissues in a specific manner. It feeds first on the reserve tissues of its host, then by degrees on the remaining parts of the body, leaving the essential organs to the last so as not to endanger its host's life prematurely.

Endoparasitism may be further complicated. Firstly, it may be primary, developing at the expense of a free-living host, or it may be secondary, if the host itself is a parasite. This latter condition is known as hyperparasitism. There are also classifications for the degree of infestation of the host. Solitary parasitism is when the parasite and its host are of more or less the same size, while gregarious parasitism refers to cases where a single host is infested with numerous small larvae. In the simplest cases, this condition results from the laying of many eggs on the same host, but it may also be the result of the phenomenon known as polyembryony. Here, the female deposits one egg only in the host's body (the host being usually considerably larger than the parasite). The embryo then develops in an unusual fashion. The fertilized egg begins to divide normally until it reaches the stage where the embryo consists of a solid mass of cells. This mass, however, consists of an abnormally high number of embryo cells. It then subdivides into 1,000 (or even more) cellular groups which finally separate and migrate to colonize the whole host. At this point, each group begins to develop as an embryo more or less normally until it becomes a larva.

This process is particularly common in some groups of Parasitica and has also been found to occur in some Aculeata. Its significance lies in the fact that it increases the reproductive potential of the species and it has been shown that such polyembryonic species generally deposit fewer eggs than those laid by normally-developing species.

To conclude this examination of the various forms of parasitism, superparasitism and multiparasitism must also be discussed. Neither is an efficient method of survival, however. In the former, too many larvae of the same species, originating from separate egg-deposits of the same or different mothers, infest the same host. In the latter, larvae of different species, all primary parasites, also infest the same host. This results in rivalry and in some cases cannibalism, which seriously endangers the development of many of the Hymenoptera, since the host is incapable of supporting for any length of time the excessive burden of parasites.

Parasitic Hymenoptera

Now that these general observations have been made, certain species of Parasitica may be examined. The numerous species have been grouped by one authority into seven superfamilies, comprising in turn 47 families.

In order of evolution, the first superfamily is the Trigonaloidea. Only one species, *Pseudogonalos hahni*, has been discovered in Europe to date. In appearance it resembles a small wasp. In the larval stage, it lives as a hyperparasite on larvae of other Parasitica or Diptera of the Tachinidae family. Both the Parasitica and the Tachinidae chosen as victims are, in their turn, endoparasites of Lepidoptera larvae, or, less often, of Symphyta larvae. In both cases, the larvae are free-living and feed on the leaves of various plants. Curiously, the female Pseudogonalos does not lay her eggs within the host, but abandons them on the leaves which serve as food for the Lepidoptera or Symphyta larvae—which ingest the eggs with the leaves, without damaging them. If these larvae are infested by Parasitica or Tachinidae larvae, the Pseudogonalos, on emerging from its eggs, may parasitize them; if not, it will not survive. Obviously this method of infestation, depending as it does on the coincidence of many factors, is very inefficient. It is therefore the reason for the relative rarity of the species, which depends for its survival solely on the huge number of eggs deposited.

More efficient methods of infestation are

followed by members of the second superfamily, the Ichneumonidae or ichneumon-flies. Within this, the Braconidae family comprises several thousand species, of slender proportions and sometimes, especially in tropical regions, of vivid metallic colouring. In many of them the ovipositor is exceptionally long.

The majority of Braconidae parasitize the larvae of Lepidoptera, some Coleoptera and Diptera. One of the commonest species, *Apanteles glomeratus*, is a small, insignificant-looking insect, well known to all would-be entomologists. Fascinated by butterflies which are colourful and easily prepared for mounting, the beginner attempts sooner or later to breed caterpillars as an excellent way of obtaining a steady flow of prime specimens. What better to experiment on than the caterpillars of the Cabbage White, easily found in the vegetable garden, and no problem to feed? When the time comes for metamorphosis, however, he receives a disappointment. Out of perhaps 100 caterpillars, not more than a third form chrysalises. The others, sickly and almost motionless, become covered in the course of a night with 10, 20 or even more tiny cocoons of yellow silk, and die. From the small cocoons, attached to the now empty remains of the caterpillars, there soon emerges a cloud of Hymenoptera, *Apanteles glomeratus* itself—a disappointment for the entomologist, but a blessing for agriculture. But for the activities of the parasite, we should have to contend with widespread infestation.

Laying the eggs

Although distributed world-wide, the vast and complex family Ichneumonidae is especially typical of Holarctic zones—that is,

Right: All the Aculeata (including the Vespidae) have larvae that feed on animal flesh; the adults are partial to nectar, ripe fruit and honey-dew. In a few cases they supplement their diet with the flesh of dead animals. The photographs show some Polistes wasps enjoying a dish of game

119

the northern temperate and sub-arctic biological regions. One of the best-known and most eye-catching species found in Europe is the large ichneumon-fly *Rhyssa persuasoria*, common throughout the Northern Hemisphere. This splendid insect, 35 to 40 millimetres (1.37 to 1.57 inches) long, not counting the ovipositor, is slender and elegant, a glossy brownish-black spotted with white, with orange-yellow legs. In the female, the ovipositor is well developed and may be 60 millimetres (2.36 inches) long. Hosts for its larvae are the wood-eating larvae of other Hymenoptera—the wood-wasps. The way in which the female *Rhyssa persuasoria* lays her eggs is extremely interesting and easily observed, especially

in coniferous woods in the mountains. The fertilized female, having flown to a fir tree, crawls over it several times, exploring it and pausing frequently to examine the surface with her long antennae, until she finds a suitable spot. Here, she attaches herself firmly by the claws with which she is equipped, extends her legs to their full length and raises the tip of her abdomen as high as it will go. She is now able, by pointing the end of her ovipositor downwards, to insert it into the bark and begins to drill a hole. It may take upwards of half an hour for her to reach her goal, sometimes 6 centimetres (2.36 inches) below the surface. The wood-wasp larva is then injected with the egg which spells its death.

Three views of a nest of the wasp *Dolichovespula sylvestris*. These nests often house a parasitic fellow-tenant as well, the wasp *Dolichovespula saxonica*

What is really amazing, apart from the hole-drilling operation carried out with such a delicate instrument, is the precision with which the insect on the surface can pinpoint its prey, apparently safe deep within the tree-trunk. It appears that this is due to the vibrations produced by the wood-wasp's jaws, perceptible even on the surface by the ultra-sensitive receptors on the Rhyssa's antennae.

A balance of forces

Other species of ichneumon-flies parasitize Lepidoptera larvae living on leaves of particular kinds of tree, and they are extremely important in controlling the biological balance of woods and forests. Sometimes, if several factors coincide, the infestation of forests by some of the caterpillars of such Lepidoptera (often moths of the species *Panolis flammea*, Pine Beauty, or similar species) can reach astounding proportions. The presence of several millions of these larvae in a pine forest could endanger its very existence, but for the intervention on a massive scale of the ichneumon-flies. In such circumstances, their population increases rapidly until equilibrium is re-established.

Even some aquatic organisms have been unable to escape the attentions of the Parasitica. The larvae of some caddisflies are infested in Europe by the only Italian member of the family Agriotypidae, *Agriotypus armatus*. The females of these Hymenoptera are small wasps about 7–8 millimetres (0.30 inches) long and black, with an ovoid gaster carrying a short, rigid ovipositor. When the time comes to lay her eggs, Agriotypus, a very competent aviator, flies off to a pond of clear water, or a stream, on whose gravelly bottom there are almost always found (sometimes in large numbers) the caddisfly larvae. These drag with them their characteristic silk case, encrusted with minute grains of sand or pieces of dead vegetable matter. The wasp, although she cannot swim, immerses herself in the water and clings on to plants or stones, covered by a fine, shining bubble of air which is retained in position by tiny water-repellent hairs. This allows the insect to breathe until she reaches the caddisfly larva and injects her egg into it.

The formation of galls

The superfamily Cynipoidea includes about 1,500 known species, of which some parasitize other insects and others parasitize plants. The latter's methods are most interesting, since the presence of their larvae causes a reaction by the host plant which provokes the formation of the characteristic growths known as galls. Those familiar with the countryside will have noticed, for example, curious yellowish balls on young oaks, perfectly spherical, the size of a large hazelnut; others, larger and brown in colour, look like a medlar fruit. Wild roses frequently have on their young, thick stems reddish-green growths covered with threads, which at first sight look like moss or clumps of lichen. These are, however, really galls, and if they are dissected with care, fat larvae of cynipid Hymenoptera of the subfamily Cynipinae (gall wasps) are visible within.

The reproductive cycle of the Cynipinae is of interest to the biologist because of the phenomenon known as 'alternation of generations'. A generation comprising both sexes will reproduce sexually to produce a generation of females only. These females, when mature, will reproduce by parthenogenesis—that is, without the participation of the male—to produce a generation which again comprises both sexes. While each species produces characteristic galls, there are great differences between the galls of different generations. Females which have been fertilized by males lay their eggs in the roots of oak trees. From these emerge larvae which cause the formation of underground galls on the roots. This generation is exclusively female and emerges from the galls in late autumn. They are wingless and crawl up to the top of the oak, where they lay their parthenogenetic eggs in the axils of dormant buds. Here, in spring, the new galls form and the cycle begins again.

However, not all Cynipinae induce formation of galls. Many of them exploit the galls produced by other species for the benefit of their own larvae, and in such cases the parasites generally develop amicably side by side with their hosts without harming them. A single gall may contain larvae other than those of the species which actually caused it, and all these larvae may be infested by different species of other parasitic Hymenoptera. Hyperparasitism may also be present, and so a very complex microcosm may be enclosed in a gall of a few cubic centimetres capacity.

Above and top: In spring, the female
Polistes gallicus builds her nest in the
most unlikely places—in this instance a
saucepan in a junkyard. The insect chews up
dried vegetable matter and moistens it with
saliva to make the nest's walls

Right: A Polistes nest (top) is generally
built in out-of-the-way and hidden positions.
In very hot areas, however, it is hung by a
strong stalk from the branch of a tree
(bottom). The cells face obliquely downwards
so that they will not be flooded when it
rains

Above: *Polistes nympha* is one of the species of social wasps, which in Europe generally form small annual colonies. The females are fertilized in the autumn, spend the winter under cover, and in spring each female then founds a new colony. The photographs show part of a tile which has been turned upside down to reveal the nest on its underside

The last superfamily of Parasitica to be considered, the Chalcidoidea (or chalcids), includes among others the family Agaonidae, to which one celebrated species belongs—*Blastophaga psenes* (the fig insect), common in southern Europe and the whole Mediterranean basin. This tiny insect produces galls within the flowers of the wild fig, also known as Caprificus or the caprifig. The wingless males fertilize the females before these abandon the gall in which they have developed. After mating, the females then leave the flowers and fly in search of another fig-tree where they may lay their eggs. On leaving the original fig-tree, they make their way through the male part of the developing fig and become laden with pollen, which they deposit when they enter the new fig to lay their eggs. The insect frequently ends up not on a wild fig but on a domestic one. Its larvae will not develop here, but the fertilization of the domestic fig is assured. The 'fruit' of the fig in domestic varieties is formed exclusively of female flowers. Many varieties will ripen without fertilization; but in others, unfertilized figs do not mature. In such cases, the fig insect is very important. Among the strains of fig which behave in this way the best known is the Smyrna fig, whose cultivators, though ignorant of entomology, have for centuries adopted the technique of 'caprification', which consists of placing flowering twigs of the wild fig among the branches of their domestic figs, in order to ensure their fertilization, thus increasing their production.

This phenomenon explains the misfortune which overtook Californian planters at the end of the last century. Having introduced the Turkish fig into California, they were disagreeably surprised when it did not bear fruit. The trees were covered with flower-buds which dropped off without ripening. The explanation was the lack of the caprifig, chosen host of the fig insect. After American entomologists had visited Smyrna in Turkey and realized the nature of the problem, it was fairly simple to import the wild fig with its attendant gall-forming insect *Blastophaga psenes*. This is a classic example of the importance of pollinating insects to the human economy.

Insects that sting

After the Symphyta and the Parasitica, the last large group of Hymenoptera is the infra-order of the Apocrita known as the Aculeata. Although this includes a wide variety of insects (both bees and ants are members) they all share a common characteristic. The females bear the 'sting' or aculeus, an offensive organ, at or near the tip of the abdomen, which has derived in the course of evolution from the ovipositor. It has lost its original function, and the eggs are directly injected through the aperture of the oviduct. The organs forming the ovipositor have undergone a structural and functional transformation, and have become adapted for injecting prey or an aggressor with the secretion from two poison glands, classified as acid or alkaline according to the reaction of the liquid they produce. The products of the two glands mingle only at the moment of stinging, and their combined action results, in man anyway, in a sharp localized pain, followed by reddening of the surrounding skin and often by swelling.

Much research has been done on the venoms of bees and wasps but there is little agreement as to their nature or the way they act. Many of the effects seem to be due to histamine set free from the cells of the victim. However, if a honeybee sting is unpleasant for humans, it is generally fatal to the insect itself. The internal lancets of the sting are provided with tiny back-curved hooks, which fasten themselves like harpoons into elastic human skin. In freeing itself, the bee leaves its sting in the victim, together with its poison glands and part of its digestive apparatus, which means it cannot long survive. If you are stung by a bee or similar insect, which leaves its sting in the wound, you should not try to remove it by grasping the part which is protruding. This only has the effect of compressing the poison glands which are still attached to it, thus causing a second injection. It is better to give a sharp, glancing blow as if shaving the affected surface, in order to extract the sting without handling it. It is also useful to know that bee venom, and that of Hymenoptera in general, has anaphylactic properties—that is, it sensitizes the human organism to further stings, with the consequence that in particularly sensitive people these may be very serious and even fatal.

Some Aculeata have perfected the most complex examples of nest-making for the purpose of caring for their offspring; indeed, these species are perhaps the most sophisticated in the whole animal world. In both solitary and social species, nests are constructed from all kinds of materials and in many different ways. These are then provisioned with animal or vegetable substances, giving the new-born larvae immediate access to an exclusive store of food and thus enhancing their chances of reaching adulthood and so of perpetuating the species.

Specialist pollinators

All bees are essentially anthophagous—that is, they feed on the sugary liquids secreted by the flowers of the higher plants. In so doing, and moving from flower to flower, they carry out an extremely important task, not only in ensuring the fertilization of the female parts of the flower by means of the pollen which the insects deposit as they enter, but in particular by facilitating cross-fertilization—that is, transporting the pollen from one plant to fertilize the ovary of another plant of the same species. But why is cross-fertilization important, seeing most plants are provided with male stamens and female ovaries and are therefore, in theory at least, capable of self-fertilization? In fact, as geneticists and biologists in general have shown, the phenomenon of bisexuality is not vital for reproduction. Reproduction by other means is possible. You have only to look at the simple

125

division of many animal organisms, not necessarily the most primitive ones, or at the cutting and layering techniques with which agriculturalists can propagate indefinitely many plants of importance to the economy. Even within sexual reproduction itself, bisexuality is not always necessary: witness the cases, more common than generally thought, of parthenogenesis, or of hermaphroditism, which occurs in species whose members possess both male and female reproductive organs. Bisexuality has another biological meaning. When two cells of different paternal and maternal origin unite, thus combining different genes or inheritances, variations in their progeny will result to ensure not only the survival of the species, its adaptability and pliability, but indeed the evolution of all living beings.

While kinship (or in the case of flowers, self-fertilization) limits the possibilities of variation, it also restricts the potential for adaptability to different backgrounds, and may favour the appearance of pathological, or at any rate negative, characteristics which would otherwise remain latent.

The majority of bees and the males, especially, of many other Aculeata act as pollinators, as already shown. From a conceptual point of view, it is interesting to note that these insects have been associated with flowers ever since their first appearance. Angiosperma—flowering plants —and pollinating insects emerged at more or less the same time on the face of the earth, and their evolution has in many ways been parallel and interdependent.

The classic botanical treatises state that the primula has two kinds of flower: one with long pistils and short stamens, the other with short pistils and considerably longer stamens. An insect entering the flowers to suck nectar from them always does so in the same position and thus will carry, on two different parts of its anatomy, pollen originating from both the short stamens and the long stamens. Obviously, in the course of visiting many flowers in succession, this pollen will brush off on

Right: A nest-building female will gladly accept help from other females, which then come to share in the running of the nest. A single female (generally the founder of the colony), however retains overall supremacy

126

Above and top: Cells and workers of a young colony of *Polistes nympha*. The queen of a new colony demotes the other females that join her to the rank of workers, which gradually lose their fertility and are reduced to rearing the brood and helping the queen. The queen herself then takes care to eat any eggs that the other females have laid

both short and long pistils, thus ensuring cross-fertilization. This clearly demonstrates the adaptation of the flower to habitual pollination by insects.

The founder of modern theories of evolution, Charles Darwin, devoted an entire work to the fertilization of orchids. Their pollen grains are grouped into two small masses called pollinia, attached by a sticky substance. An insect penetrating an orchid flower will find that these pollen masses adhere to its head and remain there as if glued on. As it visits new flowers, the male elements from flowers previously visited are thus necessarily introduced.

On some occasions the relationship between flowers and members of Hymenoptera becomes very close, even specific. This is the case with an epiphyte Mexican orchid, the well-known vanilla, which requires the specific presence of Aculeata of the genus Melipona, without which its flowers remain sterile. When it is cultivated in regions where Melipona is not found, pollination must be done by hand.

Many inaccuracies have been perpetrated about the interdependence between flowers and Hymenoptera, and in particular about the attraction which the more striking flowers have for the insects. Any discussion must proceed with caution. First of all, it is not the most beautiful or the largest flowers, nor those that humans find the sweetest-scented, which most attract the flower-loving Hymenoptera. They are rarely to be found on roses or lemon balm, but abound on the smaller and less showy flowers of ivy, poplar, maple and lime, which are extremely rich in nectar. It is purely the scent of this nectar, to us sometimes downright disagreeable, which attracts them. A field of vetch is always full of bees, even though in this plant the nectar (or rather, in this case, the sugary substance) is found on the leaves and not inside the flower. Many bees do not even penetrate the corolla of the flower, but pierce its base to suck up the nectar, without performing any pollinating function.

Robbers, profiteers and exploiters

We now come to some of the more representative species of the seven super-families and 25 families into which the Aculeata are divided.

First, the Chrysididae (cuckoo-wasps or ruby-tail wasps), about 2,000 species of small or medium-sized wasps. These are some of the most beautiful Hymenoptera, like sparkling jewels of often strikingly contrasted metallic colours. The commonest European species, *Chrysis ignita*, is less than 1 centimetre (0.39 inches) long but catches the eye of even the most uninitiated layman. Its finely sculptured head and thorax are a dazzling emerald green, while the gaster sparkles red as if on fire.

Adult Chrysididae are essentially flower-lovers and it is common to see them in high summer, especially on the flowers of the Umbelliferae. But in the larval stage they behave as cleptoparasites and exploit the larvae of other Hymenoptera, such as honeybees, mason wasps, or digger wasps. Cleptoparasitism in this case means that the cuckoo-wasp penetrates the nests which its host has prepared for its larvae in order to lay its own eggs inside. The intruding larvae feed on the stores prepared for the host larvae and sometimes even on the eggs themselves. In this contest, the host always comes off worst. The act of depositing the eggs is, however, not without risks for the female cuckoo-wasp, who is generally much smaller and less well armed than her host. However, if the intruder is discovered, so to speak, red-handed, she has recourse to an often effective stratagem. The covering of her back is hard enough to be virtually invulnerable to the sting of the host, and the concave underside of her abdomen is capable of accommodating both head and thorax. So the chrysid rolls herself up into a ball and remains immobile, 'playing dead'. After a few minutes of furious manoeuvring and attempting to sting, the host seizes the intruder in its jaws and hurls her, usually without hurting her, out of the nest.

The family Scoliidae includes some of the largest Hymenoptera. *Scolia flavifrons*, a Mediterranean species, looks like a huge wasp, up to 5 centimetres (almost 2 inches) long, with a black, hairy body, yellow head and four conspicuous yellow spots on its abdomen. In the larval state, Scoliae are parasites of large scarabaeid Coleoptera (that is, dung-beetles and chafer-beetles) whose larvae dig out tunnels in the decaying matter on which they feed. Here the Scolia finds them and paralyses them with poison from her sting. The great nineteenth-century French entomologist, J. H. Fabre, was the first to describe the behaviour of some species of Scolia when searching for their prey, immobilizing it and laying their eggs. More recent studies have shown that, contrary to Fabre's theory (otherwise extremely accurate), in this case, as with other paralysing Hymenoptera, it is not necessary for the sting to affect the nervous system directly. The poison acts by diffusing through the vital fluids of the victim and very rapidly paralyses it. The Scolia then transports its prey, by now immobile, into the farthest depths of the tunnel and lays an egg on it. When the larva emerges from the egg, it penetrates inside its victim, which is incapable of reacting but will remain alive for some time. This avoids the danger of the host putrefying, with consequent infection of the food provided.

Members of the Mutillidae family have a rather unusual appearance. They are mostly wingless, the females at least, and may be mistaken for large hairy ants, reddish-brown, white and black in colour. However, it is not at all advisable to confuse them with inoffensive ants, and certainly not to try to capture them in your hands. The resultant agonizing sting is far more painful than that of a bee.

The Pompilidae (spider-wasps) are a highly-specialized family that never vary in the prey they choose to paralyse and use as food for their progeny. Almost all the wasps in this group follow the dangerous sport of spider-hunting. Each pompilid species apparently chooses its victim from a fairly specific closely-related group of spiders. By contrast, it has been shown in experiments that the larvae are less choosy. They feed not only on spiders other than those which their mothers would naturally offer them, but also on non-arachnid organisms.

The reason for the adults' specialization would appear to be associated with the method of attack, which varies according to whether the victim is a web-weaving spider, a vagabond spider, or a spider living in underground tunnels. The chase is always risky, since the spiders are armed with formidable poisonous claws, capable of overcoming any wasp; yet the latter generally win. This is due to their greater speed and agility, so that they succeed in swiftly inserting their sting into the soft underskin which marks the border between the two zones comprising the body of the spider. The spider is almost immediately paralysed, and only then does the wasp, laboriously dragging its now inert victim, start to look for a sandy spot where it can dig out a tunnel, bury the spider, lay an egg in it, close up the tunnel after it and return to the hunt. Although this behaviour is not the most highly evolved among Hymenoptera, it is more refined than the practice of the Scoliidae who, apart from moving their prey a few centimetres into an already existing burrow, abandon both victim and egg at the place the spider was found.

Other species, which also hunt spiders, have developed an unusual technique which might be described as varying from 'breaking and entering' to 'robbery with violence'. In some species, the fertilized female waits for the female of another species to dig out a nest, supply it with food and depart. The first female then immediately enters the nest, deposits an egg in it and covers everything over. This egg produces a precocious larva which first of all disposes of the egg of the legitimate inmate and then, undisturbed, consumes its provisions. At other times, according to one authority's observations, the female

Below: Despite their appearance, these large wasps will only sting humans if molested. The stone on which this nest was made has been lifted to show the cells

'robber'—in this case one of the genus Ceropales—attacks a spider-wasp intent on carrying a paralysed spider. The spider-wasp immediately fights back and often puts her aggressor to flight. However, the struggle takes place over the body of the spider, and in the confusion of the moment, the Ceropales almost always succeeds in depositing her egg within the spider's respiratory cavity, unnoticed by the spider-wasp. Having regained possession of her prey, the spider-wasp then proceeds to bury it in the normal way. Here also, the progeny of the cleptoparasite hatches first and manages to dispose of the spider-wasp's egg. Finally, it is worth noting that some very large species of spider-wasps in hot climates are capable of taking on and defeating even the largest of the giant spiders of the genus Mygale.

Sphecidae, or digger-wasps, also excavate tunnels, but are more wide-ranging than spider-wasps in their choice of victim. They attack Diptera, cicadas, Lepidoptera, other Hymenoptera and Coleoptera, while some, such as the large Languedocian Sphex, attack large, heavy Orthoptera (crickets and grasshoppers). Members of this family also paralyse their victims, injecting poison through their sting. Here, too, the victim survives in a state of almost complete immobility until the Hymenoptera larva is fully developed. The harm done by the sting is moderate. Fabre established, by laboratory experiments, that a bush cricket of the genus Ephippigera which had been paralysed by a digger-wasp would, if the wasp larva was removed and kept in the dark in optimum conditions, survive for 17 days without food and up to 40 if fed artificially with a sugar solution. Recent research seems to show that the poison acts by diffusing through the victim's vital fluids, into the

Left: Red bees belonging to a solitary species lay their eggs in the nests of black bees. In order to occupy the nest, a red bee will position herself at the entrance (the tiny hole in the ground at the centre of the photographs) and paralyse and kill the occupants one by one as they try to come out

connections between nerves and muscles, thus altering the biochemical mechanisms which transmit stimuli.

The behaviour of digger-wasps is considered more highly evolved than that of spider-wasps. First of all, as Fabre supposed, they prepare a nest before (rather than after) finding a suitable victim with which to supply it. Furthermore, the nest itself in many cases has several cells, and is always considerably more complex than the simple cavity of the spider-wasps. This, together with the fact that many species supply their nest with more than one victim, implies an ability to return to it and to orientate themselves about reference points—a clear indication of a higher degree of evolution. Other species again, like the sand-wasp, *Ammophila adriaansei*, have passed the stage in which the mother's activity is limited to constructing the nest and provisioning it. Being more sophisticated, they provide prolonged parental care. This species, and probably others as yet unknown, build several different nests, which may be some distance from one another. Once supplied with caterpillars, the sand-wasp deposits an egg in each nest and then closes it. Subsequently, the insect periodically visits her offspring, supplying them with fresh caterpillars until the larvae reach the stage of metamorphosis.

Sociability is seen to its full extent only in successive groups, as will be shown. However, the rudiments of it are already displayed by digger-wasps, and its existence has been demonstrated in some American species within whose small communities there appears to be some attempt at division of labour.

A diversified family

The family Vespidae may be called 'true wasps'. They comprise social wasps and hornets, paper-making wasps and mason-wasps and include examples of every degree of the evolutionary cycle, from solitary species through successive stages to the formation of those complex social

133

communities which are one of the most interesting aspects of the biology of Hymenoptera.

In shape generally elongated and often very slender, Vespidae are usually strikingly-coloured with yellow and black, or yellow and brown, stripes. These function as 'warning colours', a sign of danger to would-be predators, who soon learn to respect them. (Nonetheless some species of birds, for example the honey buzzard and the bee-eater, habitually prey on them.) Associated with this is the phenomenon known as 'Batesian mimicry', whereby certain harmless species have assumed in the course of evolution an appearance similar to that of other species found in the same region but which are dangerous or inedible. This similarity clearly affords them protection. In Europe, this is the case with many moths and butterflies, especially of the family Sesiidae (clear-winged moths and hornet-moths) which closely resemble wasps, as do some flies. Others have accurately imitated the hairiness and colouring of some of the more fearsome bees.

Among solitary wasps, the genus Eumenes (a potter wasp) constructs beautiful vase-shaped nests from clay mixed with saliva. These nests, the size of a small hazelnut, are attached to brushwood or old walls. The short neck is wider at the top and through this the supply of paralysed lepidopterous caterpillars is passed.

After the next group of subfamilies, we come to the transition from the solitary state to gregariousness, and finally to true social life. This implies, principally, the establishment of a stable and enduring relationship between mother and progeny and of parental care lasting at least until the offspring's metamorphosis. Secondly, the larvae are no longer fed by means of a paralysed prey, but by mouth-to-mouth regurgitation of pre-digested substances and of secretions. The next stage is represented by groups in which some first-generation females continue to live with their mother, even when fully-grown, in the nest where they were born, without

Right: The honeybee and the more striking bumble bee are the commonest Hymenoptera that visit fields in flower. The honeybee is a most important creature in economic terms, and is also of great interest for its high degree of social organization. Note the load of pollen in the 'pollen basket' on the bee's hind leg

A nest of the bumble bee Bombus is unearthed
(below). Generally these nests take the form
of subterranean caves lined with moss and
having a waterproof layer of wax on the
ceiling. The rounded cells are shaped by the
queen (right) in triangular clumps (centre
and bottom row of this page). The two
bottom pictures on the opposite page show a
larva (left) and a worker (right)

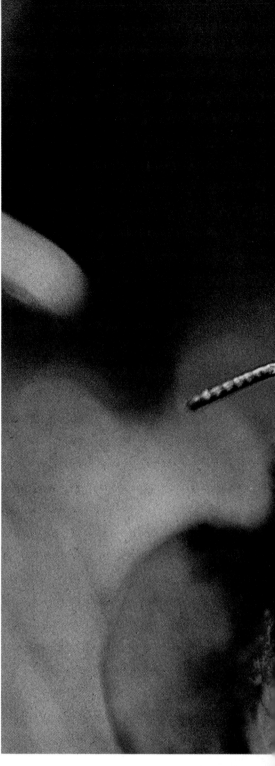

collaborating with her in any way. This is simple cohabitation, each one reproducing and caring for her own offspring.

In successive groups, the situation is similar; but the females, all still fertile, feed and care for their own and other families indiscriminately. This leads to the first stage of social life, in which only some of the females in the nest are fertile. The others, though indistinguishable in appearance, are sterile and perform the tasks of workers.

This is generally the case with paper-wasps, such as *Polistes gallica* (common on the Continent but not normally found in the British Isles), who constructs her nest under the roofs of houses in the country, or in any place sheltered from the rain. These characteristic grey, single-storied nests are attached by stalks and consist of a number of downward-inclined hexagonal cells. They are made of a lightweight but strong 'paper' made from vegetable matter chewed up finely and cemented with saliva. The fertile female who founded the colony initially welcomes other females, even strange ones, who will also begin to lay eggs. The offspring from these will, however, soon be eliminated by the founder, who reduces them to the rank of workers so that they rapidly undergo a process of sterilization.

At this stage, we meet the phenomenon of sex-determination by the mother by means of optional parthenogenesis. Among the social Hymenoptera, the fertile female (whom from now on we will call the queen) mates only once in her life. She conserves the male sperm in a special 'sperm sac' which is part of her reproductive apparatus and uses it at her discretion according to the needs of the community. Females are born from fertilized eggs, and depending on their diet will become either fertile queens or sterile workers. Males only develop from unfertilized eggs by parthenogenesis. Males do not take part in nest-building or rearing of progeny; their function is simply to fertilize the future queens and they generally die soon after mating.

The superfamily Apoidea (bees) is numerous and to be found all over the world, even in Arctic regions. Bees include both small and large species, all of them plant-eaters, and almost all of which feed on sugary liquids, especially from flowers, and on pollen. Thanks to these habits and the fact that they are usually very furry, these insects are excellent pollinators. Study of this superfamily in particular has revealed a great deal about the parallel and inter-dependent evolution of Hymenoptera and flowering plants.

As with wasps, there are both solitary and social species of Apoidea with, in addition, cleptoparasitic species developing in the nests of other bees. All larvae are fed on a mixture of pollen and honey (partially digested nectar) with the social and semi-social species also using mouth-to-mouth feeding between larvae and workers.

Within this superfamily, the family Halictidae (often known as mining or burrowing bees) provide interesting examples of the methods by which bees, initially solitary, have evolved towards a state of highly sophisticated social organization. Although in many ways this phenomenon is similar to that already noted in Vespidae, it has evolved independently. Indeed, it seems incontestable that bees of the family Apidae have evolved from Sphecidae.

The more primitive species of the Halictidae are solitary and mate in autumn, while the female builds her nest in spring. In many cases, several generations of fertile females will inhabit it successively, in mutual tolerance; or, as already seen with wasps, different fertile females build a communal nest together, but their relations do not go beyond simple cohabitation. In other cases, a long-lived founder generates a small community of her offspring, in which some of the females will be sterile and act as workers. Cleptoparasitic species occur in the Halictidae and Megachilidae, for example, with the two families Stelidae and Nomadidae composed entirely of them. These bees deposit their eggs in the already provisioned nests of other species where the parasite larvae develop at the expense of their hosts. Often the cleptoparasite lays her eggs furtively, entering the nest unseen, since she has often come to resemble the host in the course of evolution.

At other times, there is a fight to the death ending with elimination of the bees which constructed the nest. This occurs with the small solitary bee (the red and black cuckoo-bee of the genus Sphecodes) which lays her eggs in the nests of some species of social (or at any rate gregarious) Halictidae. The Halictidae dig out underground nests, generally fairly simple, though often quite large. The cuckoo-bees await the legitimate owners at the entrance to the nest, a small hole in the earth, and attack them one by one, stinging them to death. When all the owners are dead, the cuckoo-bees lay their eggs undisturbed in the already-provisioned burrow.

The family Melittidae includes some species which appear from their habits to be in a period of transition between primitive and highly-evolved bees. Megachilidae includes solitary bees which have specialized organs on the underside of the gaster for collecting pollen, known as pollen baskets. The genus Osmia constructs nests of clay and sand cemented together in almost any kind of natural cavity, even in empty snail shells. The genus Megachile (leaf-cutter bee), on the other hand, lines natural cavities with leaf fragments which it cuts out in perfect semicircles from different kinds of plants. All of them provision their nests with a 'bread' for the larvae, consisting of a thick mixture of nectar and pollen.

The family Apidae includes, besides the domestic bee which will be fully examined in the next chapter, solitary forms such as Xylocopa (carpenter-bee) as well as highly evolved social forms. They all possess a specific organ on the hind legs, modified to form a structure capable of gathering and transporting pollen. The mouth parts of Apidae are also specialized, being very elongated and particularly suited for sucking up nectar, even from deep corollas.

Above and top: Two moments in the courtship and mating of bumble bees. The male is much smaller than the female

139

Xylocopa, a large, dark-blue bee, digs out long burrows in dead wood in which the females, who are not social, prepare a series of cells filled with almost pure pollen. The subfamily Apinae, apart from the more primitive, still solitary groups, includes mainly social forms, such as Bombini (bumble bees), Meliponini (stingless bees) and Apini (honeybees). These bees construct their nests, which can be enormous, mainly or even exclusively from wax, a fatty substance synthetized from special abdominal glands. The Apinae include the domestic bee, which with its related species has reached one of the highest degrees of sophistication.

Life in the beehive

The domestic bee is the best-known honey producer but it is certainly not the only one in the order Hymenoptera. In particular, this order includes the superfamily Apoidea, to which belong numerous families of solitary bees and one family of social bees. Of the latter, two tribes, Meliponini and Apini, are of particular interest since they include several domestic species.

The Meliponini include insects living in tropical and subtropical regions of Africa, Asia, and Central and South America. They have no sting, but can be no less aggressive for that. They use their sharp jaws as weapons, and a highly irritant liquid produced by the first tract of the digestive apparatus is employed as poison. Some species, however, are docile and are bred in hives where they accumulate excellent honey. In some regions, Meliponini influence the existence of whole tribes of people, who use the wax for a variety of purposes and the honey as the basis of their diet.

The tribe Apini includes four species of the genus Apis: *A. florea, A. dorsata, A. indica* and *A. mellifera*. This first, also known as the Indian dwarf honeybee or the little honeybee, is common in India and Indonesia. It attaches its nest, consisting of a single small comb, to horizontal branches of trees. *Apis dorsata,* or the giant honeybee, is found in India, southern China, Indonesia and the Philippines. This species is wild and aggressive and not domesticated. The wax and honey are removed by the local people who rob the large combs, up to 2 metres (just over 6 feet) long, which hang from the boughs of large trees or from rocks or temple roofs. Each comb may contain up to 100 kilograms (220 pounds) of honey.

Apis indica, the Eastern honeybee, is very closely related to *A. mellifera* and is widely found all over southern and eastern Asia from India to China and from Japan to the Philippines. Bred in hives, it is remarkably docile and can survive in harsh climates.

Apis mellifera, the common domestic bee, came originally from the Old World. It is now found everywhere and in a variety of races and subspecies. The Italian subspecies or race, for example, referred to as *A. mellifera ligustica,* is found throughout Italy. The following descriptions refer to this last subspecies.

Characteristics of the worker bee

Bees are a social species, with persistent colonies comprising individuals of three 'castes' which have different characteristics. These consist of the two main reproductive castes, the fertile female or 'queen' and the males or 'drones'. The other caste is made up of sterile females, with reduced genital organs, called 'workers'.

When describing the structural,

Left: The honeycombs of the honeybee are composed of waxen cells that are mostly hexagonal—a shape produced by the juxtaposition of cylindrical cells. Each comb has two series of cells back to back. The comb hangs vertically

anatomical and physiological characteristics of the species, the example normally taken is the worker bee. This bee has a well-proportioned body with the three parts, head, thorax and abdomen, clearly differentiated. The head is flattened at the back and front and carries a pair of antennae, the compound eyes, the ocelli or simple eyes, and the mouth parts.

The antennae are considered to be the bee's principal sensory structures, since they carry the organs of touch and smell. The former consist of tactile hairs and hair-like sensillae or sense organs thickly distributed over the segments of the antennae. These organs allow the bees, even in the darkness of the hive, to carry out the most delicate operations of communication among themselves and to distinguish by feel alone whatever they approach. The olfactory sensillae are a very important means of developing social life, not only for the workers but also for the whole colony.

The compound eyes lie on either side of the head. They consist of a vast number of single eyes called ommatidia. Together these make up the well-known mosaic

Above right: Man has been able to semi-domesticate honeybees by providing them with suitable receptacles (in the form of hives) for their nests
Right: A type of hive made by certain African tribes

Top left: A straw skep, a simple type of rustic hive widely used in past centuries. In this and similar simple hives, the combs are permanently fixed inside the hive by the bees and cannot be removed
Left: A hollow tree-trunk can provide another location for a hive

vision which enables an image to be formed from a combination of the individual pieces supplied by each ommatidium. The eye of a worker contains about 6,300 ommatidia—more than the eye of a queen but about half those of a male. These variations are generally supposed to be related to the different way of life of the different castes. Workers and drones need powerful visual organs—the former for orientating themselves when flying, the latter to pick out the queen during her nuptial flight. Generally, however, the female to be fertilized is discovered mainly by the sense of smell. The eye of the queen is less developed, since her life is spent almost entirely in the darkness of the hive.

The bee perceives images from both near and distant objects and can distinguish between some colours and shapes. It cannot tell the difference between red and green, but can perceive, among others, yellow, blue, purple and white. Bees, however, are attracted by the colour and shape of flowers, as well as by scent.

There are also three ocelli, or simple eyes, lying in a triangle among the long hairs on top of the head. These do not supply an actual image, but act as photoreceptors providing information on the surrounding light-intensity.

The bee's mouth parts are adapted for licking and sucking, and especially for sipping liquids. The jaws have smooth edges and cannot cut into ripe fruit, as do those Hymenoptera which possess chewing mouth parts. The maxillae and lower lip make up the proboscis. The internal lobes of the lower lip are fused to form the ligula which is longer than all the other mouth parts and has a wide, rounded tip, the labellum, thickly covered with sensillae. A groove covered with long, thick hairs runs down the ligula, the surface of which is also covered with hairs lying in bands across it.

Although the bee's jaws are not capable of making any impression on ripe fruit every year some beekeepers face accusations from fruit growers, and particularly wine growers, that their bees have com-

mitted the most heinous misdeeds. This is probably because people often confuse bees with wasps. It is these, together with hornets, that are really responsible for damage to fruit since their mouth parts are adapted for chewing and licking, and have strong, cutting, toothed jaws. With these powerful weapons, wasps are able to attack the skin of ripe fruit to feed on the soft pulp within and once a hole has been made other insects, including bees, take immediate advantage of this food-source placed at their disposal. Specialists in plant disease have demonstrated that bees can in fact be of benefit to fruit attacked by wasps or hornets. For example, grapes which have been attacked by wasps or hornets exude a sugary juice from the pulp inside. If the wounds are not quickly closed microorganisms cause acidity to develop or moulds to appear. Grey grape-mould is particularly harmful, since if humidity is high it spreads within a few days to all the grapes in the vicinity of those attacked by the wasps, until the whole bunch is destroyed. However, the bees, by licking the sugary juice exuding from the grapes, dry them out and this partial or total desiccation discourages agents of disease from establishing themselves. In addition, the bees eat and so eliminate the rotting fruit on which these micro-organisms thrive.

The thorax of the bee, as in all insects, consists of three segments—prothorax, mesothorax and metathorax—but the segmentation is not clearly visible because of the thick covering of fur. The last two segments carry two pairs of membraneous wings on the back. These wings have a mechanism for hooking together so that forewings and hind wings beat in unison during flight. The three segments of the thorax also carry, on the side and underneath, the three pairs of legs which are

Right: Bees (top) contrasted with wasps (bottom). The bee's mouth parts are elongated and are of the sucking type. The mouth parts of the wasp are shorter and are adapted for licking and lapping up sweet sugary foods

differentiated according to the various functions they perform.

On each of the first pair of legs is a comb-like device consisting of a two-lobed spur at the end of the inner edge of the tibia, and a semi-circular notch with comb-like spines arranged in a circle at the top of the inside of the first joint of the tarsus. When the leg is bent, the spur closes the opening of the hollow, thus forming a hole through which the bee passes its antennae in order to clean them of dust and pollen grains. The second pair of legs, on the mesothorax, differ from the first pair since they have no 'comb' and are also a great deal stronger.

The hind legs, on the metathorax, have two joints, the tibia and the first tarsomere, adapted specially for pollen-collection. The tibia is flattened and on its outer surface, towards the further end, is a hollow, known as the pollen basket. Long, thick hairs growing on the inside of the tibia point towards the pollen basket. The first joint of the foot, known as the first tarsomere, is wide and flat, and on its inner surface is the so-called 'brush' consisting of

crosswise bands of tiny, stout, dense bristles.

The bee, entering the corolla of the flower to suck up nectar, becomes covered with pollen. A very rapid movement of the first pair of legs and then of the second pair gathers up the pollen lying thickly in the fur of the thorax and collects it on to the brush of the hind legs. The insect then crosses its legs and deposits the pollen from each brush in the pollen basket of the opposite leg. There, moistened with nectar and honey, it accumulates in globules awaiting transport to the cells of the comb where it will be stored.

The abdomen of the worker bee has a convex back and flat stomach. It consists of ten segments or urites, each of which has a tergite, a strong plate on the upperside, and a sternite, a solid plate on the underside. Of the forepart, the fourth, fifth, sixth and seventh sternites each possess two wide oval lateral areas, called 'mirrors' since they are shiny and very thin. Below these are the wax glands, whose secretion passes in liquid form through the thin skin of the

Of all insects, the bee has the most intimate relationship with flowering plants. The photographs on these two pages show bees contentedly at work among the petals of flowers of various colours, gathering nectar and pollen for food and at the same time cross-fertilizing the flowers

mirrors before solidifying in thin scales.

In the membranes between the sixth and seventh tergites is the scent gland, also called 'Nassonoff's gland' after its discoverer. This gland emits a distinctive odour, different for each family, to which other bees are very sensitive, so that it serves for recognition and as a signal.

At the tip of the abdomen, the worker bee carries a sting. This is part of the genital system—even if not used for laying eggs. The sting, or aculeus, is a long, thin shaft, widening at the point nearest the body into a hollow bulb. This shaft consists of a grooved stylet which is extended to form the bulb, and of two narrow lancets armed with ten or so little, backward-facing teeth. The lancets and the stylet form a channel which opens at the end of the shaft. At either side are two valves, the sting valves, which are covered with little barbs and with sensillae.

The sting is activated by special muscles and is connected to the bee's poison glands. The barbs make it an offensive weapon, but it may also be a suicidal one if injected into the elastic skin of mammals and not into the rigid outer casing of rival bees or other arthropods. If the sting is inserted into elastic tissue, such as the skin of a mammal, it stays lodged in it so that when the bee tries to fly away the sting remains in the victim and is torn away from the insect's abdomen together with part of the intestine.

Bee venom is formed from the secretions of two separate glands, one acid and one alkali. The former consists of two small glandular masses which lead, via an appropriate duct, into a long common channel ending in the so-called reservoir of the gland, a large pear-shaped sac, the narrow end of which is connected by a short channel to the bulb of the sting. At the base of the bulb itself is the opening of the alkali gland, which is tiny and tubular. The secretion of the two glands mingle only at the moment of emission, so that the bee itself is not damaged by the presence of the poison in its body.

Vital mechanisms

The internal structure of the bee presents some interesting details. The digestive apparatus begins with the mouth, followed by the pharynx, whose cavities can be dilated with a complex of powerful muscles. The pharynx works like a suction pump and is used to suck up liquid food. After the pharynx comes the oesophagus, a long, thin tube extending through the thorax into the abdomen, where it widens to form the crop or 'bursa melaria' (honey-stomach), an expandable reservoir where the nectar is stored on gathering flights, prior to being transformed into honey. The crop is followed by the proventriculus, a narrow part which is invaginated into the crop; it has an X-shaped aperture provided with four triangular lips. The posterior opening is guarded by a well-developed valve. The proventriculus serves to pump food from the crop into the stomach and when closed prevents the food returning when the bee regurgitates honey from the crop. The final tract of the digestive system is the wide rectal cavity which can be dilated and which increases enormously in size during the winter months when healthy bees do not evacuate within the hive, but retain excrement in the rectum. This is emitted outside on a mild day on the so-called 'cleansing flights'.

Also connected to the digestive system are the salivary or labial glands, and the pharyngeal glands. The saliva from the former aids digestion and transformation of the nectar into honey. The latter secrete the famous 'royal jelly', of fundamental importance to the life of the colony since it is this substance which determines the development of a queen and which constitutes the elixir of life for the queen herself.

As with most insects, bees breathe through the tracheae—elastic tubes whose walls are lined with a thin, hard layer, with a special spiral reinforcement to keep the tracheal tube open. The tracheae end externally in porthole-like openings, the tracheal spiracles or stigmas, which have

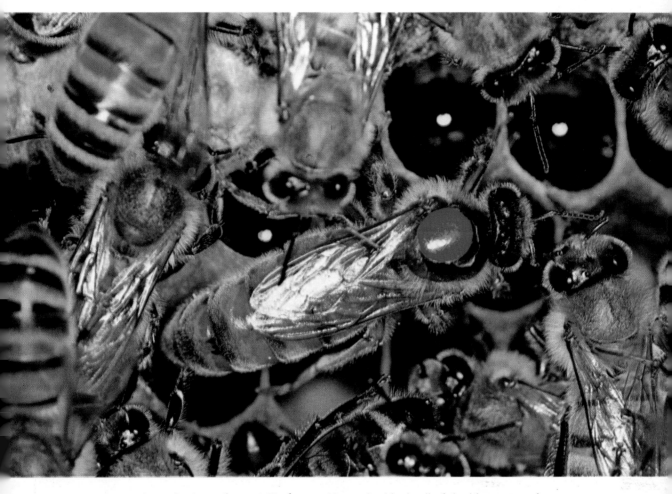

special devices for closing them. Each spiracle gives rise to a trachael branch which divides into finer and finer ramifications to eventually become the tracheoles, very fine tubes which carry oxygen to each individual cell. In bees, some tracheae have inflatable pouches, called air sacs, which fill with air and thus lessen the specific gravity of the bee during flight. They also store oxygen during the long winter rests and can, in flight, compress the rectal cavity, and, in the male, extend the copulatory organ.

The circulatory system is similar to that of other insects, with a dorsal pulsating longitudinal 'heart' and the blood circulating through vessels and cavities. Bees are incapable of regulating their own body temperature in any way. They can, however, generate heat by muscular activity and can cool the colony by bringing in water and causing it to evaporate by

Above: In this detail of the hive, some of the cells can be seen to contain small white eggs laid by the queen (marked with red paint), one egg in each cell

Left: The queen bee (in the centre) is
permanently surrounded by an attentive throng
of maids-in-waiting who take great care of her
Above: Three scenes taken while the queen
was in the process of laying eggs

153

fanning their wings. It has been found that in winter the temperature of the inner group of bees, with the queen at its centre, is 20–25°C (68–77°F), while from spring to autumn the temperature of the brood is 35°C (95°F).

The nervous system of the bee is highly developed, especially the brain, with the mass of nerve-centres lying above the oesophagus in the head. There can be no doubt that bees are pre-eminent among Arthropoda for psychic faculties. They are guided by remarkable instincts which lead them to carry out a chain of varied activities in their brief life span, from the simple but varied and well-coordinated tasks of the first few days within the hive, to the labour in the field where they are able to find their direction by the sun compass even on cloudy days and to transmit information to other workers by their special dances.

When considering the reproductive system, the worker bee, a subordinate, being an unfertilized female, must be largely disregarded, although she sometimes lays eggs, all of which become drones. In the queen the reproductive apparatus consists of two large ovaries, each of which is formed of numerous lesser ovaries leading into a oviduct. The two oviducts unite in a common duct opening into the vagina which widens into an oval sac known as the 'bursa copulatrix'. The vagina receives the duct from the spermatheca, a pouch in which the male sperm can be preserved after mating for a period of up to five years. By a special mechanism of the genital ducts, eggs deposited in cells of 5 millimetre (0.20 inch) diameter are fertilized and produce worker bees; those that are laid in cells of 7 millimetre (0.27 inches) diameter—the drone cells—are unfertilized and produce males by parthenogenesis. The male genital organs consist of two small testicles and two ducts, each of which has a seminal vesicle ending in an accessory gland which secretes a liquid that mixes with the sperm and perhaps assists in preserving it. The two accessory glands

Right: The head of an almost fully developed pupa shows the large brown eyes and the antennae folded across the lower part of the face. When the larva is full-grown and about to change into a pupa, the workers make a cap of wax and pollen across the cell mouth

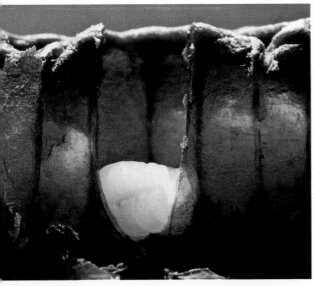

Opposite page, top row: Bees' eggs, each lying in its own cell. Centre and bottom rows: Larvae in various stages of development. The younger ones lie in pools of honey, on which they feed This page from top, and from left to right: Successive stages in the development of a larva. In the bottom left photograph the pupa has been taken out of its cell; at bottom right the pupa, shown in its cell with the cap removed, is surrounded by workers

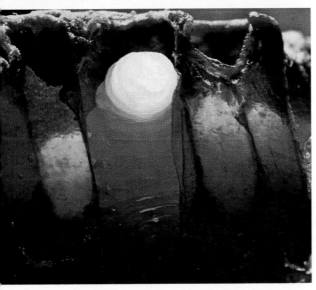

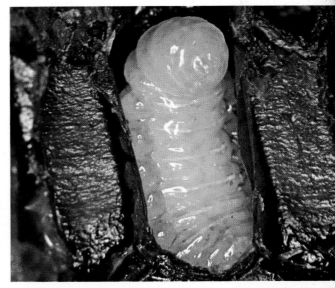

unite to form a common duct, the ejaculatory duct, which leads to the very complex copulatory organ.

The reproductive class

The queen is easily distinguished from the workers, mainly because her abdomen is so much larger. Her eyes are smaller, having about 5,000 ommatidia as opposed to the worker's 6,300. The mouth parts are reduced and the ligula is very short and cannot be used for sucking nectar. The sting is still an offensive weapon but is used only against other queens. The hind legs do not have the structural modifications necessary for pollen-gathering. Nassonoff's gland is absent from the abdomen, but groups of glands exist in the third, fourth and fifth segments and there are the mandibular glands which produce a secretion known as 'queen substance' which maintains the cohesion of the colony. The queen substance is taken up by the workers from the queen and passed on to the other workers in the course of this 'mutual feeding' or 'food-sharing'. If the queen substance is no longer present the bees realize they have no queen. The worker feeds both the queen and the drones, inserting into their mouths the food which she has stored in the fore part of her own digestive system. The wax-making glands that are in the queen's abdomen do not function.

The male is larger than the worker but smaller than the queen. The eyes are relatively huge, consisting of 13,000 or more ommatidia. The mouth is small, with a short ligula, too short for sucking nectar. The drones must therefore be fed by the workers. The hind legs are not adapted for pollen-gathering. The sting, typical of the female sex, is absent. While the fore-wings of the worker reach to the end of her abdomen, those of the male are longer. The queen's wings are similar in size to those of the workers, but appear much shorter on account of the fact that her abdomen is very much larger.

Conception and development

The queen mates only once in her life, during the nuptial flight. This takes place on a sunny day, when the virgin female leaves the darkness of the hive, circles it a few times in order to be able to recognize it later, and soars to a great height, followed by numbers of drones attracted by the pheromones she produces. Mating takes place during this flight: for the successful male it is also a death sentence, since his copulatory organ breaks off inside the queen. She, after mating, returns to earth, frees herself from the inert body of the drone and re-enters the hive. The workers help the queen to remove the male's genital organs and feed her abundantly. After a few days the queen begins to lay her eggs: this activity will occupy her for the rest of her life. A queen can live for five years and may lay up to 2,000 eggs a day.

A bee's egg is slightly curved and pearly white, about 1.4 millimetres (0.05 inches) long and 0.4 millimetres (0.01 inches) wide. It is deposited on the bottom of a cell together with a substance which ensures that it sticks. The eggs may be fertilized or unfertilized. The former produce females, the latter males. Development of the embryo takes three days. The new-born larvae are whitish, without legs or eyes. They go through five moults which take five days in the case of larvae from fertilized eggs, and six days for those from unfertilized eggs. In the first two or three days of life, all the larvae are fed on royal jelly produced by the young worker bees. After this, only the larvae destined to become queens, living in larger cells called queen cells, continue to be fed with royal jelly; the others are fed on pollen mixed with honey.

On the sixth day, the mature larvae stop feeding and the cells are closed, when full, with a waxen seal by the workers. Each larva now wraps itself in a very light web of silk, within which, after achieving the final larval moult, it becomes a pupa, straw-coloured to begin with but gradually growing darker. After pupation,

during which the bee has changed gradually from a larval form to an adult insect, it breaks the seal of its cell and emerges. From egg-laying to emergence of the adult bee requires 16, 21 and 24 days respectively for a queen, a worker and a drone.

Above left: Cross-section of a comb in which the queen is depicted busily laying eggs. Cells may be seen containing honey, pollen and water, as well as larvae and pupae at various stages of development
Top: A worker with its pollen basket fully laden
Above: A drone is larger than a worker and has better-developed eyes

Tasks of the worker bee
During her short life the worker bee carries out in stages all the tasks necessary to her society. In the first ten days after emerging from her cell she works exclusively in the beehive. From the first to the third day, as her body grows darker and bigger, she cleans the cells as soon as they have been vacated by her companions, so that the queen may lay more eggs in them. She also helps to keep the brood warm. This requires a temperature of not less than 28°C (82°F) and is produced by the young workers huddling together on top of it.

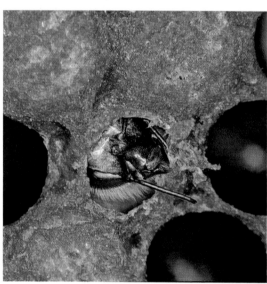

The photographs on this page show the
hatching of a worker bee. The top two show
a comb cut open to reveal the insect about
to leave its pupal position
Above and left: Having chewed out an opening
in the cell, the bee extends its pair of
antennae
Right: The camera has caught the final
stages of the struggle by the bee to get
out of the cell. The young worker finally
emerges and takes its first steps in the
outside world

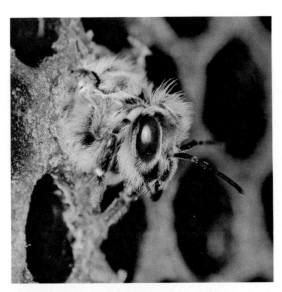

Above: Two workers, intent on their appointed task, clean out recently vacated cells so that they may be ready to receive a fresh batch of eggs from the queen

From the third to the fifth day the worker feeds the larvae with honey and pollen, taking the food from the cells where it has been stored. From the sixth to the tenth day she consumes vast quantities of pollen in order to produce royal jelly for the young larvae, for the 'princesses' and for the queen herself. In this period the pharyngeal glands of the worker are fully active.

During the second ten-day period the worker continues to carry out most of her tasks within the hive, and also makes her first flights outside it. Inside, she stores the pollen brought back by the foraging bees, ventilates the hive, produces wax for comb-making, cleans the hive by removing old cell-caps and the bodies of her dead companions, acts as a sentinel at the entrance to the hive and makes further orientation flights.

From the twentieth day after emerging from the cocoon, the workers act as foragers, gathering nectar, honeydew, pollen, propolis (or bee-glue) and, if necessary, water, within a maximum radius of 3 kilometres (nearly 2 miles) from the hive.

Nectar is a sugary liquid exuded by plants and converted by the bees into honey. It is produced by the nectar-secreting glands inside the corolla of a flower. The presence of sugary substances in plant juices slows down evaporation and thus makes it available to the bees over a long period. Nectar production and its sugar concentration vary widely from plant to plant, and even in the same plant depending on conditions. For example, in optimal conditions, secretion is greatest in the morning, drops to nothing after midday, and increases again towards evening. In consequence, the activity of the foraging bees follows this same rhythm.

There are two occasions on which bees will ventilate the hive. It is done, firstly, when the combs are in danger of melting because of excessive internal and external heat, thus threatening the loss of honey, provoking robbing and even the death of the whole colony. This may be caused by the narrowness of the entrances, leading to overcrowding of them, or the accumulation of combs and stores. Secondly, ventilation is necessary when nectar is present in quantities large enough to block the usual air currents which carry away the water vapour produced by the nectar evaporating.

In both cases, the 'fanning bees' gather on the alighting-board of the hive, raise their abdomens and beat their wings rapidly in order to send a draught of fresh air into the hive. They also fan between the combs to encourage evaporation of the honey. The beat of wings may be strong enough to make a deep rumbling noise rather like that of a saucepan of boiling

Top: A worker bee sets out in search of nectar and pollen
Above: Worker bees return from foraging. Pollen is just visible on the legs of the lower bee

water. A beekeeper should try as far as possible to spare his bees this strenuous work by widening the entrances and doing all he can to ensure a natural flow of air.

Young bees construct the combs from wax produced by their abdominal wax-glands. To produce wax, they must eat a lot of honey as this encourages the secretion of wax. The bees use their jaws to grasp the thin scales of wax and apparently use their legs to manipulate them into shape. Thus, with all the young bees working together, the combs are built up, each consisting of numbers of cells lying at a slight angle to the horizontal. The cells are arranged on both sides of the comb. Each cell is hexagonal and the system of construction solves a difficult architectural problem: it achieves the maximum number of cells on a given surface area and makes the structure extremely strong.

A comb consists of worker cells, drone cells, transition cells, storage cells for honey and pollen, and queen cells. The worker cells are so called because the larvae of the workers are bred in them. They are hexagonal, about 11–12 millimetres (0.47 inches) deep and 5.5 millimetres (0.21 inches) wide. The drone cells are similarly shaped, but about 13 millimetres (0.51 inches) deep and 7 millimetres (0.27 inches) wide. The transition cells are intermediate between worker and drone cells. Pollen and honey are stored separately in storage

cells which, when full, are closed with a white, waxen, impermeable seal. The seals of brood cells which contain pupae are brown and porous. The queen cell is only constructed when the colony feels the need to breed a new queen. The cell, at the side or bottom of the comb, is shaped like an upside-down acorn, 20–25 millimetres (0.78–0.98 inches) deep and approximately 8 millimetres (0.31 inches) wide. The inner walls are absolutely smooth.

Sentinel bees: myth or reality?

Many beekeepers talk of sentinel bees, which put up strong opposition to any attempt on the part of strange bees or other

The bees shown on these two pages are acting as an air-conditioning unit, fanning the air with their wings as hard as they can in order to circulate cool air within the hive. The internal temperature is thus prevented from rising to a dangerous level on a hot day

enemies to enter the hive. One observer has described the work of these bees. 'Some bees stand guard at the entrance, both during the day and on summer evenings and night. Sometimes at night, in early spring, when there are no enemies to fear, there is only one bee, the fastest and boldest, who takes upon herself this office and who can be seen running in all directions, on the alighting-board and over the front of the hive, watching for the enemy. Sometimes there are two or three rather than one; but in August, when the Death's-head Hawk-moth roams around the hives, the sentries are more numerous. These sentries allow free passage to the collector-bees of their own hive, though they often require them to yield up a drop of the nectar they have collected; but, by nature not very welcoming, they attack

enemies attempting to enter the hive and also bees from other colonies who seek refuge without bringing honey in their honey-stomachs, not to mention the unfortunate beekeeper, if he should appear in front of the entrance. In July, annoying flies gather, attracted by the scent of honey. If the sentry does not feel she can cope single-handed with the enemy, she re-enters the hive and gives a little cry, like a thin

Every action in the bee's brief life is devoted to the collective good. The pictures on these two pages show the process of trophallaxis or the exchange of food. Many substances can only be used by these insects after having been pre-digested in the stomach

whistling, to call to her aid a squad of bees or even the whole colony.'

According to a leading Italian bee-keeper, however, sentinel bees are nothing but a myth: in practice no bee has a specific task, but all bees capable of flying will give the alarm and come to the defence of their colony. Nevertheless, modern research indicates that a colony is in fact guarded by bees which stand around the entrance and dart out if they see a swift movement from a possible enemy. The guards do not remain long at their posts, but are changed constantly.

Explorers and dancers

When a worker bee discovers a field full of flowers, the field is invaded soon afterwards by a swarm of other bees from the same hive. The 'explorer' bee does not always accompany the others back to the field, which may be several kilometres or miles away from the hive; obviously she must somehow be able to indicate to her companions exactly where to find the new and rich sources of nectar. The researches of Karl von Frisch, a Nobel prizewinner in 1973, have yielded valuable information about the bee's language, orientation and sensory faculties. After patient and prolonged investigation von Frisch deciphered the code by which the explorer bees, attracted by the colour and scent of the flowers, indicate to their companions where to find these new sources of nectar. The information is transmitted in the darkness of the hive through surprisingly precise messages expressed by dances on the combs. The three reference points on which this remarkable signalling depends are the hive itself, the food source, and the sun, whose position is known exactly even on overcast days, due to ultra-violet radiation.

If the flowers are less than 100 metres (330 feet) from the hive, the explorer bee performs a rapid circular dance, consisting of eight or ten revolutions in about 15 seconds. If they are more distant, up to a

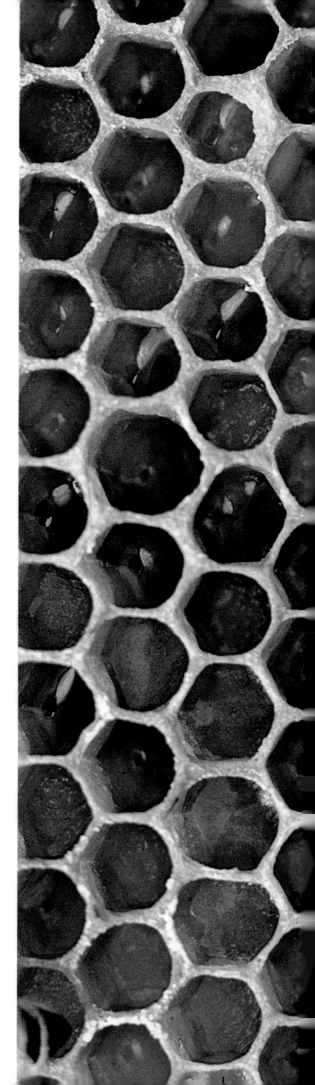

168

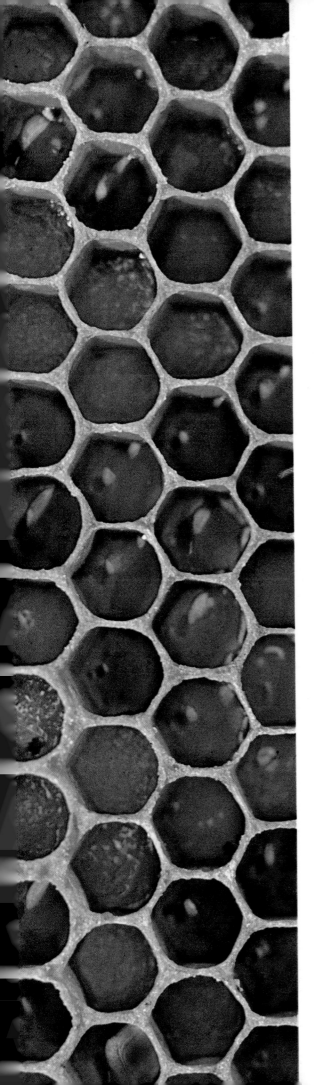

Above: The young workers build a comb, a
process that is governed by elaborate but
logical rules
Top: Workers build the royal cell

Left: The structure of the individual cells
is such as to allow major constructions to be
built with a minimum of raw material

Left: A highly organized society such as that of the bee relies heavily on means of communication. A rigid code of dance movements enables the bees to pass on important information about the location of food in the vicinity of the hive
Bottom left: The 'circular' dance
Below and above right: By means of the 'tail-wagging' dance, a bee can indicate with a fair degree of accuracy the direction in which food is to be found by relating it to the position of the sun relative to the hive

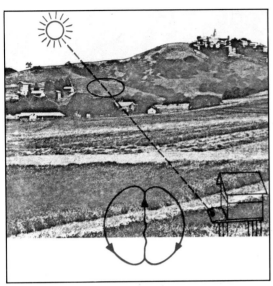

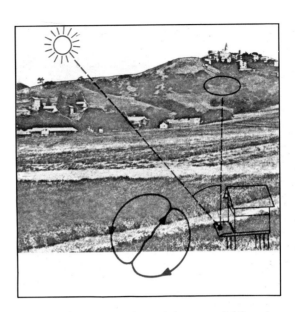

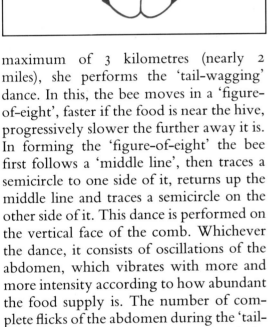

maximum of 3 kilometres (nearly 2 miles), she performs the 'tail-wagging' dance. In this, the bee moves in a 'figure-of-eight', faster if the food is near the hive, progressively slower the further away it is. In forming the 'figure-of-eight' the bee first follows a 'middle line', then traces a semicircle to one side of it, returns up the middle line and traces a semicircle on the other side of it. This dance is performed on the vertical face of the comb. Whichever the dance, it consists of oscillations of the abdomen, which vibrates with more and more intensity according to how abundant the food supply is. The number of complete flicks of the abdomen during the 'tail-wagging' dance gives a measure of the distance from the hive, each extra flick indicating an increase of some 75 metres (about 240 feet).

The 'tail-wagging' dance therefore supplies two important facts: the amount of nectar available and its distance from the hive. But there remains the problem of the direction of the food source. The way in which this information is conveyed is remarkable. The 'middle line' of the 'tail-wagging' dance makes an angle with the vertical equal to the angle between the sun's rays and the food source. The foraging bees, as soon as they have all the necessary information, then leave the hive and fly off in the direction indicated, even if

the sky is overcast, as if they could see the sun perfectly well. This is because bees are sensitive to ultra-violet light and to the pattern of polarized light in the blue sky even on cloudy days.

The raw materials of the hive

Especially in years when there is little nectar production, the bees gather honeydew—a sugary excretion of aphids (the common plant-lice) and coccids (scale-insects) covering the leaves on which they feed. Honeydew makes a dark, thick honey as opposed to the clear, pale honey made from nectar. Pollen is sometimes called 'bee-bread'. It is the bee's source of protein and not a constituent of honey although a few grains are bound to be found in it.

Propolis, or bee-glue, is a kind of resin gathered by the bees from buds and branches of various trees such as poplars, willows and pines. This sticky substance is far from welcome to beekeepers, as once they get it on them it is very difficult to remove. For bees, however, it is very important for a whole series of tasks within the hive. In a very thin layer, it strengthens the combs, it lines all the walls of the hive to keep out damp, and it is used to stop up any cracks and to reinforce any spaces which could be points of weakness. It is also smeared on the bodies of intruders such as moths, snails or rodents which may have penetrated the hive to feed on its rich stores. For the beekeeper, this substance is a nuisance, for the bee a necessity; it even has various commercial applications. Propolis when melted gives a yellow wax which remains malleable; burnt like incense it perfumes its surroundings with attractive fragrance; dissolved in alcohol and filtered, it is used as a polish for wood and as an attractive golden-yellow varnish for metals. Obviously there is no question of industrial exploitation, since the expense of obtaining it and the small amounts in which it is produced prevent it being widely used.

Bees need vast amounts of water for dissolving the crystallized or congealed honey in the combs, and also for dissolving the pollen with which to feed the brood. Some beekeepers consider that there is a particular category of bees specializing in collecting water which is brought back to the hive and then distributed among the bees who thus serve as reservoirs. Water is collected from leaves damp with dew, from damp earth or from puddles.

Beekeeping methods

Bees have been kept since earliest times and honey has always been much prized and considered a heaven-sent food fit for the gods. The ancient Greeks, and in particular the Romans, cultivated the art of beekeeping and consumed great quantities of honey and wax. Honey was considered a great delicacy and wax was widely used for making writing tablets. In Roman times beehives were constructed out of wicker, cork, earthenware and wood. They came in a variety of shapes and sizes and had movable comb-frames. It was the practice to collect only part of the honey, and not to kill the bees. In short, the Romans understood the basic principles on which modern beekeeping is founded.

In the Middle Ages, beekeeping declined, probably as a consequence of the earlier introduction first of cane sugar and

Right: Top view (above) and section (below) of a cell used as a pollen store. Pollen and honey are stored separately by the honeybee; pollen is mainly stored near the brood so that it can be readily fed to the larvae

Left: A beekeeper wears a protective veil while examining his stocks of bees
Bottom left: The frames holding the combs of an artificial hive must be constructed with mathematical accuracy if the bees are to be persuaded to use them

then of beet sugar which quickly replaced honey as a sweetener. However, about the middle of the nineteenth century, it regained popularity, thanks largely to technical discoveries which made modern systems of beekeeping possible. The most important of these discoveries was the hive with movable combs, which replaced the more primitive and less satisfactory hive with fixed combs.

With fixed–comb hives, the beekeeper is unable to influence the growth of his colonies or counteract their weaknesses, and is powerless to prevent or combat enemies and disease. But above all, he is unable to extract the honey and wax without killing the bees and destroying the combs.

Before dealing with the hive in detail, however, a definition is required. A hive is the dwelling provided by man for the bees he keeps. When this hive is populated with bees and furnished with the waxen constructions known as combs, it is called a

Below: A ceaseless to-ing and fro-ing of bees on the threshold of their hive occurs as they set about their missions of exploration or plunder

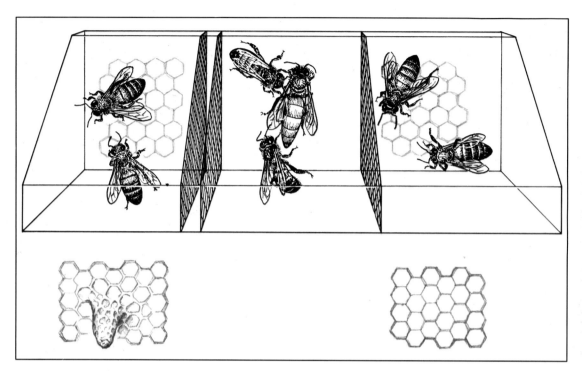

'colony'. A collection of colonies in a particular place is called an apiary.

The fixed-comb beehives used all over the world vary widely according to locality both in shape and in the materials used for their construction. They include sections of hollow tree-trunks, closed at the top with a slab; pieces of cork joined together to make a tube closed at the top with another piece of cork; elongated boxes minus one of the smaller sides; and barrels without bottoms and old tubs. Many are also made of earthenware, tufa, wicker or straw.

Most fixed-comb hives are positioned vertically—that is, with the open end nearest the ground. If this sort of hive is raised clear of the ground, the bees come and go easily underneath. If not, holes are made in the lower half of the front wall to allow the insects to go in and out. In horizontal hives, such holes are unnecessary since the bees enter by the open end, or mouth. In all fixed-comb hives, the bees attach their combs to the inner surface, helped in this by a system of hardwood battens which the beekeeper arranges between opposite walls so as to give the insects a solid basis for their construction.

Above: The life of the bee colony revolves around the queen, who rules it—and indeed keeps it in existence—through the secretion of pheromones (external chemical messengers). The bees in the left-hand compartment, who are unable to receive the queen's pheromones by touching her, since they are separated from her by a double screen (she is the large bee in the centre compartment), have set about building a royal cell in order to raise a new queen. Those in the right-hand compartment can touch the queen through the single screen and receive her pheromones, so they do not set about raising another queen

Right: For a variety of reasons—to give her special attention, for study, for removal to another hive, or because of the presence of two queens—it may occasionally be necessary to isolate a queen in a separate container

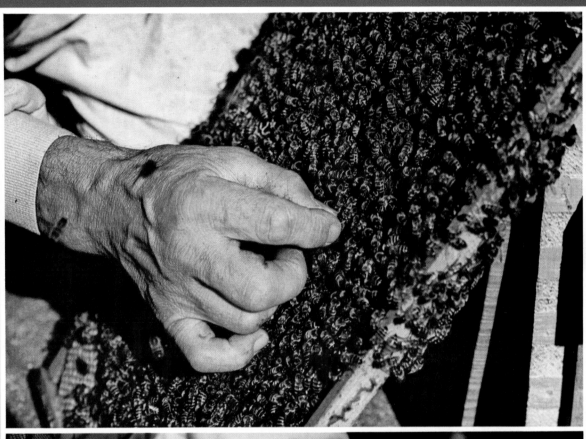

In fixed-comb hives, however, because the combs are immovable, the honey can only be fully gathered if the family is destroyed. This is generally done after the colony has swarmed a few times. Killing the bees is not advisable since this destroys, along with the colony, the young queens, who are very precious as they are still in the prime of reproductive activity. Sometimes, in order to avoid such wholesale massacre, the honey is only partially collected. This means, for example, removing the upper part of the sealed combs from vertical hives, and some of the honeycombs from the front of horizontal hives. To do this, the colony must be 'smoked' so that the work can be done in relative peace. Indeed, it has often been said that without a 'smoker' beekeeping is impossible; but this apparatus must be handled with care and the smoke should not be too great. A smoker basically consists of a bellows and a firebox. The

bellows keep the fuel smouldering without flame and blow the smoke from it out through the mouth of the firebox. This is cylindrical in shape and is closed at one end, while the other end is fitted with a conical cap, which can be lifted to insert the fuel: rags, dry grass, corrugated paper and similar material. A good smoker should not go out, and even if left to its own devices should continue to burn as long as the fuel supply lasts. It should also provide a powerful jet of smoke, since this is the only weapon capable of subduing the bees available to the beekeeper.

The movable-comb hive became a reality towards 1850 when, almost at the same time, two apiculturists, L. L. Langstroth in America and Baron von Berlepsch in Germany, invented movable rectangular frames which the bees could fill with comb. This meant that the combs could easily be taken out, something that was impossible with fixed-comb hives.

Left and right: The royal cell inside this tiny cage contains a larva that is fed on royal jelly and will grow into a queen

The Berlepsch or German-type hive was used for a time in Europe, but the Langstroth or American-type hive is the one most frequently used today. This has a removable roof so that the frames can be lifted out from above. The comb-frame of the modern hive seems at first sight a very simple structure and yet it took a long time to produce such an obvious device. In fact, its invention was only possible after long and careful study of the habits of bees.

Bees invariably leave a space of about 8 millimetres (0.31 inches) between the various elements of their home so that they can circulate freely in the gaps without, however, wasting space. If the distance were less, the bees would soon fill up the space with propolis, welding the two elements together to form a compact block. If it were greater, the excess space would be filled with small supplementary wax constructions. The innovation lies in the fact that these frames, although in themselves nothing more than wooden constructions, are suspended in the hive by two lugs, extensions of the top member. When the combs are built out, they are 7–8 millimetres (0.31 inches) from the other parts of the hive. Thanks to this simple device, the frames are completely movable and can be easily lifted out without in any way damaging the combs, since the bees have not felt the need to weld them to one another nor to the rest of the hive.

Elements of the hive

The Langstroth hive has been subject to many variations, some of doubtful value, by various beekeepers who have tried to adapt it to particular conditions and to certain strains of bees. Roughly speaking, however, a hive of this type consists of the following basic parts: the nest or brood chamber; the queen excluder; the 'super' or honey storage chamber; the movable

floorboard; the entrance-block; the ceiling (usually called the coverboard or crownboard); the roof; the division board or dummy board; and 12 brood frames and 12 super frames.

The brood chamber is a box which usually has standard measurements of 51 × 41.25 × 24.10 centimetres high (20 × 16.24 × 9.44 inches). At the top of two opposite walls are 'rebates' or channels which allow the frames to be suspended from their lugs. These do not weigh directly on the rebates but instead on two small metal supports, since it is more difficult for the bees to glue these with propolis. The 12 brood frames measure externally 23.18 centimetres (9.12 inches) high by 44.80 centimetres (17.63 inches) wide. If one frame is removed, room is made for a dummy board, a small partition the same size as a brood frame which allows the capacity of the brood chamber to be altered as required.

The queen excluder is a metal mesh, with slots too small for the queen but yet allowing workers to pass through. This is placed between brood chamber and super to prevent the queen laying eggs in the honey stores. The super, a box the same size as the brood chamber but only half as high, fits neatly on top of the brood chamber. Its 12 frames are like those of the brood chamber but, of course, are not as high.

The movable base is a board with fillets on three sides and exactly the same size as the brood chamber, which fits on top. There is no fillet at the front, thus creating a space about 25 millimetres (1 inch) high between the base and the brood chamber the whole width of the front, which serves as an entrance for the bees. This is not too large an opening if the bee colony is well developed, though it might be if the colony is under-developed. In such

cases a special piece of wood is used for an entrance-block which can alter the size of the hive entrance according to the requirements of the season and the size of the family. If the colony occupies the whole brood chamber and the weather is not cold, the entrance-block is placed with a 20 centimetre (8 inch) opening towards the bottom. Otherwise a somewhat smaller opening is placed at the bottom, thus protecting the bees not only from the cold but, with some modifications, also from their enemies, especially mice.

The coverboard, or crownboard, fits tightly across the top of the hive. If it does not fit well, heat from the hive is lost through the cracks, and strange bees, ants, moths and other parasites will be able to enter. The coverboard must therefore be accurately constructed. Generally, it consists of at least two pieces of wood. Apart from other considerations, this means that the whole hive need not be uncovered during visits of inspection. The bees are therefore not exposed to the cold and there is less risk of robbing.

The roof, which may be flat, sloping or gabled, protects the hive, which is normally kept in the open, from excessive cold, heat, and inclement weather. It may be made of wood, asbestos lumber, sheet metal or other materials. A good space is left between it and the ceiling. In summer, this allows free circulation of air; in winter the space is filled with straw, hay or paper to insulate the hive.

Frames are the foundations on which the bees construct their wax combs. The production of wax requires, albeit indirectly, a high honey consumption; so, as wax costs far less than honey, thin sheets of beeswax embossed on both sides with a pattern of the hexagonal bases of worker cells are placed in the hive. These beeswax sheets, called 'starters' or 'foundations', were invented by the Bavarian cabinetmaker J. Mehring in 1857. They are, or should be, made only with pure beeswax without any additions such as paraffin wax. Special embossing machines use either dies,

The hive is defended against intruders with ruthless determination
Top left: A bee and a wasp fight to the death
Left: A fight between two bees from different hives

under pressure, or cylinders to produce an impression of worker-cell foundations on both sides. By supplying the bees with these starters, just when they are in optimum condition for producing wax, perfect combs are obtained with minimum energy on the part of the insects and with the least possible honey consumption. In fact, the bees, being provided with an already near complete comb, need only manipulate it to their liking, working the wax until it is of the normal thickness for a cell base. The wax removed is used to start 'drawing out' the side walls of the cells, and any small quantity of wax which may be required to finish these is then produced by the bees. The use of a starter not only reduces honey consumption but also has other advantages. First, it limits the production of drones, who not only do not work but consume quantities of food. This can be done since the leaves are embossed only with worker cells. The bees can, if necessary, construct male cells at certain places in the artificial comb, but in far smaller quantities than normal. Secondly, if the size of the cells stamped on the starter is increased, larger workers than normal for

Below and right: The violent battles that are observed between members of different hives suggest that bees are able to recognize each other, perhaps because a characteristic odour is carried by all bees in the same hive

that particular strain will emerge. Larger workers, because of their greater pollen-gathering potential, in turn mean greater production.

Swarming for survival

The honeybee is a social species which creates persistent colonies and, given particular conditions, it can perpetuate itself indefinitely. A fully developed colony may number as many as 100,000 bees, the overwhelming majority of which will be workers. The queen is the driving centre of the whole hive, in that hers is the task of continually laying the eggs from which new bees will develop. There is normally only one queen but one or more others may be allowed to lay if the founding queen is old or failing. The drones appear only from spring to the end of summer or

Overleaf: A fight between two queens is a dramatic event that ends with the death or flight of one of them

183

autumn and then only in limited numbers. At the end of autumn the males, now useless and capable only of absorbing great quantities of food without giving anything in exchange, are stung to death by the workers.

Obviously, if the egg-laying activity of the queen or queens continues, the hive will reach a point where it can no longer contain the whole family. To survive, it must divide, and it does this by swarming. In the over-populated hive, one of the queen cells, constructed by the workers in anticipation of this very happening, contains a 'princess'—a queen in the larval state. The old queen, accompanied by a large number of workers and some drones (only a few, since she is no longer a virgin, having been fertilized, albeit a long time ago) now leaves the hive to form the 'prime' swarm. Swarming generally takes place towards noon on a sunny day; the swarm gathers in the familiar cluster on the ground, on a branch of a tree or in a hedge. It remains here for a short time and, if it is not captured by a beekeeper for a hive of his own, it flies to a place which will be the site of a new colony.

Meanwhile, in the hive which the swarm has left, the new queen is born. As soon as she emerges, she stings to death the princesses which are about to emerge from the other queen cells, and the workers help her in this. The massacre does not however take place if the 'swarming instinct' is still present in the hive. In response to this, the new queen, like the old one, abandons her hive, followed by more workers and by many males attracted by her still virginal state. This constitutes a 'second' or 'cast' swarm and may even be followed by others. Thus the original family is subdivided into smaller ones, each of which may quickly grow, in favourable conditions, to its maximum development.

Royal sweetmeats

The best-known products of the bee are honey, wax and royal jelly. Honey derives

Right: The presence of two queens in one hive does not necessarily result in bloodshed; more commonly it leads, shortly before a new queen emerges from its cell, to the swarming of a large part of the colony. This swarm hangs from a low branch of an apple tree

Above: A swarm piled up in the grass,
preparing to search for, or to build, a new hive

from the action on nectar in the honey-
stomach of an enzyme (invertase) which
converts almost all the saccharose in the
nectar into simple sugars, glucose and
levulose, which are easily assimilated by
humans, who obtain energy and heat from
it while having no difficulty in digesting it.

Separation of the honey from the combs
is carried out by special machines called
extractors, which remove the honey without damaging the combs. This operation
calls for skill and experience, even in
removing the combs from the hive to take
them to the extractor, since they may be
'robbed' by bees from other colonies, with
serious consequences. This type of robbing
may occur if the hive is left uncovered for a
period, allowing strange bees to enter and
steal the honey. Usually stronger colonies

left the darkness of the hive. Both products have recently been exploited commercially in the wake of extravagant claims for their virtues. Science, however, is still investigating. The demand for pollen is ever-increasing and some beekeepers tend to supply more and more of it, even to the detriment of their bees. This is a dangerous course, since if too much pollen is removed the hive will deteriorate rapidly.

Bees are, of course, of fundamental importance to agriculture as pollinators of cultivated crops. The pollinating activity of bees is necessary even where there are other pollinating insects; and in fruit-growing, thanks to a variety of very complex phenomena, bees are indispensable. They are not, however, properly protected and can be destroyed by the short-sighted use of pesticides on flowering crops.

The enemies of bees

Bees have many enemies and contract many diseases. Among their occasional enemies are the brown bear, the badger, the hedgehog, and some birds such as the honey-buzzard and the bee-eater. But even greater damage may be done by some species of arthropods.

The mite *Acarapis woodi* reproduces in the tracheae of bees, with consequent serious damage to the respiratory system. Some spiders weave their webs close to hives, or in places much frequented by bees, and are quite successful in capturing and killing them.

The name wax-moth is commonly given to two species of Microlepidoptera, *Galleria mellonella,* the greater wax-moth, and *Achroea grisella,* the lesser wax-moth. The females of these lay their eggs, singly or in small heaps, in comb cells, on the comb itself, or on the floor of the hive. From the eggs emerge larvae, which bore tunnels into the wax and feed on it. The bees try to fight these unwanted guests but seldom succeed since the larvae, as they inch their way along the tunnels, line them

prey on weaker ones until they reduce them to starvation. Such robbing is certainly harmful, but equally so is the kind which occurs when a few bees at a time penetrate into a hive which is not theirs. Here the theft of honey is less, but there is a danger of disease being spread within the hive by the intruding bees.

Honey is not used solely for food, whether mixed with other substances or not, but is also used to make hydromel, or mead, an alcoholic beverage. Beeswax finds many applications in industry and much of it returns to the beekeeper and his bees in the form of beeswax 'starter' sheets.

The development of royal jelly and pollen follow, as it were, parallel lines. The former is made by young bees, while the latter is gathered by adult bees who have

Above: The bee's enemies include the Death's-head Hawk-moth (*Acherontia atropos*)
Left: A beekeeper removes a swarm, which he will then transfer to a new hive

with silk which gives protection against the bees' stings. Wax-moths, if present in large numbers, can destroy the combs.

The wax-moth is small, but the Death's-head Hawk-moth, *Acherontia atropos*, is far larger and is a giant among moths. It is a glutton for honey and enters the hive to suck up great quantities through its short proboscis. It is often killed by the bees, however, when, full of food and with belly swollen, it can no longer squeeze out of the hive it has raided.

Another enemy is the bee-louse, *Braula coeca*—a small, wingless, reddish insect with rudimentary eyes. It is often found on the thorax of bees, especially on hive-bees and queens, but rarely on the foragers. It is not a parasite in the true sense of the word and lives by sucking up honey, pollen and royal jelly when it is hungry straight from the workers' mouths. If there are no more than one or two of these insects on a bee's thorax, they may pass almost unnoticed, but if the host (generally the queen) is heavily infested, their presence can be harmful. In fact the queen, irritated by the bee-lice, and short of food since they eat it before she can, lays far fewer eggs. The consequent reduction in size of the family is detrimental to the colony.

The commonest means of defence against this insect, at least up to the present time, is tobacco-smoke. When blown into the hive, it does not kill the bee-lice but dazes them, causing them to fall to the floor of the hive where they can be swept up and destroyed. More efficient, and very effective if carried out with perseverance over a period of time, is a chemical known as phenothiazine. If burnt in a tightly closed hive, it does not daze the bee-lice but kills them, without harming the bees or contaminating the honey.

The principal bee diseases are caused by protozoa, bacteria and viruses. Nosema disease is due to a protozoan parasite, *Nosema apis,* which affects the mid-gut. Bee paralysis is caused by a virus and spreads easily, especially in May. Two very serious brood diseases, American Foul Brood and European Foul Brood, are due to bacilli. Both can be treated with antibiotics, but with careful and efficient beekeeping their spread and even the initial infection of the hives can be avoided.

Camouflage
and mimicry

In zoology, the various ways in which animals make themselves virtually invisible in their environments are termed cryptic coloration, crypsis or camouflage. Concealment is usually achieved by colouring which blends with the surroundings (for example, those green grasshoppers and bush-crickets and butterflies of the genus Kallima which look like dead leaves) or by the imitation of the shape and colour of the dominant features of a creature's habitat (such as the well-known leaf insects and stick insects, certain bush-crickets belonging to the subfamily Pseudophyllinae which also resemble leaves, and many other species). The term mimicry is used when a harmless insect imitates the shape and colouring of a poisonous species which is feared and shunned by predators, or a species simply distasteful—a phenomenon known as Batesian mimicry. In this connection, poisonous species are usually red or orange (the so-called warning colours), so that members of other groups of insects are alerted to danger. Very similar warning colours are also found in insects belonging to groups which are remote so far as the 'race history' of the organism is concerned, such as Coleoptera, Lepidoptera and Hemiptera. In the same way, predatory insects sometimes meticulously copy the

livery of their prey (predatory mimicry) in order to be able to mingle with them undetected and capture them easily. Many parasites also resemble the shape and colouring of their hosts as much as possible in order to be able to live undisturbed in their nests. Robber-flies that closely resemble bees, such as the South American *Mallaphora tibialis*, catch and feed on bees, while their wood-inhabiting larvae may tunnel in the same wood as carpenter-bees, on whose larvae they may feed.

The beautifully patterned wings of butterflies and moths merit detailed examination and provide numerous examples of mimicry. Sometimes these are the sole means of attracting members of the opposite sex; and in many other cases they offer a highly effective means of defence. This usually involves butterflies and slow-flying moths (such as *Automeris* and other Saturniidae) which may have leaf-like wings complete with veins and sometimes small blemishes. When such a butterfly is motionless on a branch with its wings raised, it is practically invisible. But there is always a chance that a bird may become suspicious and give it a quick bite in case it is edible. Some of these insects have large 'eye spots' on their hind wings which they can flash, showing the bird a terrifying 'face' with two huge wide-open eyes. Then, taking advantage of the predator's momentary amazement, the insect manages to escape.

Lastly, there are some particularly odd

Left: Many insects achieve a measure of protection from their enemies by resembling the plants amongst which they live. Top: Flatids imitate a twig in bloom. Centre: A leaf-insect. Right: A stick-insect. Bottom: A cryptic orthopterous insect

cases, like the butterflies of the genus Thecla which have small inconspicuous heads while the ends of their abdomens form a very eye-catching false head. So when a predator is poised to strike, the butterfly can make a quick getaway in the opposite direction to that in which the ambush is set.

Among the more remarkable exponents of crypsis are numerous orthopterous insects, ranging from the bush-crickets mentioned earlier belonging to the subfamily Pseudophyllinae and those of the subfamily Phaneropterinae, all of which resemble leaves in shape and colour (some being green and others twisted and dried up), to members of the order Dictyoptera suborder Mantodea which are particularly interesting from this point of view. The cryptic coloration and shape taken on by mantises must be considered in the context of the change from a herbivorous diet to predatory habits. This has resulted in the insects' need to conceal themselves as effectively as possible from the eyes of their prey so as to catch them unawares. Pink or purple Praying Mantises with petal-shaped legs stand motionless on the blossoms they resemble; others are perfectly hidden among dry shrivelled leaves which they match, not only in colour, but in shape and also in the pattern of their veins.

Real masterpieces of mimicry are found among members of the order Phasmida, which are similar to mantises. As they are harmless, plant-eating insects, the art of concealment among vegetation is in fact their only form of defence against predators. The well-known leaf insects and stick insects (of the genera Phyllium and Bacillus) belong to this group. The outer structure of their bodies is greatly modified so that leaf insects look just like leaves and stick insects like fine, bare twigs. They are both quite large, 8–10 centimetres (3–4 inches) long. In spite of their appearance, they would be visible if they moved at all quickly; they are therefore extremely slow and prefer to move at night.

Both larvae and adult Lepidoptera also provide remarkable examples of mimicry besides those previously mentioned. The upper sides of the wings of moths of the genus Thysania (family Noctuidae) are dappled like the bark of a tree in the same subtle shades of grey and brown, so that the insect is almost invisible on a tree-trunk when its wings are spread out. Other species which live in woods are the colour of the dead leaves on which they frequently alight. *Krananda semihyalina*, *Auophylla magnifica*, and *Belenoptera sanguinea* are such examples. There are also endless examples of harmless and edible moths, flies, beetles and other insects that mimic wasps, bees and a number of other poisonous insects— for example, the hornet clear-wing moth (*Sesia apiformis*) and the wasp longhorn beetle (*Clytus arietis*).

The pattern and colouring of the wings of the milkweed butterfly (*Danaus plexippus*), whose blood is poisonous to predators, are very well copied by an edible species, *Limenitis archippus*, which would be much in demand among predators if it were not for its suspicious appearance. But there are even more fascinating cases of mimicry among larvae. Some caterpillars of the Geometridae family, for example, are perfect copies of the twigs they live on in terms of shape and colouring. They adopt an extraordinary position when resting, stiffening their body as much as possible, while the back remains attached to the twig by a silk thread secreted from the mouth, so that they form an acute angle to the branch. Any predator would have to examine them very closely to see that they were caterpillars and not merely forked twigs.

Even more remarkable are the caterpillars of the species *Pachypasa lineosa* (moths of the family Lasiocampidae) which look so like the branches of conifers, their ideal habitat, that they often deceive the human eye. Members of the species *Flatida floccosa* live in groups of six or seven, so that side by side on a branch they resemble an inflorescence. The South American bush-cricket, *Cycloptera excellens*, is a remarkable

Mantises are camouflaged so that their
prey may be deceived and more readily
captured. Right: A mantis that resembles
leaves and flower buds. Bottom left: The
Indian mantis is brown and resembles the
dead leaves on a forest floor
Bottom right: This is not a wasp but a
harmless moth, achieving protection through
its resemblance to a venomous insect

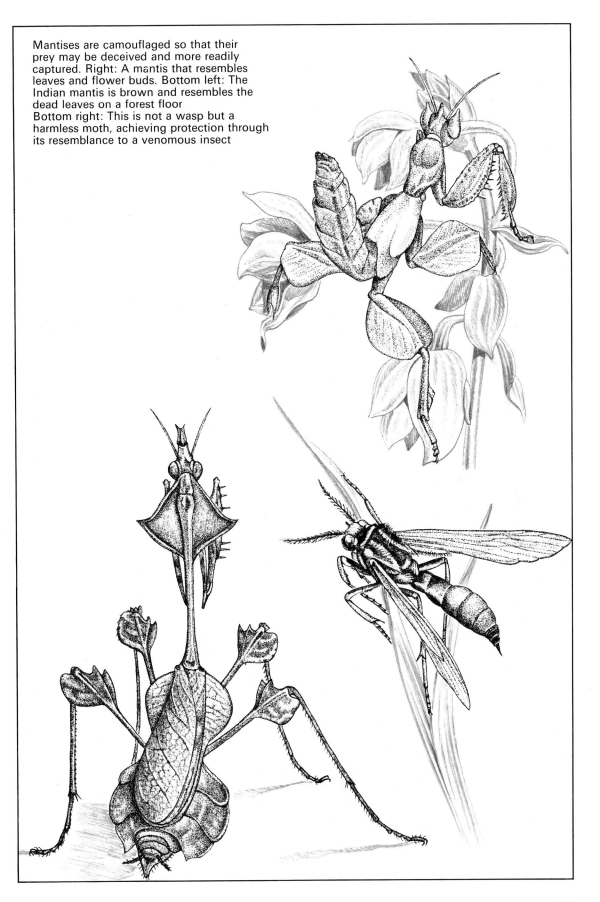

dead-leaf mimic, even having clear areas suggesting rot-holes.

These are just a few of the more striking examples. Many others have not been covered, however, and can only be mentioned briefly. The homopterous insects have outgrowths on their backs resembling the large thorns on the trees in which they live, while the Longicorn beetles (Cerambycidae) look very like the distasteful beetles of the family Lycidae. The young of certain beetles and of lacewings (family Chrysopidae) cover themselves with excrement and also cast skins and those of dead prey in order to blend with their background and escape the attention of their natural enemies.

Below: An American moth of the genus Automeris with its wings closed (left), and open (right) to show the deterrent 'eyes'

Butterflies and moths

Of all species of insects, butterflies are without doubt the best known and among the most beautiful. Their brilliant colouring and graceful flight give pleasure the world over. The insects commonly known as butterflies and moths belong to the order of Lepidoptera, a name derived from the combination of two Greek words and meaning 'with scale-covered wings'.

Lepidoptera are terrestrial insects and rarely aquatic. They have four membraneous wings, the size of which can vary considerably. The head, which is usually quite separate from the thorax, carries a pair of compound eyes which are generally well developed, and sometimes a pair of simple eyes as well. The antennae, of which there are two, are many-jointed and vary in length. They can be comb-shaped or club-shaped, thread-like or branched into various shapes and this variety of forms, also found in their other organs, reveals the manner in which the two sexes differ markedly in shape, colour or size. In most families of Lepidoptera, the mouth parts are so complex as to be distinctive features of the order. The majority of butterflies and moths have mouths adapted for sucking, but a few are helped in their search for food by mouths which are also capable of biting. The very primitive family known as the Micropterygidae differ most from this

Left: An adult male *Plebeius argus* (the Silver-studded Blue butterfly). The species shows marked sexual dimorphism, the females being brown and the males a vivid blue

201

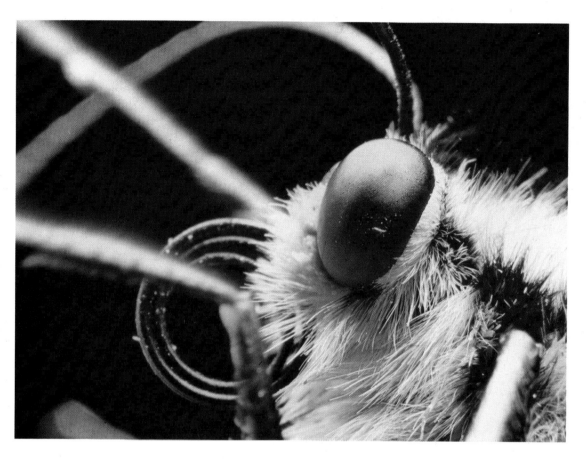

Above: Close-up of the head of a Swallowtail butterfly showing the insect's large compound eyes and its coiled proboscis
Above right: The same insect shown feeding through its extended proboscis

norm, as their mouths are adapted for chewing. The mouth parts of the larvae of Lepidoptera can also chew, as befits their way of life. In the majority of Lepidoptera, the mandibles are totally wanting while the first maxillae are elongated and joined along the underside to form a sort of tube, known as the proboscis. In some cases, this is very long and coils up under the head. This type of proboscis is known as a haustellum, and a series of hardened half-rings alternating with stretches of membrane enable it to coil up. The haustellum is controlled by numerous short muscles. It winds up when they contract and is thought to unwind as a result of the increased pressure of liquid circulating in its vessels, forced into them by muscular contraction.

Lepidoptera feed through the proboscis, drawing in food by means of a pump which is modified from the pharynx. For this purpose, the proboscis is uncoiled and inserted into the corollas of flowers or into

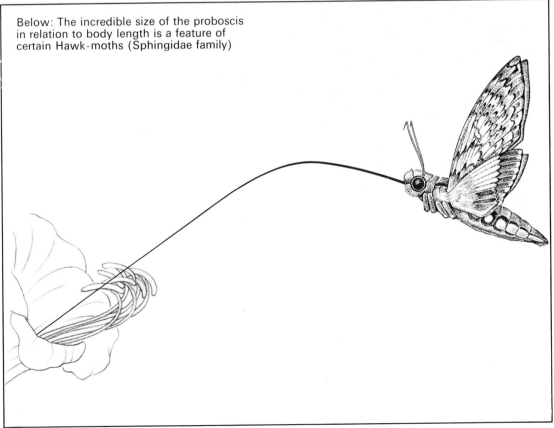

Below: The incredible size of the proboscis in relation to body length is a feature of certain Hawk-moths (Sphingidae family)

Top: Close-up from above of the head of a Swallowtail butterfly (*Papilio machaon*)
Above: The feathered antennae of the Saturniidae are very highly developed, particularly in the males, who can detect, even at considerable distances, the scent of females ready to mate

Right: A male *Hipparchia semele* (Grayling butterfly). The inner side of the wings shows patches of brilliant blue. These patches have a characteristic and penetrating odour which attracts the female during courting

liquid food. This operation is greatly facilitated by the length of the proboscis which may be as much as 30 centimetres (almost 12 inches) in some species. Butterflies and moths with special diets have a modified version of the proboscis. For example, the well-known Death's-head Hawk-moth (*Acherontia atropos*), (a member of the Sphingidae family, has a very short, thick proboscis which enables it to bore through the layer of wax with which bees cover their honeycombs.) In other families of Lepidoptera, the mouth parts are either rudimentary or totally atrophied; the oral orifice is often partly or completely closed when the mouth is atrophied.

The three segments which comprise the thorax are generally fused together, with two pairs of wings and three pairs of legs. The forelegs of some butterflies are reduced in size as are the hind legs of some moths, while the females of some case-bearing Psychidae ('bag-worms') have no legs at all. Butterflies and moths are, in fact, born to fly.

Lepidoptera number some of the fastest flying species. *Macroglossum stellatarum* (the Humming-bird Hawk-moth) can travel at more than 70 kilometres (43 miles) per hour, which makes it one of the fastest insects known.

In theory, the third part of the body of a butterfly or moth, the abdomen, consists of ten segments which are not always easy to distinguish because those at the end merge into the external reproductive organs. The outer structure of certain abdominal segments (the second to the eighth in the male and the second to the seventh in the female) also generally lacks distinctive features. But in two groups of moths there are hearing organs near the base of the abdomen. Each has a stiffer upperside and underside separated by membraneous areas at the sides. As already noted, the remaining segments are modified to form the reproductive organs, with the result that it is often difficult to distinguish the tenth segment. The structure of the male and female genital organs is now the most reliable guide for distinguishing and classifying different species of certain families of Lepidoptera.

Scale-covered wings

One of the loveliest sights in nature is to watch a butterfly alighting on the corolla of a flower or gliding along, letting itself be carried by the wind. The organs responsible for flight, the wings, are among these insects' most distinctive features. They are often fairly large, with the forewings usually bigger than the hind wings, and held open by a network of veins. These are the minute channels which branch out inside the wing and contain vessels, nerves and air-tubes. For a long time, these venations or nervures were thought to provide important clues for distinguishing the different species. But

new techniques have now superseded this method, at any rate for the majority of families.

As is the case with most higher insects, the two forewings are generally linked to the hind wings during flight so that the wing-beat is synchronized. The way in which the two pairs of wings are coupled together varies from one group to another. In the more primitive Lepidoptera, such as the Micropterygidae, the inner margin of the forewing bears a projecting lobe. Opposite, on the margin of the hind wing, there is a group of bristles. When these two structures meet, the wings are coupled together as if they were a single unit. In other, more highly evolved Lepidoptera, each wing carries special hairs for hooking on to the opposite wing, or the two pairs of wings are joined as they expand and overlap.

At rest, the wings fall into a variety of

Above : Detail of the wing of a
Swallowtail butterfly. In the course of
evolution, the wing patterns have become more
complex, each family of butterflies having
its own characteristic arrangement

positions. They can be placed at an angle to
each other like a roof, they can lie horizontally on the abdomen, or they can be raised
with the uppersides touching. Sometimes
they remain wide open in the flying
position. The hind wings occasionally fold
back and are tucked under the forewings in
the rest position. There are endless variations in the shape of the wings, not only
according to species but also, within the
same species, according to sex. In those
groups of Lepidoptera which are most
primitive from the point of view of
evolution, as for example numerous members of the superfamily Tineoidea, the
wings are often oblong and narrow; in

other groups they are wider and usually noticeably triangular, with the outer edges rounded, particularly on the hind wings. The outer edges of the hind wings of certain butterflies and moths extend in lobes or threads, commonly known as 'tails'. These can be very long in such families as the Uraniidae, for example. The wings of certain groups of Microlepidoptera, such as the Orneodidae (Many-plume moths) and the Pterophoridae (Plume moths), are extraordinarily beautiful. The borders are perforated or 'torn' into ribbons, lending them an air of exquisite delicacy which is unique.

As a rule, Lepidoptera have a larger ratio of wing-surface to body than other insects. In certain Morpho and Ornithoptera butterflies, the wingspan can be as much as 25–30 centimetres (about 10–12 inches), while their short, narrow bodies are barely noticeable. The reverse is true of some moths of the Sphingidae family (Hawk-moths). They are very fast flyers and as a result their wings are long and narrow; their bodies are large in order to accommodate the powerful muscles needed for flying. Though the wingspan of some of the larger butterflies, such as *Thysania agrippina*, may exceed 30 centimetres (12 inches), some members of the Nepticulidae family (moths) have a wingspan of only a fraction of this.

Atrophy plays a major role in the modification of wings, and this phenomenon has been observed frequently in certain isolated species or groups. It usually affects both pairs of wings and rarely occurs in the male. In fact, the females of many butterfly and moth families tend to fly far less than the males, although their wings seem normal.

The phenomenon of reduced wing-size is known as brachypterism and includes various intermediary stages from an almost imperceptible reduction in the size of the wings to a total absence. So far, brachypterism affecting both sexes has been recorded in only two species of Microlepidoptera found in the islands of the Antarctic.

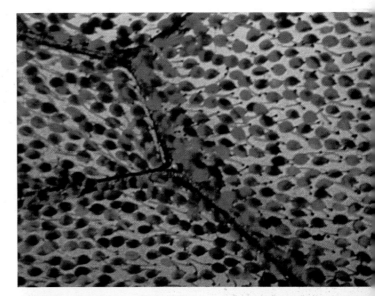

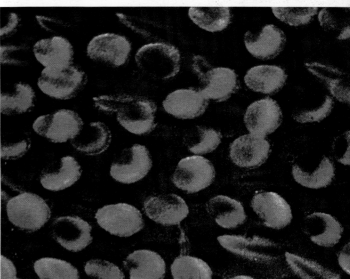

Above and top: Two close-ups of the wings of two tropical Lepidoptera. The coloured scales are arranged in overlapping fashion like roof-tiles

The species whose families are brachypterous or totally wingless usually belong to the faunas of cold or mountainous regions or else to species from the steppes or subdesert regions. Although there is clearly a connection between these phenomena and the environment the cause as such has not yet been established.

Most of a butterfly's wing is covered with a great many scales. Besides partly or completely covering the wing, they provide the characteristic colours and variety of patterns which make Lepidoptera, particularly those from the tropics, so attractive. The scales are hollow appendages, produced by specialized cells in the skin. They are usually fairly wide and thin. Ridges often linked by supporting crossbands run lengthwise down their outer surface. These are reinforced internally by small cuticular bars which cross them, parallel with the shortest side, and usually contain pigments. Their further edges may be smooth, lacy, fringed or of some other shape. The edge of each scale is provided with a stalk-like structure which fits into a special 'pocket' on the wing. The scales are arranged in either a regular or an irregular pattern, like tiles on a roof, or in two overlapping layers. The wings may not be completely covered by scales; areas devoid of scales appear transparent. In addition to the simplest types of scale there are other, specialized kinds such as the 'androconia' scales which are connected to scent glands. These are found on the wings of males of various species and secrete volatile hormones or pheromones which act as sexual stimulants.

Sources of colour

The colours of butterflies and moths come from two distinct sources. They may be due to optical phenomena such as interference or the diffraction of light on the scales, as happens when the surface of a soap bubble appears iridescent. The dazzling blues of the famous Morpho butterflies of the Brazilian fauna or those of certain

Below: The wing membrane is transparent and colourless; areas which lack scales therefore show up as 'holes', as is the case in some Saturniidae
Bottom and lower right: The colouring and metallic sheen of the wings of some Lepidoptera are produced not only by pigments present in the wing scales, but also by special optical effects related to the angle of the illuminating light-rays

members of the Lycaenidae family, which
is found all over the world, are examples of
colours which are physical in origin. These
colours usually change and seem to flicker
on and off according to the angle of vision.
For example, members of the Apatura
genus are a magnificent purple viewed
from the side. Whites are also physical in
origin. They are caused by the dispersion,
reflection and refraction of light by the
scales. These physical colours are also
known as structural colours.

Another source of colour in butterflies
and moths is chemical. Here the tints are
derived from the colour of the pigments
themselves, which are chemical substances

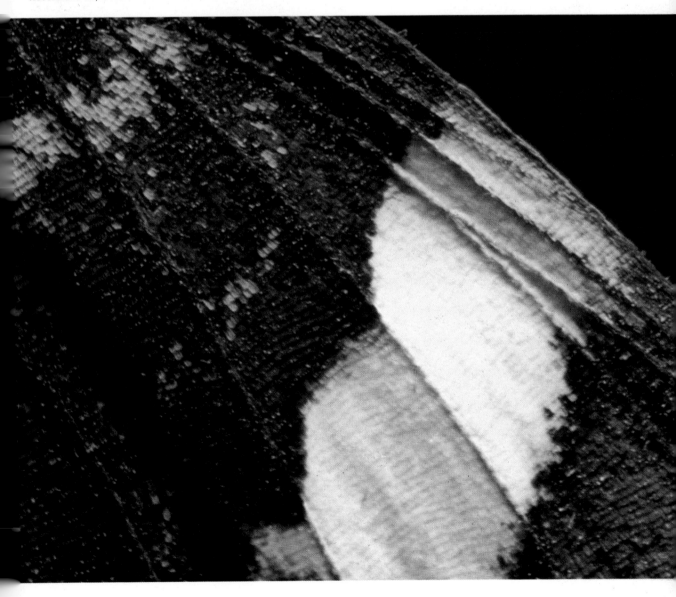

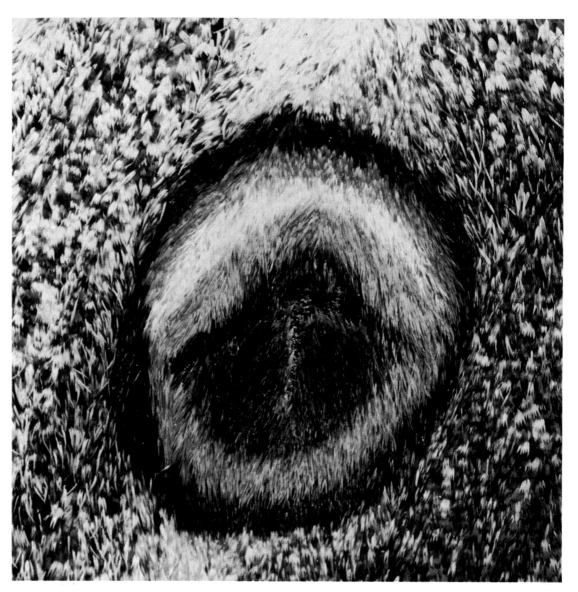

present in the insect's body. These substances can absorb certain light-waves while reflecting others. In the realm of chemical colouring two categories may be distinguished according to their origin: pigments can be endogenous (that is, formed by the creature itself) or exogenous (derived from external origins and generally absorbed through food). The colouring of butterflies and moths is generally, however, a combination of both physical and chemical phenomena.

Colours are of particular importance in the life of Lepidoptera. Sometimes the two sexes differ so much that at first sight they seem to belong to different species: individuals with different colouring may belong to the same species. This is because they belong to generations which have matured at different times of year and therefore under different climatic conditions. A well-known experiment involves exposing larvae—such as those of *Aglais urticae* (the Tortoiseshell)—to the cold, to obtain individuals with abnormal colouring (in this instance with smaller black spots and duller colours).

Mimicry—a form of defence

The most significant aspect of the coloration of wings in butterflies and moths is

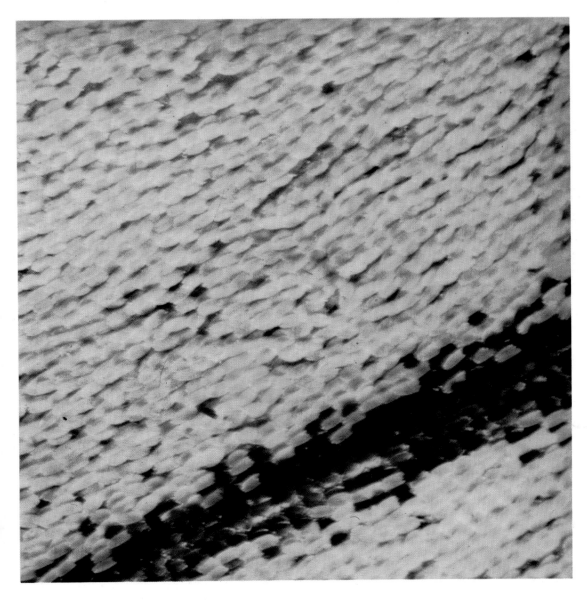

mimicry—when their colours and patterns merge with the environment or resemble those of other species or other insects. This happens to members of two families, the Heliconiidae and the Ithomiidae which are found only in the tropical regions of the New World, except for a few species which have moved on to temperate zones. These butterflies form an amazing group of mimics and include species which are well-protected against predators, both by their smell and their unattractive taste, when they are not actually poisonous. They are also very tough and can survive the kind of rough treatment which would kill most other butterflies or moths. They are among

The scales on a butterfly's wings may take a number of different forms—rounded, oval, finger-like or thread-like
Above: A highly enlarged detail of the wing of a Swallowtail butterfly
Above left: An 'eye-spot' on the wing of *Saturnia pyri*

211

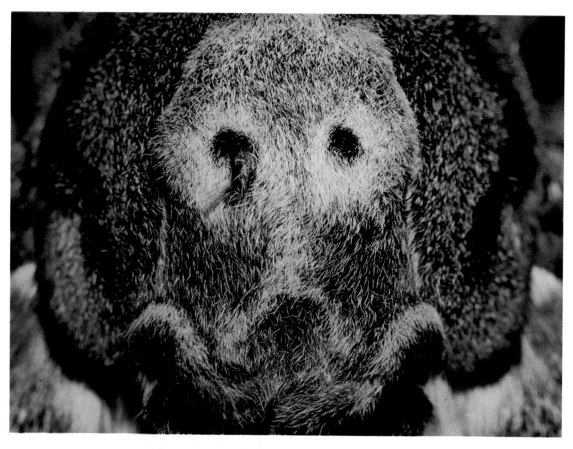

Above: Close-up of the upperside of the
Death's-head Hawk-moth (*Acherontia atropos*)
showing the characteristic skull-like
pattern that gives the insect its name

the most eye-catching species in the tropics,
if not the most common; for this reason
they are often seen in collections.

Besides their repellent characteristics,
these butterflies have also developed vivid
and distinctive colouring and conspicuous
patterns which make them instantly recognizable to would-be predators such as
monkeys, lizards and especially birds. The
species are also mimicked by other defenceless edible species. Remembering unpleasant experiences with the inedible
species, predators refrain from attacking
the other species too, as they look identical.
This is known as Batesian mimicry.

Müllerian mimicry is similar. It occurs
when two common and protected species
resemble each other and therefore serve as a
mutual defence against predators. Yet
another kind of protective resemblance is
found among Lepidoptera. Sometimes
certain butterflies and moths imitate the
shape or colour of leaves or other features
of their environment, in order to hide from

their enemies. This is usually known as crypsis or cryptic coloration. For example, when its wings are open, *Kallima inachis* (the Indian Leaf butterfly), a beautiful Asiatic insect, is very colourful and stands out clearly against the background. But, at the slightest hint of danger, it closes its wings, the undersides of which exactly match the colour of the leaves and branches on which it normally settles. Even the shape of the closed wings, including the pattern of veins, resembles these leaves. But this type of protection is never foolproof. If it were, the numbers of protected species would be disproportionate to that of other species, and the ecological balance would be upset.

Another case of adaptation to the environment is found in *Biston betularia* (the Peppered moth), a member of the Geometridae family. In the words of the entomologist E. B. Ford, this species represents 'the most striking example of evolution which has ever actually been

Below: Another detail of the body of the Death's-head Hawk-moth. The entire body is covered with thread-like scales crowded close together like a coat of fur

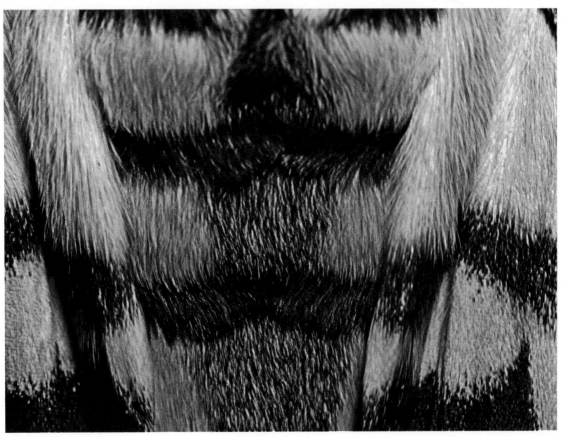

witnessed in any living organism, plant or animal'. This moth's ordinary livery is white, spotted with dark markings, and it merges fairly easily against lichens on tree-trunks. There is also a dark form which was relatively rare until about a century ago. Industrial development and the resulting increase in smog made tree-trunks and undergrowth darker, so the white form of this moth was unable to harmonize with the background in order to escape its numerous predators. Consequently, the dark variety became dominant, and with the additional help of powerful natural selection it almost entirely replaced the white variety. It is also reasonable to suppose that this phenomenon occurs in other species located in heavily polluted industrial zones, though the results of research on this subject are as yet far from conclusive.

The evening of the Great Peacock moth

Lepidoptera come second in the insect world in terms of the number of species, totalling at present about 160,000 known species. However, every year several hundred new species are discovered throughout the world and the number of still unknown species is possibly extremely high.

Although Lepidoptera can be very destructive at the larval stage, they are generally harmless and even useful and desirable as adults. A garden without butterflies can be a cold, almost artificial place. Indeed, Sir Winston Churchill once obtained a great many live butterflies from a collector and had them released at an important party to create an evocative and memorable atmosphere.

During the mating season, the males —particularly those with a very short lifespan—start searching frantically for females. Day-flying species undoubtedly use their eyes to help them in their search, but success depends chiefly on the sense of smell. As already mentioned, the females can release pheromones which, on reaching the males' olfactory organs (most of which are located on the antennae), lure them irresistibly to the place where mating will take place.

In his *Souvenirs Entomologiques*, J. H. Fabre gives a masterly description of this fascinating occurrence. It concerned *Saturnia pyri*, the Great Peacock moth. This is a large moth with dark, thickly scaled wings. The males have distinctive comb-shaped antennae, while those of the females are

Right: The Hornet Clear-wing moth (*Sesia apiformis*) mimics the Hymenoptera in every particular, from its body colouring to the structure of its transparent wings. Its resemblance to the dreaded hornet provides protection against predators

Left: This Death's-head Hawk-moth is well camouflaged against the bark of a tree

215

quite normal. Fabre described the incident as follows:

'It was a memorable evening. I shall always think of it as the evening of the Great Peacock moth. In my presence, on the morning of the 6th May, a female leaves her cocoon on the table in my zoological laboratory. I cover her at once, as she is, still damp from the moisture of the nest, under a woven metal bell jar. From the start, I have no particular plan in mind. I take her prisoner because of my lifelong observer's habit of wishing to see everything when it first appears. And this is the wonderful thing that happened. At about nine o'clock that evening, while my family is going to bed, I hear a terrific noise in the room next to mine. My son Paul, half undressed, is rushing to and fro, running, jumping, shouting and knocking over chairs as if he's gone mad. I hear him calling out: "Quick! Come and look at these moths, they're as big as birds. The room's full of them!"

'I hurry in. The boy's excitement and exaggeration are quite understandable. It's a real invasion, the like of which has never been seen in our house: an invasion of gigantic moths. Then I remember my morning prisoner. I go down with my son to my study which occupies the right wing of the house. Even the kitchen is full of them. It seems as if the Great Peacock moth has taken possession of my house. What ever will it be like upstairs in the room where the female, which is certainly the cause of this great invasion, is imprisoned! Candle in hand, we go into the room. The spectacle before us is quite unforgettable. With a soft fluttering of wings, the huge moths fly round the bell jar, linger for a moment, fly off again, come back, rise to the ceiling and come down again. There are about forty moths in all, including those in other parts of the house. They have come from all directions. Who knows how they were summoned? But here are forty suitors hurrying to pay homage to the young nubile moth born that morning in the mystery of my study.'

Above: Moths usually rest with their wings spread; their protective markings are on the upper surface. Butterflies, by contrast, generally rest with their wings closed and their protective markings are on the lower surface

Left: Adult of *Kallima inachus* (the Indian Leaf butterfly). With its wings closed, this butterfly bears a startling resemblance to a dry leaf and is thereby protected from predators. When it spreads its wings, however, it turns out to be coloured bright blue, orange, black and purple

Top right: Lycaenids mating. The male can only be distinguished from the female by his slightly paler colouring
Bottom right: *Philosamia cynthia* moths mating. Moths rarely mate on the wing, but butterflies do so frequently

Below: *Saturnia pyri,* one of the largest of European Lepidoptera, is also found in Mediterranean countries

Reproduction

Mating often takes place in flight. Sometimes, especially among day-flying Lepidoptera, the male remains motionless, waiting for the females to pass by before pursuing them. It is also not unusual for him to pursue any butterfly that happens to be in the vicinity for fear of missing an opportunity. Mating is then sometimes preceded by a courtship parade during which the male may emit an odorous substance which excites the female. The males of some families, such as certain papilionids and nymphalids, secrete a special substance during mating which, once released, becomes sack-shaped and congealed and sticks to the end of the female's abdomen. This is known as the sphragis or mating seal.

After a while, with timing varied according to the species concerned, the eggs are laid. Generally this takes place immediately after mating, but in some species it may happen much later. The female carefully chooses a place to deposit the eggs; in most cases, they are laid on the food-plant.

The female's reproductive organs can in fact be one of three different kinds. Individuals of the 'monotrisian' type have a single genital orifice which serves for mating and laying eggs. The second type, known as 'exoporian', have two genital orifices, one for mating and the other for egg-laying, both of which are located on the same abdominal segment. Members of a very primitive family—the Hepialidae (Swift moths)—belong to this group. The third and final group includes Lepidoptera of the so-called 'dytrisian' type. These are females which have two separate genital orifices situated on two different abdominal segments.

Once laid, the eggs are usually abandoned by the mother since they do not require special care. They can be of various shapes and colours. A thick, tough outer covering forms an interesting sculptural shape. It can be notched, deeply engraved or covered in hairs. Only species which in

Above and top: The mating of *Philosamia cynthia*. The moths cling on to a support with their legs and bend up the tip of the abdomen to enable copulation to take place

Top right: Processionary moths (*Thaumetopoea pityocampa*) shown mating. As the male flies, he trails the female along behind him while she flaps her wings to help him as best she can

Bottom right: *Philosamia cynthia* mating. The process may last as long as four hours

some way protect the eggs from outside agents have weak shells. The outer covering has an opening at one end, known as the mycropyle, and its function is to permit the entry of one or more sperms. Some time after the egg has been laid, the embryo develops and the egg then opens to release a larva which, in the case of Lepidoptera, is known as a caterpillar. Lepidoptera undergo total metamorphosis: before reaching adulthood they have to go through the stages of being larvae and pupae or chrysalises.

The caterpillar is clad in a non-elastic covering which it has to change when this gets too tight for its growing inner body. This process is known as moulting, and in the course of the life of a larva it happens several times before the larva changes into a chrysalis and then into an adult insect. In Lepidoptera, reproduction sometimes occurs without the participation of a male. This phenomenon, parthenogenesis, may be of two types: spontaneous and artificial. In special circumstances, such as the accidental absence of males, certain species undergo spontaneous parthenogenesis. The females of these species are also capable of normal mating when they find a male. The parthenogenetic females give birth to both males and females. Other species reproduce only by parthenogenesis and never as a result of mating with males, and only females of these particular varieties are known.

As far as artificial parthenogenesis is concerned, innumerable experiments have been conducted on various species. By means of chemical, physical or mechanical agents, eggs laid by unfertilized females have been successfully reared. Until now, this has only been achieved with the silkworm (*Bombyx mori*). Individuals born as a result of artificial parthenogenesis exhibit varying degrees of abnormality in their genetic make-up.

The determination of the sex of Lepidoptera by chromosomes is different from that in other insects. The normal chromosome complement of an individual may be referred to as 2a and the sex chromosomes of each sex as XX and XY. In the vinegar-fly (*Drosophila melanogaster*), the male's chromosome formula is 2a + XY, while the female's is 2a + XX. In Lepidoptera it is the other way round: the males have a chromosome complement of 2a + XX, while the females have 2a + XY. As with the majority of animal organisms, this phenomenon affects the sex of the offspring. In particular in Lepidoptera, the appearance of anomalous individuals called gynanders or gynandromorphs can be witnessed, and it is this which, as a rule, produces individuals whose physical characteristics are half male and half female. This is evident in species exhibiting marked sexual dimorphism. For example, if the male of a species has yellow wings while the female's are white, the gynander will have its right wings of one colour and its left wings of the other colour. Gynandromorphism can happen in different ways, but always some accident in development occurs so that certain cells receive chromosomes leading to the development of the opposite sex from the rest of the body. If this happens at the first division of the nucleus in the egg, then one half of the resulting insect will be female and the other half male.

Long-distance migration

Lepidoptera, like other insects, sometimes take part in what may be called 'social phenomena'. Some day-flying species congregate for the night's sleep, as has been noticed several times with certain Lycaenidae and Nymphalidae butterflies, and sometimes these species meet to form communities. But migration is far and away the most important social phenomenon. It happens frequently, particularly to members of the Danaidae family, but a great many other families also have migratory species.

A migratory swarm may consist of one or more species. During the flight, the butterflies or moths fly singly or in groups.

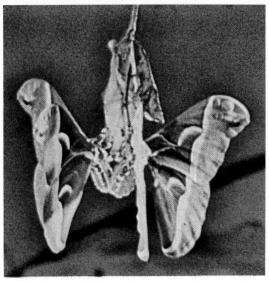

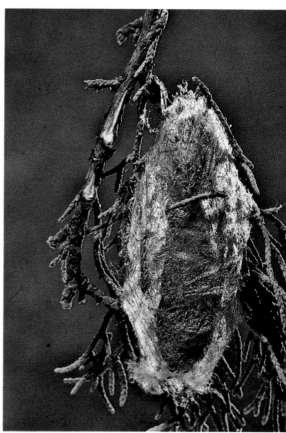

According to latest statistics, certain swarms are made up of billions of individuals and are capable of obscuring the sun. Such swarms are an astonishing sight. They can cover an area thousands of kilometres or miles long and a few hundred kilometres or miles wide. Their route is always clearly established, but varies according to the species concerned and the time of year.

The distance covered by migrating butterflies and moths is impressive. Some species normally fly from Africa to northern Europe, others from North America all the way to Australia. But unlike birds and mammals, butterflies and moths, in common with almost all migratory insects, fly only one way. They make the outward journey but never (or at least rarely) return to their country of origin. So far only one case of seasonal migration with a return flight has been recorded by naturalists. The species involved belonged to the genus Danaus—*Danaus plexippus,* commonly known as the Milkweed or, in the United States, the Monarch. This butterfly is very familiar in the regions it inhabits because of its great size, powerful flight and its habit of not seeking hiding places. For these reasons, it is the best known of the migrant butterflies.

In the autumn these butterflies can be seen virtually throughout North America, travelling south in large numbers and often concentrated along the coasts. It is not unusual to see them flying over big cities: they have been seen, for example, passing over the centre of New York. At night, swarms several thousand strong come to rest together, often choosing the same resting places used by numerous swarms in earlier years. The butterflies head south towards tropical or subtropical regions where they spend the winter, often in a semi-dormant state.

In spring the northward flight begins, but this is never as compact, orderly or extensive as the mass movement in the autumn. During the journey the females deposit eggs on plants of the milkweed

Far left: Eggs (top) and larvae (centre and bottom) of *Pachypasa lineosa;* the larva is able to camouflage itself extremely well
Top left: Cocoon of the same species. The transparent wall of the silken cocoon allows the pupa to be seen
Left: Two adults mating. The male's antennae are turned back along his body

family, which are herbaceous plants or shrubs, rarely trees, whose tissues often produce a milky liquid. They are sometimes shaped like cactus plants and have simple leaves. Nutritious plants like these provide food, and the new-born larvae feed ravenously and strip them almost bare. As soon as the Danaus caterpillars become adult butterflies, they leave the area and continue the journey north, sometimes going as far as Canada. These are the butterflies that migrate southwards in the autumn.

A great deal remains to be learned about the migration of the Milkweed even though extensive research has been conducted in recent years. Research is carried out by research laboratories. A large number of specimens are caught, marked and released for recapture elsewhere. It is hoped that co-operation between laboratories in the countries where this migration takes place will reveal in future more about this remarkable occurrence.

Italy's main migratory butterflies belong to the Pieridae family (the Colias and Pieris genera) and the Nymphalidae family (Vanessa genus). Certain species of moths of the Sphingidae and Noctuidae families and the Microlepidoptera also have migratory habits. Every year these species migrate north from southern Europe and Africa to central Europe and even Britain and Scandinavia. One or more generations may appear during the course of a year in the regions they travel to. This is the case with the Red Admiral, the autumn specimens coming from the eggs laid by migrants. As the adults rarely survive the winter, these migrant species are sometimes unable to maintain themselves in their new environment. This is true of two large Sphingidae moths—*Acherontia atropos* (the Death's-head Hawk-moth) and *Herse convolvuli* (the Convolvulus Hawk-moth). Man has also contributed to the presence of species belonging to the fauna of other regions by deliberately or accidentally transporting either larvae or adults into new areas.

Enemies of butterflies and moths

As already shown, adult butterflies and moths often try to escape from vertebrate enemies through mimicking distasteful species or by their cryptic coloration. Yet, in spite of this, Lepidoptera are still among the insects most relished by predators. This may be because many caterpillars feed openly on vegetation and are more or less helpless, despite their resemblance to the leaves and possession of irritating hairs.

The chief enemies of butterflies and moths are mainly insects: they include beetles, hornets, ants, mantises and many others. These parasitic or predatory insects attack larvae in particular. Among the worst culprits are the species which devote special care to their offspring, endeavouring to procure abundant food supplies for them either by laying their eggs inside the caterpillar or by paralysing their prey and then carrying it off still alive to their nests. Other animals which feed on butterflies and moths are spiders, frogs, toads, lizards, bats, monkeys and above all birds. On account of his activities, man, too, must be added to the list.

In certain regions inhabited by primitive peoples, the plump, fleshy larvae of some species of butterflies and moths are regarded as a great delicacy by the natives. But man's influence makes itself particularly felt through the often indiscriminate use of pesticides which, though intended by manufacturers and users alike to rid crops of pests, also have a harmful effect on all other insects.

Today, unbridled hunting by collectors is not least among the causes of the destruction of butterflies and moths. Far from carrying out scientific research, the sole aim of some is to amass flawless specimens of the largest possible number of species. This activity flourishes in tropical zones where an abundance of magnificent multicoloured specimens are easy to catch. Consequently, the number of specimens and species readily found of more spectacular kinds is now diminishing appreciably.

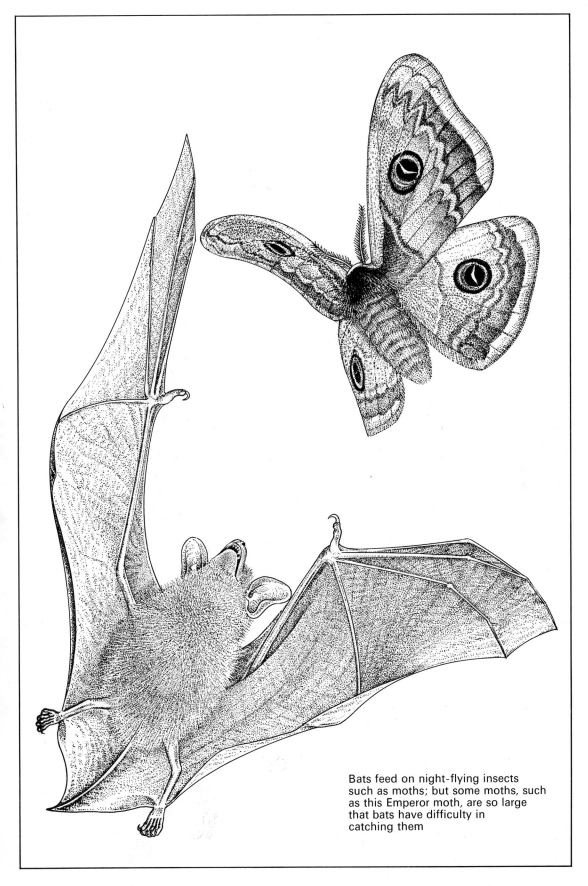

Bats feed on night-flying insects
such as moths; but some moths, such
as this Emperor moth, are so large
that bats have difficulty in
catching them

Lepidoptera are subject to a number of often fatal diseases due to the attack of viruses, bacteria, fungi and protozoa. The most serious and dangerous of the virus diseases is undoubtedly the so-called polyhedral disease which causes crystalloids composed of virus proteins arranged in a well-defined pattern to appear in the cell. The disease attacks caterpillars which become swollen and show destruction of the hypodermis (the cellular layer lying beneath the cuticle), blood-cells and other internal organs. Because of the enormous economic damage it causes, breeders of silkworms greatly fear this disease to which silkworms are particularly susceptible. Disease-inducing bacteria also attack and kill Lepidoptera with ease. Such diseases are highly virulent and contagious.

Mycoses, like other diseases, are also greatly feared by silkworm breeders. Certain fungi of the genus Beauveria find their way underneath the cuticle and the young fungus spawn digests the chitin and causes great damage to silk factories. This fungus can even penetrate a chrysalis, harden its tissues and finally mummify it so that it never emerges as an adult butterfly or moth at all.

Microsporidia, which are parasitic protozoa, also affect Lepidoptera, particularly caterpillars. The victim develops poorly and may even lose weight; it becomes lethargic and loses its appetite. The protozoon destroys the hypodermis, causing dark, dead patches full of spores to appear on the surface of the infested area. Unfortunately, this disease is transmitted through eggs to offspring, with disastrous results which are hard to eradicate in a single generation.

The sense organs

Scientists have often used Lepidoptera in experiments for their increasingly detailed research into the physiology, anatomy and behaviour of insects. In the late nineteenth century, S. Exner and E. Müller published their theories on vision in insects, and the application of these theories in the study of Lepidoptera has proved them to be valid.

The compound eye of the butterfly or moth is formed by the juxtaposition of a large number of basic elements, the ommatidia. Each ommatidium is formed by a corneola, a crystalline cone, a retinula or sensitive part and some accessory cells known as 'pigment cells'. In moths' eyes, a special reflecting layer—the tapetum—is usually found between the pigment cells and the crystalline cone. It consists mainly of fine air-tubes filled with air, and gives moths' eyes that dazzling effect characteristic of cats' eyes at night.

There are two kinds of sight in Lepidoptera. They can see either by 'apposition' or by 'superposition'. In Lepidoptera with the former type of vision, each ommatidium is separate from those next to it because of the pigment cells so that it receives only those rays of light which are able to cross its own corneola. In this case, the image seen comes from the combination of as many points as there are ommatidia. This kind of vision is typical of day-flying species which are usually good flyers.

In species that fly in the evening or at night, however, the ommatidia are not optically isolated from each other. The sensitive part of the compound eye therefore simultaneously receives rays of light which have penetrated a group of neighbouring ommatidia, not a single ommatidium. The overall image is therefore the combination of a number of overlapping images and is consequently brighter.

There are innumerable intermediary stages between these two visual systems. In fact, the pigment can migrate in the pigment cells when going from dark to light, thus transforming the visual system from one type to the other. There are 'fast' eyes which can transform the visual system in a matter of minutes and 'slow' eyes which take several hours to adjust.

Right: The Red Admiral butterfly (*Vanessa atalanta*) is commonly seen sunning itself on flowers, particularly in the autumn

Ants carry lycaenid larvae, which produce a sweet secretion, from the flowers they feed on back to their own nests. The butterfly larvae feed on the ant larvae and turn into pupae the following spring. Adult butterflies eventually crawl out of the ants' nest to produce eggs and start the cycle again

Applying the techniques used for bees, some writers have studied colour perception in butterflies and moths. *Aglais urticae* (the Tortoiseshell butterfly) is very sensitive to light rays from blue to violet and from yellow to red but is virtually blind to the green to yellow-green band of the spectrum. When fluttering over flowers in search of food, certain species of pierids alight spontaneously on specially prepared blue or purple sheets of paper but are less likely to settle on red or yellow sheets. They, too, are almost blind to green, blue-green and grey. Oddly, females of these species prefer emerald green or blue-green foliage when laying eggs, and ignore blue or yellow. This is clearly a special physiological reaction connected to their condition at the time. All members of the Pieridae family are similar to human beings in their perception of green, red and yellow. As a rule, moths are nocturnal and so do not need colour vision, but the Elephant Hawk-moth (*Deilephila elpenor*) flies and feeds at dusk and is able to distinguish the blue–purple group of colours from yellow-green. Similarly, the day-flying Humming-bird Hawk-moth (*Macroglossa stellatarum*) prefers to feed from blue-coloured flowers.

Lepidoptera are quite advanced in their perception of shapes, too. Even caterpillars which are known to have rudimentary vision, distinguish shapes fairly accurately. Given a choice of two identically shaped objects which differ in height, they select the higher one. In such cases, the perception of shape is due to the lateral ocelli distributed over a large part of the surface of the head. The front of the head is continually bobbing around, enabling the caterpillar to explore a wide visual field. Certain ocelli may form clear reversed images.

Caterpillars, butterflies and moths have also been used in experiments on the functioning of the various sense organs, with excellent results. Research into the organs affecting the sense of taste has shown that caterpillars seem unable to distinguish sweetness from bitterness, acidity and saltiness. They are quick to recognize pleasant or unpleasant tastes, however. Nearly all adult butterflies and moths have special organs for tasting sugary substances. These are located in their feet. A number of receptors are found there with the sole function of transmitting taste stimuli to the central nervous system. This type of taste is known as 'tarsal taste'.

In certain species of the Pyrameis, Danaus and Pieris genera, for example, if the wings are immobilized in the rest position and the feet are touched with a small brush soaked in a sugar solution, the insect will immediately uncoil is proboscis as if to dip it in the corolla of a flower. This experiment shows that, because of tarsal taste, Lepidoptera can tell instantly whether they have settled on a flower or on some other sort of vegetation. Certain species have feet which are also very sensitive to other substances such as quinine or saline compounds.

The nervous system of Lepidoptera has also been investigated in order to identify the location of various nervous functions. The male and female of a particular, rather large moth, are able to mate and behave and react in an apparently normal manner even after decapitation — that is, after being deprived of most of the systems controlling their activity. Detailed examination has revealed that the reflex which leads to mating has its centre in the last abdominal ganglia of the central nervous chain; and since they are still intact, they function without difficulty. This experiment confirmed what had already been observed in the Praying Mantis, a beautiful predatory insect.

During mating, the female Praying Mantis eats the male, starting with his head. Certain observers had noticed that the male seems unaware of this amputation and, if anything, completes the sex act more easily. Experiments reveal it to be a relatively simple matter due to two phenomena. Firstly, as already mentioned in connection with butterflies and moths, the reflexes governing copulation are centred in the last abdominal ganglia which are independent of the brain. Secondly, the suboesophageal ganglion inhibits the sexual activity of the Praying Mantis. It is understandable that mating is easier when the head (and therefore the suboesophageal ganglion) is removed.

Classification of Lepidoptera

Lepidoptera are found in virtually every part of the world where there are flowering plants, even at high altitudes. The number of species living in the colder regions is rather limited, but sufficiently humid, hot regions have a much larger butterfly and moth population. Since caterpillars are almost exclusively plant-eating, the major factor affecting their distribution may be the availability of food-plants.

Families of the order of Lepidoptera can be classified with the help of dichotomous keys. These are tables compiled by various authorities on the basis of characteristics which are constant within the same category but variable in different categories. But dichotomous tables inevitably fall short of perfection, mainly because the characteristics identifying certain families are not precise.

The order Lepidoptera is now divided into four suborders according to the structure of the mouth parts, wing venation and the arrangement of the female's genital openings. As a generalization, it may be stated that the presence of mandibles indicates Zeugloptera or Dacnonypha; if the venation of hind and forewings is similar, Monotrysia; but if the venation of wings is dissimilar, Ditrysia, which group includes the greatest proportion of the order.

Females of the Zeugloptera (Micropterygidae), Dacnonypha (for example, Eriocraniidae) and Monotrysia (such as Hepialidae, Nepticulidae and Incurvariidae) have nine or ten recognizable abdominal segments. The reproductive organs are of the monotrysian or exoporian

type and the included species are therfore primitive from an evolutionary point of view. The Micropterygidae, generally small moths, are unique among Lepidoptera in that they feed on solid food as adults. This is explained by the fact that their mouth parts are of the chewing type. They therefore constitute a completely separate group and their classificatory position is still uncertain. The Micropterygidae include about 80 species found in most of the earth's temperate zones, particularly north of the Himalayas and in New Zealand.

The Eriocraniidae do not have chewing mouth parts although they have non-functional mandibles. The side processes of the maxillae form a short, rudimentary trunk for sucking which is perfectly functional. The family includes about 20 species with wide distribution.

The Hepialidae include large and medium-sized species with a wingspan of between 2 and 23 centimetres (0.78 to 9 inches). The female genital organs are of the exoporian type. Members of this family are fast flyers, both during the day and at night, and their bodies are often brightly coloured. They include about 300 species with virtually world-wide distribution.

Species belonging to the Nepticulidae family include the smallest Lepidoptera and can have a wingspan of only 2 millimetres (0.07 inches). Their size is directly related to the lives they lead as larvae. The caterpillars burrow tunnels into leaves, thus earning the name of 'leaf-miners'. The 'mines' or tunnels sometimes cover the whole leaf and take various forms such as blotch-like patches and blisters. Broadly speaking, every species has its own characteristic 'mine' or at any rate one which differs from those produced by other leaf-mining moth families. The form and arrangement of larval excrement inside a 'mine' provide an accurate indication of whether the tunnel has been burrowed by a lepidopterous insect or by some species belonging to another order.

The Nepticulidae family is found all over the world and includes about 300

Photographs showing the structure of the
heads of butterflies and moths
Above: Detail of the compound eye and
proboscis of *Pieris brassicae,* the Cabbage
White butterfly. The mouth parts consist of a
double-barrelled suction tube
Right: The 'face' of a male *Philosamia cynthia*
Below: The thick 'fur coat' of *Thaumetopoea
pityocampa*
Bottom right: Head and forelimbs of *Actias
selene* (the Luna moth)

Butterflies are day-flying insects and are
often seen on flowers, from which they obtain
nectar which is their chief source of food.
Moths, by contrast, fly at night and most of
them hide during the day
Far left from top: *Plebeius argus* (the
Silver-studded Blue butterfly); a butterfly
of the species Satyrus; another satyrid
lands on a leaf
Left: *Melanargia galathea* (the Marbled White
butterfly)
Above: *Melitaea didyma* (the Spotted Fritillary
butterfly)
Right: *Smerinthus ocellata* (the Eyed Hawk-moth)

species. The males of certain species of the Incurvariidae family have incredibly long, fine, thread-like antennae which may be as much as four times as long as the body including the head. The adults sometimes fly in broad daylight, flaunting superb, many-coloured or iridescent liveries. A common species in oak woods in Europe is *Adela viridella* (the Green Longhorn) which is a brilliant golden green.

The suborder Ditrysia comprises all the remaining Lepidoptera and it is often divided by amateur entomologists into Rhopalocera (day-flying butterflies with clubbed antennae) and Heterocera (moths, mainly night-flying, with antennae various but not clubbed). Another division is into Macrolepidoptera and Microlepidoptera based mainly on the size of the adult. Although these terms are still used in general books such as this, they are not employed in specialist writing.

Beneficial and harmful species
Another member of the Incurvariidae family, belonging to the Prodoxinae subfamily, is important because of its close relationship with an American plant, the yucca. *Tegeticula yuccasella* is the best-known species. The female carries a special long tentacle on each maxilla with which she gathers a small amount of pollen, which may be even larger than her head, from the anthers of the yucca flowers. She then carries the precious load to another flower and deposits it on the tip of the stigma, part of the flower's female organs. Thus this small insect cross-fertilizes the flowers, since each of the pollen grains can push a pollen-tube into the ovary. In this case, pollination is not merely a by-product of the insect's movements inside the flower, as happens with bees, wasps and other insects which pollinate flowers while visiting them in search of food. In fact, after entering the flower, the Tegeticula lays one or two eggs in the ovary of the inflorescence so that the caterpillars have food available as soon as they emerge.

Right: *Parnassius apollo* is common in the Italian Alps. Similar looking species of Parnassius are found in mountainous areas of the world including the United States, but not in Britain

234

Although they feed on the yucca seeds, the caterpillars—of which there are only one or two—always leave a certain number intact, and these in due course produce new plants. The yucca therefore benefits from the insect's action while the insect is nourished and sheltered by the plant. No more striking example is known of interdependence between insects and plants.

The Tineidae family includes species which are commonly known as 'clothes-moths'. Their larvae are often found in houses where they attack carpets, wool mattresses and clothes, causing considerable damage. Most Tineidae caterpillars weave silky cocoons which are usually covered with material taken from their immediate surroundings. However, the problem is much less serious than it once was for various reasons, the most significant probably being the invention of dry cleaning. An Asiatic member of the Monopis genus is particularly interesting because it is one of the very few Lepidoptera whose larvae are born alive. Females have been known to carry as many as a dozen caterpillars in a special enlarged duct in the abdomen.

The Pyralidae family is important from the economic point of view. The most representative species appears to be the cosmopolitan meal-moth (*Pyralis farinalis*) which, as its name implies, causes serious damage to grain and cereal stores. *Ephestia kühniella* (the Mediterranean flour-moth), which also belongs to this family, is easy to rear and is frequently used in laboratory experiments.

Most caterpillars belonging to the Tortricidae family build their nests from twisted vegetable matter. They also cause a great deal of damage to agriculture. One has only to think of the notorious apple pest which is none other than the larva of *Cydia pomonella,* the Codling moth, a member of the Tortricidae family.

Many moths used to be classified as Macrolepidoptera, the most significant being the Cossidae, the Lymantridae, the Geometridae, the Sphingidae, the Noc-

tuidae, the Saturniidae, the Bombycidae and the Lasiocampidae. Unlike the larvae of most Lepidoptera, the Cossidae caterpillars feed on wood and cause much damage to specific trees. Among the more notable are the reddish *Cossus cossus* (the Goat moth) and *Zeuzera pyrina* (the Leopard moth). The Lymantridae are not very striking to look at, but their caterpillars include some remarkably beautiful and unusual specimens. The most common species is *Lymantria dispar* (the Gipsy moth), which also does considerable damage to trees.

The Noctuidae family may well be the largest of all Lepidoptera. It comprises about 20,000 species, some 2,000 of which are found in the Palaearctic region (generally Europe and Asia north of the Himalayas). There are enormous variations in the many species, which is only to be expected in such an extensive group. Some of the smallest species have a wingspan of less than 8 millimetres (0.31 inches), while at the other end of the scale there is a tropical species in the New World with a wingspan of 32 centimetres (12 inches). The colours of the Noctuidae are usually fairly drab; there are few brightly coloured species in the family. Many species cause serious damage to crops.

Geometridae moths hold their wings outstretched in such a way that their hind wings are exposed. 'Geometra' means 'surveyor' in Italian, and the name 'Geometridae' comes from the characteristic way the caterpillars loop as they move, as though they are measuring out the ground. The Sphingidae include medium and large moths with sturdy, torpedo-shaped bodies and long, narrow wings that create an aerodynamic effect. They are all excellent flyers and usually have highly developed proboscides. They hover above flowers with long corollas to suck out the

Right: Linnaeus's earliest successors in both botany and entomology used hand-painted colour plates to illustrate the species they described and named. Shown here are various moths with a caterpillar and a chrysalis

236

185. e.

185. d.

185. a.

185. g.

185. b.

185. f.

185. c.

185. h.

185. i.

El. Hochecker et Fassin pinx.

nectar. The most eye-catching species is undoubtedly the Death's-head Hawk-moth (*Acherontia atropos*), so called because of the skull pattern on the moth's thorax. This species has a short, powerful proboscis which it sometimes uses to pierce honey-combs and suck out the honey.

The Saturniidae include some of the largest and finest moths. They sometimes have spectacular antennae of an unusual shape and size. The striking European species is *Saturnia pyri,* with a wingspan of 16 centimetres (6 inches). But there is also *Philosamia cynthia* which was originally imported from the East, together with its food-plant, at a time when the silkworm was in danger of being wiped out by disease. Unfortunately the silk from its cocoons proved useless for various reasons, and the species became naturalized and is now fairly common in Italy. The best known of the Bombycidae moths—the mulberry bombyx or silkworm (*Bombyx mori*)—was introduced to Europe from its native China. The main significance of this moth is its economic importance, though this is becoming less relevant today. The family Lasiocampidae are stout-bodied, hairy and sexually dimorphic, with fast-flying males and larger, sluggish females. Their caterpillars are very hairy, the hairs sometimes having irritating properties.

Day-flying Lepidoptera

Butterflies are day-flying Lepidoptera with clubbed antennae; they used to be called Rhopalocera. Unlike moths, butterflies hold their wings vertically above their backs when resting. The most important families known as butterflies are the Hesperiidae, Papilionidae, Pieridae, Lycaenidae and Nymphalidae.

The Hesperiidae are usually small or medium sized, with very sturdy bodies. They have triangular forewings, while the hind wings are rounded and sometimes elongated in a long, tail-like appendage. This family comprises about 3,000 species, most of which are tropical. The majority of

species are found in South America.

Although they are a relatively small family amounting at present to about 600 species, the Papilionidae are very well known. The species differ considerably in size: some may have a wingspan of as much as 25 centimetres (10 inches) while others do not exceed 5 centimetres (2 inches). Their wing coloration is sometimes vivid and astonishing colour combinations can be seen. The family includes numerous important subfamilies which are found nearly all over the world. The Papilionidae include species which generally show marked sexual dimorphism. Some males have long tails on their hind wings, but these are not always found in the females. In the species *Papilio dardanus,* there are two kinds of female, one with a tail and one without.

Dimorphic species with brilliantly coloured males and dark, drab females are often found in the Ornithoptera. This genus includes the giants of the Papilionidae family with species which are in great demand among scientists and butterfly collectors. The renowned entomologist Sir A. Russel Wallace, who spent many months hunting Lepidoptera in New Guinea and the neighbouring islands, recorded his delight at capturing a splendid specimen: 'I had the good fortune to capture one of the most magnificent insects the world contains, the great bird-winged butterfly, *Ornithoptera poseidon*. I trembled with excitement as I saw it coming majestically towards me, and could hardly believe that I had really succeeded in my stroke until I had taken it out of the net and was gazing, lost in admiration, at the velvety black and brilliant green of its wings, seven inches across, the golden body and crimson breast. It is true I had seen similar insects at home, but it is quite another thing to capture such oneself—to feel it struggling

Right: The early illustrators of natural history books did not have photographs to help them and needed to work with meticulous accuracy. The moths in this plate belong to the family Noctuidae

263. a.

263. c.

263. d.

263. b.

263. f.

263. g.

263. e.

263. i.

263. h.

M. El. Hochecker pinx.

F.L. Swebach Desfontaines sculp.

between one's fingers, and to gaze upon its fresh and living beauty, a bright gem shining amidst the silent gloom of a dark and tangled forest. The village of Dobbo held that evening at least one contented man.'

The most outstanding of the European species of Papilionidae with tails on their hind wings are undoubtedly the beautiful Swallowtail and the Podalirius. These butterflies fly between March and September on the plains and in the mountains. The Zerynthia and Parnassius are tailless, but

Below: The butterfly *Colias hyale*. In this species the female, shown here, is not as dark as the male

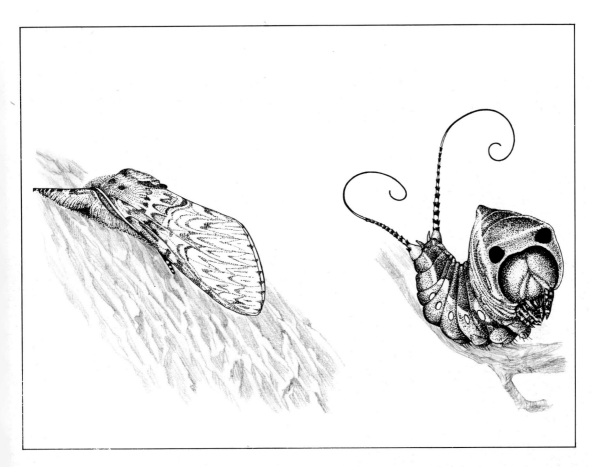

Above: Adult and larva of *Cerura vinula* (the Puss moth). To escape from predators the adult (left) tends to blend into its environment while the larva (right) relies on the element of surprise by extending a pair of long, red filaments from the end of its body

equally interesting and beautiful. The latter includes alpine species, found at great altitudes in the mountains of Europe and Asia.

The large Pieridae family, with more than 1,000 species, includes a number of butterflies which are universally familiar. Members of this family are small or medium-sized and they nearly always have white, yellow or orange wings with a varying number of black spots. Almost invariably, however, they show marked sexual dimorphism, at least in their colouring. Migration occurs in certain species of the family, with swarms of millions of butterflies travelling great distances. In the past, the simultaneous emergence from their cocoons of a large number of butterflies led to the fantastic legend of 'rainstorms of blood'. What actually happens, however, is that the ground and plants above which the adult insects have emerged look as if they have been covered with blood-coloured spots. These are in

The sequence of
photographs on these
two pages show a
processionary moth
(*Thaumetopoea
pityocampa*) newly
emerged from its
puparium. After its
long confinement
within the chrysalis
the moth spreads out
and dries its wings

fact drops of meconium, a reddish fluid which is ejected from the anal opening of the adult butterfly after it emerges.

Certain species of the Pieridae family living high in the mountains appear to be viviparous to a greater or lesser extent, probably as a result of adaptation to the particularly harsh climate. The larvae of some species feed on cabbage leaves, frequently causing severe damage to the crops. Because of their diet the adults of these are called Cabbage Whites.

Of all Lepidoptera, the most brilliantly coloured belong to the Lycaenidae family, which consists of about 3,000 species with world-wide distribution; they are most commonly found in the tropics. They are usually small, or at any rate never large. Sexual dimorphism is nearly always very marked in this family, too. The males of the species *Lysandra bellargus* have magnificent silver-blue wings, while the females are reddish brown.

Many species of Lycaenidae lead unusual lives, both as caterpillars and as butterflies. The larvae of certain species have myrmecophilous glands which secrete a liquid that is attractive to ants. For this reason they are welcomed and carried into ants' nests, where they sometimes live symbiotically. Caterpillars of the very rare British butterfly *Maculinia arion* (the Large Blue) are carried by ants and deposited in the ants' nests. A caterpillar of this species is initially plant-eating, but stops feeding after the third moult and wanders around until an ant, attracted by the special secretion from its glands, captures it and carries it away. Once inside the ants' nest, the caterpillar does not return the compliment but feeds on its hosts' larvae. Caterpillars of other species of the Lycaenidae family are fed by ants by food-exchange. This consists of regurgitated food being passed from mouth to mouth, the ant obtaining a sweet substance in exchange. Some butterflies of the Lycaenidae family compete with certain ants in feeding on the honeydew secreted by particular scale-insects. The butterflies hold themselves erect on their legs, keeping their abdomens out of reach of the terrible jaws of the ants.

Certain species, though basically plant-eating, show a strong taste for cannibalism. Other species are exclusively carnivorous and therefore predatory. It is also not unusual to come across butterflies and moths feeding on liquid food of animal or vegetable origin. In hot countries, members of the Lycaenidae family can be seen feeding on the liquid oozing from the eyes of large herbivorous mammals, thus transmitting to other individuals the germs of any diseases which may be present. Beautiful multicoloured butterflies often settle on people's arms or necks because they are partial to sweat, which they suck with their proboscides. Others feed on the liquid in manure heaps or excrement.

The Nymphalidae include perhaps some of the best-known butterflies such as *Aglais urticae* and *Inachis io* (the Tortoiseshell and the Peacock) which appear as soon as spring arrives, having spent the winter as adult butterflies. The first warm rays of sunlight lure them out of their hiding places. At rest, the Nymphalidae, like other butterflies, hold their wings vertically, the uppersides facing each other. Since the wings often have lacy edges and the undersides are more or less uniformly dark, these butterflies are hardly distinguishable from the foliage on which they settle.

Species belonging to this family are medium-sized or very large, and are usually brilliantly coloured with vivid wing patterns. Many tropical species which are very popular with collectors and taxonomists belong to the Nymphalidae family and include, among others, the Danainae and Morphinae tribes. The Danainae include species found in the tropics both in the Old and the New World. *Danaus chrysippus* (the Plain Tiger) and *Danaus plexippus,* which are widely known, are imitated by other butterflies because of their ability to evade predators

Right: *Melanargia galathea* (the Marbled White butterfly) takes nectar from a flower

or else because they are quite inedible. *Danaus plexippus* undertakes remarkable migrations and is the only butterfly or moth to make the return journey.

The Morphinae include some magnificent butterflies. They have huge wings but their bodies are comparatively small. The males are a marvellous shining, metallic blue and for this reason are often used to decorate jewellery and ornaments. The females are much less exotic, however. The Morpho genus is typical of the forests of tropical America. The Nymphalidae family, which has more species than any other family of the butterflies, numbering about 5,000, is found all over the world.

Metamorphosis
of the caterpillar

Caterpillars, the larvae of Lepidoptera, undergo total metamorphosis and as a result are remarkably different from adult butterflies and moths. They provide an interesting example of adaptation to their environment.

Butterflies and moths lay their eggs in various ways. Depending on the family or species concerned, the eggs may be laid singly on leaves or stalks, or in clusters on the upper or lower surfaces of leaves. They are usually attached to the foliage with a sticky substance secreted by glands connected to the female's genital organs. Certain species, particularly among the Satyridae, deposit their eggs in flight in such a way that they fall on suitable ground—generally meadowland—for the future caterpillars. Female Lepidoptera are certainly gifted with a remarkable instinct for choosing appropriate places for their offspring to hatch.

It is easy to distinguish different species of butterflies and moths whose eggs have been deposited in unusual ways. For example, *Malacosoma neustria* (the Lackey moth) of the Lasiocampidae family, lays its eggs in a ring cluster around the fine twigs of fruit trees or other specific trees. *Ennomos magnarius,* a member of the Geometridae family, also has its own distinctive method of laying eggs: they are deposited in a long, vertical line up a tree-trunk.

Left: Larva of *Smerinthus ocellata* (the Eyed Hawk-moth). The spiracles through which it breathes can be clearly seen along its side

Some females coat their eggs with special protective substances which are sometimes very resistant to outside agents. These substances may either be secreted by the mothers or they may simply be hairs or scales from the area around the ovipositor and the anal opening. Female Psychidae generally lay their eggs inside the pupal skin from which the females emerge either partially or completely.

After a period of incubation, a minute larva emerges from the egg, which has either been fertilized or has developed through parthenogenesis. Since it requires food immediately, the mother has to make sure she lays her eggs on or near the foliage which will serve as a food-plant for the new-born caterpillars. The female almost invariably dies after laying the eggs; in any case, butterflies and moths rarely care for their young.

The anatomy of the caterpillar

A caterpillar's anatomy is not as simple as it might appear at first sight. Caterpillars are generally fairly long and cylindrical or spindle-shaped, and some of them are slightly flattened. The head is always well developed and distinct from the rest of the body. It tends to be round, though occasionally it may be flattened. The cuticle covering of the head is generally almost bare, with very few hairs on it. Some groups of Lepidoptera have heads like tortoises which can be drawn back into the

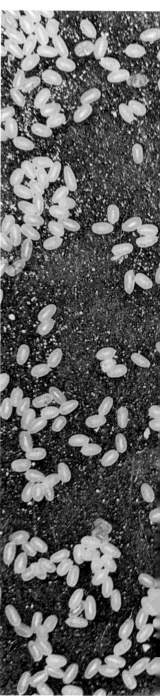

first segment of the thorax and disappear altogether.

Being larvae, caterpillars do not carry compound eyes but have a number of lateral ocelli—the stemmata—and the position of these corresponds to the future location of the compound eyes in the adult insects. The ocelli look like small, rounded, transparent lenses and there are usually six

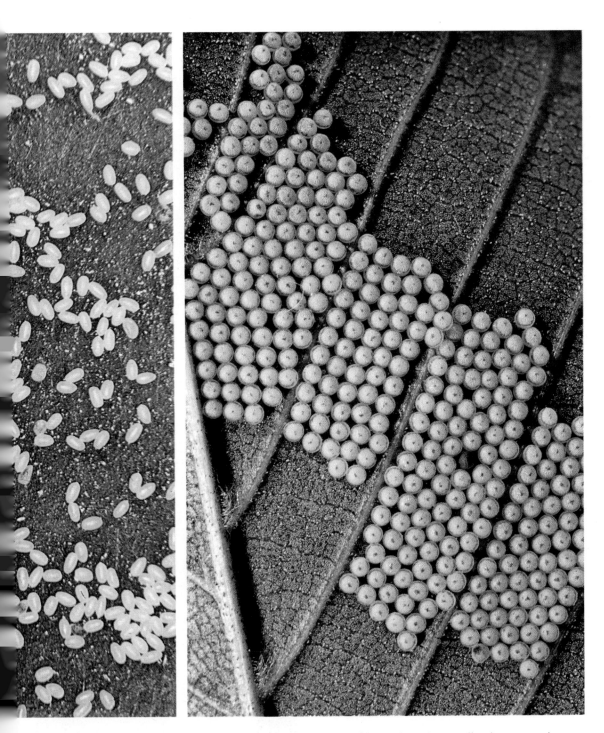

on each side. Five of these are arranged in a semicircle with the sixth in front of them. Some caterpillars have no ocelli at all and others appear to have compound eyes although these are simply closely connected ocelli.

Two antennae may be distinguished on their heads. These are usually very short and lie on either side of the head. They have

Butterflies and moths are all oviparous and lay their eggs in large numbers in places that will provide a favourable environment for the new-born larvae, such as along a stem or on the underside of a leaf. The photographs on these two pages show the differently shaped eggs of three species of Lepidoptera

251

fewer component parts, or segments, than in the adult insect—generally not more than three. In repose, the antennae may be withdrawn into cavities on either side of the head next to the principal jaws, and in this position only the tips of the antennae are visible. These tips are covered with sensory receptors.

The mouth parts of caterpillars are typically of the chewing type, unlike those of most butterflies and moths apart from the Micropterygidae. Certain parts of the mouth are modified for the production of silk, which is a characteristic of virtually all caterpillars. The upper lip or labrum is never very conspicuous and typically carries six pairs of bristles on the upperside and numerous sensory organs on the underside.

The principal jaws are usually very strong as they are used for seizing food and for the preliminary chewing. The size of their crests and the sharpness of the points vary according to diet. Unlike butterflies and moths which do not have chewing mouth parts, the lower lip or labium is formed, as usual in insects, by the fusion of the second maxillae along the middle line. The spinneret, situated in a part of the labium known as the prementum, is an

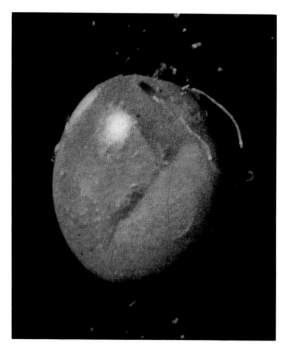

Right: Stages in the hatching of a sphingid larva. High-speed photography was used to capture these three views of what is a very rapid process

elongated tube, often narrowing to a point, from which the silk emerges. The tube is usually membraneous but is often reinforced by harder bands.

As in adult insects, the thorax consists of three segments. These segments are clearly recognizable because each carries a pair of jointed legs which are usually short and cylindrical or flattened and usually end in a well-developed claw. In some leaf-mining Lepidoptera the thoracic legs are considerably reduced or non-existent. In some species the first thoracic segment, the prothorax, is wider than the others in order to leave room for the head to withdraw into if necessary.

Typically, there are ten abdominal segments, some of which may carry prolegs—soft, fleshy false legs which look like true legs. Prolegs are an effective aid in walking, and are divided into ventral and anal prolegs according to where they are situated. They are inclined to be broader at the base and are controlled by powerful bundles of muscles. Each proleg can act as a suction device, helping the caterpillar to cling to the surfaces across which it moves. A series of hooks which are arranged in a circle around the foot also makes gripping easier. The layout and number of hooks vary considerably from one species to another and are therefore used as criteria for classification. This is also true of the way hairs or bristles are arranged, particularly in the area of the head and anus.

There are a number of paired, symmetrical openings—two on each segment—on the sides of the body. These are the spiracles or breathing pores. There is usually one pair on the prothorax and eight pairs on the first eight abdominal segments. Being a different colour from the body, the spiracles are often clearly recognizable. Although their tracheal systems may not be greatly modified, the breathing pores of the small number of caterpillars living in an aquatic environment are partly or totally obliterated and therefore function poorly or not at all. This problem is solved in various ways. Respiration may be via the integument of the body which has become fairly thin and permeable to oxygen, or the larvae may capture oxygen rising to the surface of the water or air bubbles left adhering to the submerged parts of plants. In other instances, gills may be developed.

One type of gills called tracheobranchiae are developed from the skin and are usually thread-like or flattened: the very intricate extensions of the air-tubes branch into

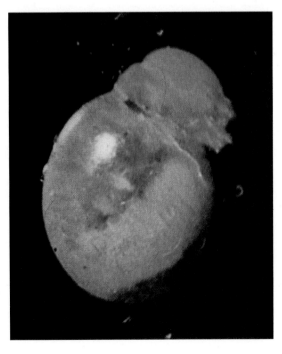

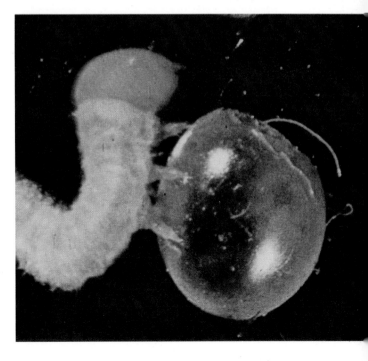

them. The latter come from the main paired tracheal trunks running along the sides of the body. The tracheal system is of the closed type. This means that respiration occurs through these small air-tubes, with oxygen passing through the body wall. There are often bundles of muscles that enable these organs to move the water around the tracheobranchiae so that the insect has a plentiful supply of oxygen.

Blood gills are similar to tracheobranchiae though of different construction. They have an extremely thin cuticle, and their function and location vary, but they simply carry the haemolymph or blood-like circulating liquid and very rarely have any tracheal branches. Blood gills are rare in Lepidoptera; to date only three American species having them—belonging to the genus Cataclysta—have been recorded and studied. Here too, respiration takes place through the body wall. The captured oxygen travels in solution into the haemolymph which acts as a carrier and thus performs a respiratory function.

The caterpillar's digestive system differs from that of the adult butterfly or moth. It is usually short and broad, it runs in a straight line down the body cavity and is rarely curved. Three parts may be distinguished, each with a different structure and significance. The first section, known as the oesophagus or stomodaeum, is short and connects the mouth aperture to the mesenteron or middle section of the intestine. An important valve, the cardiac sphincter, is found at the point where the two parts of the alimentary canal meet. It is provided with numerous circular muscular fibres which enable it to close. Another valve, the pyloric valvule, separates the mesenteron from the proctodaeum, the final section of the intestine.

The stomodaeum and the proctodaeum both have the same embryological origin and their cavity is covered with a cuticle like all the rest of the body surface. The mesenteron, however, has a different origin from the other two sections; it has no cuticle and is the centre of almost all the digestive and absorption functions.

The silk-glands

A number of glands, most of which have a digestive function, are connected with the alimentary canal. The silk-glands are the most conspicuous of these; they are the labial glands, corresponding to the true salivary glands of other insects. In caterpillars the salivary function is taken over by another pair of glands which open on the mandibles. In Lepidoptera, these glands are only present in the larval stage. The paired labial or silk-glands open on to the labium and are often extremely long, sometimes as long as the caterpillar's body. The gland is divided into three parts, each with a different function. The part farthest from the outlet is narrow and produces the silk in conjunction with the second, wider part. The latter is known as the reservoir. The third part, next to the mouth, is a narrow, winding tube. These glands lead into a common duct, part of which is modified and controlled by powerful bundles of muscles which dilate their cavities. They culminate in the spinneret on the lower lip.

The silk, produced in a liquid state, solidifies on coming into contact with the air. This is due to oxidization and not, as was once believed, to drying; it even

Left: The body-shape and ornamentation of caterpillars varies a good deal. Top left: *Celerio nicaea*; centre left: *Eueidis dianassa*; bottom left: *Acronycta aceris*; centre: *Loxostege similalis* hanging from a silken thread; below it is *Actias selene*; right: *Opsiphanes tamarindi*

Below: Detail of the extendible appendages of *Cerura vinula*. As it extends these red filaments, the caterpillar simultaneously emits a jet of repellent fluid from the front part of its body
Bottom: A plant-eating caterpillar feeds on a leaf

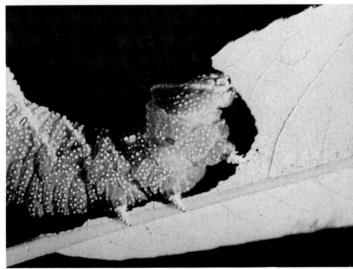

solidifies under water. The silk emerges in the form of long, tough threads with an inner fibre consisting of fibroin and an outer one consisting of sericin which envelops it. Fibroin and sericin are both proteins. The inner fibre of the silk thread has two strands formed by the juxtaposition of threads secreted by the two paired glands pressed together by the wall of their common duct. This part, known as the 'press' or 'thread-crusher', regulates both the thickness of the thread and the quantity of silk emitted; it can cut the thread if necessary. While the caterpillar's head has a glandular system of great importance, the rest of its body also has groups of cells with equally useful secretory functions.

Deterrent and seductive organs

The thorax of caterpillars of the Papilionidae family typically contains a secretory organ which can be extended and is known as the osmeterium. Its principal function is to act as a deterrent, besides being scented and possibly excretory. A very prominent gland with a distinctive, strongly aromatic secretion is associated with this organ. When the caterpillar senses danger or when it is simply disturbed or excited, it extends the osmeterium by pumping a large amount of blood into it. Since it is usually brightly coloured, this organ looks quite terrifying and gives the caterpillar a powerful and fearsome appearance. When no longer needed, the osmeterium is retracted by muscle action.

There are other glandular organs on the abdomen that can be protruded. They are not, however, common to all caterpillars, being found only in certain groups, and operate in the same way as the osmeterium in the Papilionidae family.

The moth family Lymantridae may

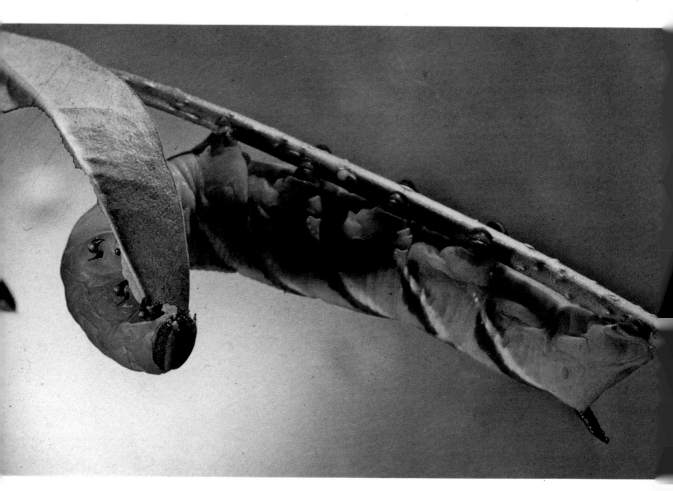

have a defensive organ about three-quarters of the way along the body. A central orifice connects a pouch, that can be pushed outwards, with associated glands. Besides secreting repellent substances, this organ has hairs that can stiffen and become poisonous to would-be predators.

The so-called myrmecophilous organs are very important for caterpillars of the Lycaenidae family. Some members of the family live as larvae in ants' nests where they receive care and nourishment. In certain cases, without the ants these caterpillars would become incapable of feeding themselves and would die of hunger.

There are usually three myrmecophilous organs arranged in a triangle on the rear half of the caterpillar's back; like the previously mentioned organs, they can be protruded. They secrete two types of substance: the secretion from the front gland is sweet while that produced by the

Below and below left: Two photographs of the caterpillar of *Sphinx ligustris* (the Privet Hawk-moth). It lives on plants, like almost all caterpillars, and is equipped with chewing mouth parts and has a large appetite

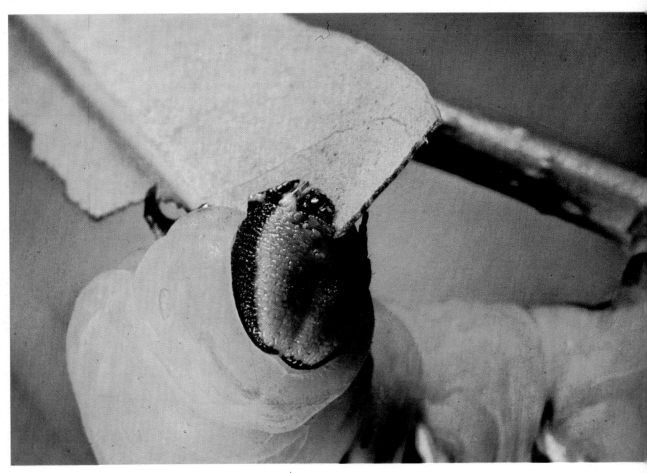

other organs is scented. Ants are greatly attracted by the first type of secretion and tickle the front gland with their antennae. Under the pressure of the blood, this gland swells up and secretes small drops of the sweet substances which the ants suck avidly. The larvae of the Lycaenidae family live in symbiosis with the ants, deriving mutual benefit from the association.

Some caterpillars are covered with thick hairs which may be carried on highly coloured outgrowths. But European processionary caterpillars of the Thaumetopoeidae family, which march in Indian file from pine trees, looking for all the world as if they are taking part in a procession, are covered with quantities of fine, stiff hairs which can easily be detached. The hairs are hollow and contain a stinging fluid secreted by a gland. On coming into contact with foreign bodies, they break open and eject their contents. Obviously, it is not advisable to touch one of these caterpillars; and even after the skin has been shed and the caterpillar is dead the hairs are still dangerous since they retain their stinging capacity for a long time. Hairs which have been detached from the cuticle and blown along by the wind may also find their way into the upper respiratory tracts or the eyes where they can cause intense and painful irritation, sometimes with grave consequences.

The moulting process

Newly emerged caterpillars are usually very small. The cuticle which completely covers the caterpillar is not elastic so it cannot expand to contain the internal organs of the growing body, which therefore has to cast off its old skin several times, replacing it on each occasion with a new, enlarged one. This phenomenon is known as 'moulting' and takes place anything from two, as in certain species of leaf-mining caterpillars, to ten times.

Caterpillars which produce females frequently moult once more than those producing males. Caterpillars often attach themselves to a surface before moulting, sometimes covering it with a thick web of silk threads to which they anchor themselves securely. Once the moult has been completed, the old useless skin, known as the exuvia, is either cast off and abandoned or more often than not devoured by its former occupant, in which case the hard 'capsule' of the head is not normally eaten as it is often too tough and indigestible.

Moulting is not as simple a process as it might appear at first sight. In the first place the number of moults is influenced not only by the sex of the caterpillar, but also by hereditary factors, and temperature and food supplies among other external factors. Just before the moult, the hypodermis secretes a liquid which dissolves the inner layers of the cuticle and severs all connections between it and the rest of the body, thus forming a chamber between the cuticle and the hypodermis. This chamber is filled with fluid and is known as the exuvial chamber. Among other things, it acts as a lubricant and makes it easier for the old skin to slip off and the newly clad insect to emerge. The new skin starts to form at almost exactly the same time as the old skin is being shed. There is frantic activity in the cells of the hypodermis to produce the necessary materials in a relatively short time, but before the old skin is shed the caterpillar's new skin is ready.

Caterpillars of the same species always shed their skins in the same way. They usually attach themselves firmly to a surface and inhale large quantities of air in order to increase their internal pressure. By writhing energetically, they eventually manage to rupture the old skin—often along predetermined fracture lines down the back—and liberate themselves. Sometimes the new cuticle is a different colour from the cast-off skin.

These are the mechanical aspects of moulting. From the physiological point of view, however, moulting is directly controlled by the central nervous system, particularly by the brain. Part of the brain

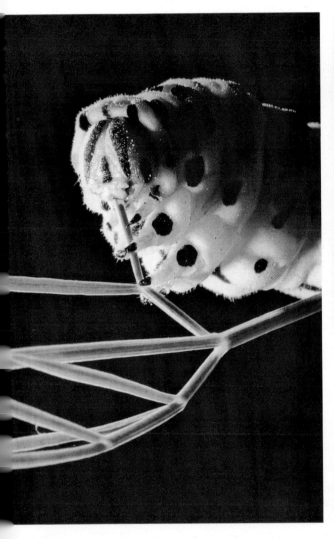

Above: Front of the body of a Swallowtail butterfly caterpillar
Right: Head and thoracic legs of *Philosamia cynthia*. Lepidopterous larvae have three pairs of thoracic legs ending in a curved claw, and five or more pairs of abdominal legs or 'prolegs'

is actively secretory though maintaining its nervous functions intact. Its secretion, or rather neuro-secretion, travels via the nervous system to other organs outside the brain. These are paired, symmetrical, more-or-less spherical glands. They, too, are composed of nerve cells with a secretory function, and because of their anatomical position—which is usually close to the heart—are known as the 'corpora cardiaca'. On being stimulated in this way, they discharge a cerebral hormone into the circulatory system. This hormone, which is probably derived from the neurosecretion, activates the prothoracic glands, the typically larval organs situated in the first thoracic segment. The hormone produced by the prothoracic glands is known as ecdysone or the 'moulting hormone'. The brain thus exerts an overriding control over periodic growth by moulting.

There is another pair of glands, the 'corpora allata', situated just behind the corpora cardiaca. During larval life they produce a hormone known as the 'juvenile hormone', which controls the formation of the larval cells at each moult. As long as this hormone is produced, the larval form is retained; when production of it ceases, the adult insect is produced. Thus the moulting hormone brings about moulting but the juvenile hormone decides the form of the insect. The corpora allata resume secretion of a hormone in the adult insect which appears to be identical to the juvenile hormone, but it now acts as a stimulant to mature the sexual glands of the young adult.

Pupation—the last moult

After the required number of moults, the caterpillar, which is now considerably larger, stops feeding and searches for a suitable place to accomplish the last major act in its life as a larva—its transformation into a chrysalis. This is known as pupation. On reaching a suitable spot, which may be on a plant, under the ground or in some other protected place, the caterpillar attaches itself to the surface. Chrysalises of the so-called naked type (those without any additional protective covering constructed partly or entirely by themselves) generally use a silk thread. Others make a protective silk cocoon, often very thick, within which they transform into adults over a period of time.

Different groups adopt surprisingly different methods of attaching themselves to a surface. Chrysalises are therefore divided into various categories. Naked chrysalises can be either suspended or girdled, while protected chrysalises can be enclosed either above or below the ground or inside a cocoon made of living vegetable matter.

During pupation, the chrysalis sheds its larval exuvia completely; as this shrivelled, shrunken skin often remains attached to the base of the pupa enormous efforts and contortions are required to disentangle it. The whole process may take a considerable time. Caterpillars which are to be transformed into suspended chrysalises pupate head down. The caterpillar fixes a silk pad to the surface and hangs from it by its anal prolegs. Once the butterfly or moth has emerged, the back of the chrysalis remains attached to the silk pad. In the case of girdled chrysalises, the caterpillars attach themselves to the surface with a silken thread, like a safety belt, around the thorax or, very occasionally, the head. Once freed from the old skins, these chrysalises also remain attached to the surface by the girdle and the tip of the abdomen.

During the resting pupal stage, the chrysalis remains more or less motionless. Some chrysalises are completely immobile while others are able to move their abdomens or their appendages, particularly when they are disturbed or when the time to emerge is approaching.

The name chrysalis comes from the Greek language and means literally 'small golden object', but this rarely matches the appearance of the pupa. The chrysalis generally looks very different from the caterpillar and may already bear some resemblance to the adult insect. It is, in fact, easy to distinguish the three sections into which the body of the adult will be divided. The abdominal segments are already recognizable. The integument is usually hard, tough and almost hairless. It often bears outgrowths and spines, and its colour varies a great deal. The compound eyes are already distinguishable on the head. They are well developed although almost certainly not yet functional. The antennae are as long as those in the adult and, except in rare instances, are folded along the underside between the legs and the wings, closely pressed or soldered together as well as to the body.

Unlike the caterpillar, which typically has chewing mouth parts, the chrysalis, except that of the Micropterygidae, has

Some of the details of caterpillars' bodies
Above: Detail of the prolegs of *Philosamia cynthia*, showing their little hooks and suckers
Right from top: Spiracles and prolegs of *Smerinthus ocellata*; close-up of the claws on the thoracic legs of *Saturnia pyri*; detail of the prolegs of a caterpillar as it climbs a stem

261

sucking mouth parts, although they may be rudimentary. The proboscis, like the antennae, is folded back and soldered to the underside, but in certain of the Sphingidae it is free and curving. The mouth parts are never functional except in those rare species which, prior to emerging as adults, inhale a large quantity of air into their digestive systems.

All the characteristic organs of the adult insect are recognizable in the thorax. At first sight, though, the six legs do not always appear to be in the correct sequence. They are usually tightly grouped, and the feet of the final pair of legs sometimes appear between those of the first and second pairs.

The undeveloped forewings can be seen inside their more or less triangular sheaths (pterothecae) on the second segment of the thorax. They are much shorter and smaller than the wings of the adult. In a mature chrysalis, the full-sized wings are tightly folded. The hind wings, borne on the third segment, are difficult to distinguish because they are nearly always concealed by the forewings.

Like adults, chrysalises have ten abdominal segments but without the prolegs found in caterpillars; some of the segments are, however, hard to distinguish. The spiracles are clearly visible and are of the same number as those found in the caterpillar, although the final pair is rudimentary and non-functional. Even species which pass the larval state in an aquatic environment breathe through the spiracles as chrysalises; and as far as is known, chrysalises never possess either tracheobranchiae or blood gills, even if they had them as caterpillars. The last abdominal segment—at least in the more highly evolved families—bears a hooking device known as the cremaster, which enables the chrysalis to attach itself firmly to a surface. It is well developed, particularly in suspended chrysalises.

As usually happens with the oral orifice,

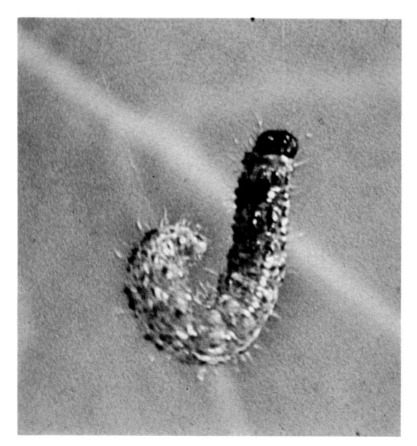

Left: The caterpillar is able to secrete a tough silken thread through its mouth which enables it to climb back on to a leaf or stem if it should fall off. The thread is just visible as a fine line emerging vertically from the head; the diagonal white line is a leaf-vein

the anal orifice is closed and the only visible sign of its presence is a hollow or groove. Similarly, the male genital orifice and that of the female with monotrisian reproductive organs is indicated by a single groove on the outside of the chrysalis; females of the dytrisian and exoporian type have two grooves. This makes it relatively easy to identify the sex of the chrysalis of the latter. The sex of a chrysalis can also be distinguished by sexual dimorphism which can, at times, be quite marked. In an extreme example, a female chrysalis of the Psychidae family is partly or completely devoid of pterothecae since the adult will lack wings.

With so many different families and species of Lepidoptera, there are bound to be several kinds of chrysalis. The more primitive groups typically have free chrysalises which means that all but the last three abdominal segments, the wings, the legs and other appendages are free rather than being soldered together and to the

Below: A pair of white butterflies courting. The male is seen flying up to the female on the flower

body. Consequently, they are to a certain extent mobile.

Another kind of chrysalis is known as 'incomplete', with wings, appendages and some abdominal segments being mainly free. The appendages cannot be moved, however, and are therefore non-functional, although, by twisting its abdomen energetically, helped by the spines and outgrowths on it, the chrysalis is able to move quite a lot. There is also a third type of chrysalis characteristic of the more highly evolved Lepidoptera, particularly the Rhopalocera. This is the obtect chrysalis in which the wings and appendages are usually firmly glued both together and to the body and the abdominal segments are also soldered together. The chrysalis is therefore totally immobile and can only move a small part of its abdomen.

Emergence of the adult

After a time, which varies considerably from one species to another, the chrysalis reaches maturity. In chrysalises with an almost transparent cuticle, it is possible to see clearly the internal structure and the colours of the folded wings of the butterfly or moth a few days before the insect emerges. Generally, however, maturity is signalled by the progressive darkening of the pupal case.

A little while later, what is perhaps the most beautiful phenomenon a naturalist can observe takes place: the emergence of the butterfly or moth from its pupal case. Precisely when this occurs depends not only on the individual insect but on a great many external factors, the most important undoubtedly being temperature and light. Every species has a definite emergence period which is not only seasonal but is tied to specific times of day. In fact, it is unusual for day-flying species not to emerge in the morning, while night-flyers generally emerge in the afternoon or evening.

Constrained in its pupal case, the butterfly or moth breaks the skin of the chrysalis and forces its way out head first.

Some species have powerful pointed outgrowths on their heads which rupture the cuticle in the desired place. Emergence from the chrysalis is by no means a simple operation considering that some species have subterranean chrysalises, others have chrysalises enclosed in plant tissue, while many are enclosed in thick silk cocoons.

When the time comes to emerge, those subterranean chrysalises which are free or incomplete and therefore have reasonably mobile appendages bore tunnels in the ground leading to the surface. Once the cuticle has been ruptured, the adult insect will immediately find itself above ground without having had to make any effort to get there. The chrysalises enclosed in plant tissue generally emerge in the open, too; and in any case, species of the leaf-mining variety do not have particularly thick or tough vegetable walls to perforate. Species with naked obtect pupae simply have to rupture the pupal case and then make the considerable effort needed to extract themselves. Obtect pupae below the soil or in cocoons emerge within their shelters and the adults have to force their way out.

Once species with cocoons have broken the pupal case, the silk threads can be severed by pressure from the head or by means of appropriate organs, or they can be partly dissolved by a liquid secreted by glands inside the insect's body and discharged via the mouth parts. In other instances there are weak places in the cocoon where the threads are much less closely woven, allowing the emerging adult to push its way through.

The way chrysalises rupture their outer casing varies a great deal. Generally, the cuticle of an obtect chrysalis remains whole, apart from the fracture line, while that of an incomplete chrysalis must crumble into fragments so that the adult insect can emerge. Once the head has

Right: Caterpillar (top) and adult (bottom) of *Mimas tiliae* (the Lime Hawk-moth). The caterpillars feed on the leaves of lime trees and also on elm leaves, causing considerable damage

Top: The Swallowtail butterfly caterpillar
as it appears after its last moult. Its body
coloration enables it to blend with the leaves
of fennel and wild carrot on which it feeds
Above left: Chrysalis of the same species,
with the insect inside it
Above: Empty chrysalis after the adult has
emerged
Right: The adult Swallowtail has dried off
and now pauses on the empty chrysalis case
before making its maiden flight

emerged from the case, the imago or adult butterfly or moth breathes in a large amount of air through its mouth parts. Then, with the aid of its legs and by twisting the rest of its body, it manages to complete the operation in a comparatively short time. The exhausted and sluggish butterfly or moth remains firmly attached to the surface, on or very close to the pupal skin. Its crumpled, shapeless wings certainly give no hint of their beautiful patterns and the insect looks ugly and deformed.

Little by little, the wings dry and expand with the help of the air and of internal liquids which are forced under pressure into the wing veins. The cuticle covering the wings also stretches and grows harder from contact with the air. Then, after anything from a few minutes to a few hours, the butterfly or moth reaches full maturity: it has become one of the most beautiful insects in the world.

While waiting for the moment when it can start to fly, the adult rids itself of all the waste products that have accumulated in its body during the pupal stage. Because the anal orifice of the chrysalis has been closed, and since excretory products are discharged into the final tracts of the digestive system in insects, the great quantity of waste matter that has collected can only be expelled when the anal orifice becomes functional. The substance that is finally ejected, known as mcconium, contains a considerable amount of water and is sometimes bright red.

Not until the meconium has been expelled and a sufficient time has elapsed—which varies from one species to another—for its wings to gather strength, does the butterfly or moth take flight. Only then can the tremendous changes that have taken place between the larval, pupal and adult stages of the insect's life be really seen. The adult bears no resemblance whatsoever to the caterpillar. Its mouth parts, except in rare instances, have been modified from the chewing to the sucking type, two pairs of wings have appeared, and its entire structure has been revolutionized. This is typical of those insects

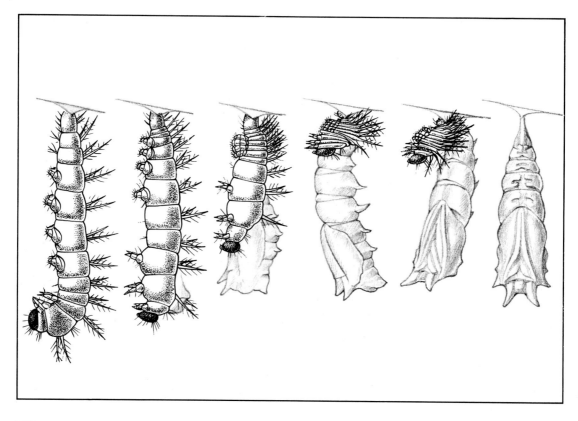

Above: The caterpillar of *Apatura ilia*, the Lesser Purple Emperor butterfly, has a characteristic pair of red-tipped, bluish horns
Right: Chrysalis of *Apatura ilia*. At the head end, near the leaf-vein, the remains of the caterpillar's abandoned head-covering, cast off during the last moult, can still be seen

Left: Stages in the pupation of *Inachis io*, the Peacock butterfly

which undergo complete metamorphosis, in contrast to those whose metamorphosis is only partial. The larvae of the latter resemble the adult insects and the transformation is gradual, without any sudden, dramatic changes.

A variety of diets

Most caterpillars are plant-eating and prefer to feed on higher plants, making no distinction between herbaceous plants and trees. They even feed on the foliage of plants and trees that are poisonous to humans or certain animals, without suffering any ill effects. Lepidoptera show no preference for any particular part of the vegetable matter they are eating. Some species attack the foliage, others tunnel in the wood or feed at the roots, while still others feed on the fruit and seeds. It is true to say that whereas adults are virtually harmless if not actually beneficial to man and crops, through pollination activity, caterpillars are among the most harmful and voracious creatures imaginable.

Caterpillars position themselves on the leaves and proceed to devour them, starting at the edge, so that in a matter of minutes nothing is left but the stalk and a few ribs. When infestation is on a massive scale, the voracity of mature caterpillars is exceeded only by that of locusts. Certain wood-eating species may spend more than two years as larvae, having to absorb a disproportionate quantity of food because of its low nutritional value. Clearly, they constitute a serious pest for agriculture and forestry.

The behaviour of leaf-mining caterpillars is particularly fascinating; they bore tunnels inside the thickness of a leaf or stalk, leaving the outside undamaged. If the leaf is held to the light, the tunnels can be seen. Depending on the species of caterpillar, these tunnels follow a clearly defined course, intersecting once or twice or not meeting at all. Sometimes caterpillars bore rounded areas rather than tunnels. These are in the form of blotch-like patches or

Left: The chrysalis (top) and adult (bottom) of the Death's-head Hawk-moth. The superstition which holds that this insect is a harbinger of disaster probably arose not only because of the markings on its back, but also because of a peculiar sound that it can make by squeezing air through its proboscis

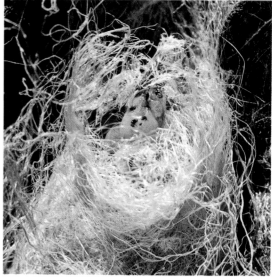

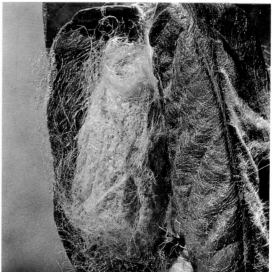

Above: A caterpillar of *Saturnia pavonia* (the Emperor moth) builds its cocoon
Above right: A caterpillar of *Philosamia cynthia* puts the final touches to its cocoon before pupating
Right: The completed cocoon shown during the quiescent pupal stage
Below: The same cocoon, opened along its length, shows the insect inside undergoing its transformation

272

blisters. The Nepticulidae, Lithocolletidae, Elachistidae and some members of the Coleophoridae families are very skilful at this. In the majority of instances, the latter construct a case by cutting a piece of leaf and joining the edges with silk threads. The caterpillar comes part-way out of the case and bores into a small area of the leaf, periodically moving on to virgin areas which it ravages in the same way.

Tortricidae caterpillars are generally expert at rolling leaves. With the help of strong silk threads which they fix to crucial points, they wrap the leaves around with apparent ease and build their nests inside. There, they will spend their lives, including the chrysalis stage, well-protected from the outside world.

Though the caterpillars of most Lepidoptera are plant-eating, a great many feed on a wide variety of other substances. Some have a liking for such items of vegetable origin as dead wood, corks, dried mushrooms, stored flour and cereals, dried fruit, all kinds of provisions including chocolate, and even parts of the nests of social Hymenoptera, particularly of bees and wasps but also of ants. Certain members of the Tineidae, Gelechiiadae and Pyralidae families are among the worst offenders at attacking stored foods and often cause enormous damage if they are not dealt with promptly and ruthlessly.

Other Lepidoptera, particularly those classed as Microlepidoptera, feed on the corpses of animals or on other substances of animal origin. More than any other family, the Tineidae are merciless in their attacks on groups of insects, embalmed higher animals, birds' feathers, hairs, fur, wool and all kinds of man-made fibres. A familiar example is the common clothes-moth that used to be seen regularly in most homes but is now rarer on account of the moth-proofing of fabrics and the widespread use of man-made fibres. In fact, the adult moth is not actually responsible for the damage to clothing and there is little to be gained by killing it. It is the caterpillar which should be ferreted out and destroyed,

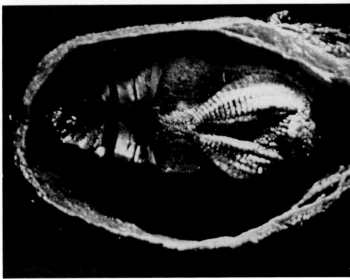

Top: End portion of the cocoon of *Saturnia pavonia* showing the hole through which the moth emerges
Above: Within the cocoon is the chrysalis itself. This is generally an obtect pupa —one in which the rudimentary organs are covered by an outer cuticle

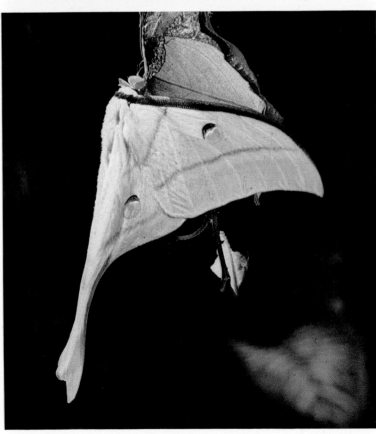

The illustrations on these two pages show the slow expansion and trying of the wings of a newly emerged *Actias selene* (Luna moth). The adult may have to wait hours for its wings to dry completely before making its maiden flight

though more often than not it is overlooked and left in peace.

Other species feed on all types of dung. A few—although the economic damage they cause is considerable—eat beeswax and spend part of their lives inside beehives. The best known of these is undoubtedly *Galleria mellonella* (the Greater Wax moth), a member of the Pyralidae family. When infestation is on a large scale, the damage it causes to beehives is serious. Lepidoptera also include predatory species. They will attack other insects or their eggs, of which they are particularly fond. Ants are among the most frequent victims of these aggressive species of Lepidoptera, which are immune to ant bites and which decimate their broods and young larvae.

Fortunately, there are not many parasitic Lepidoptera and it is usually other insects that suffer from them, though some species are known to infest such vertebrates as the sloth. Their methods of attacking sloths and the substances they derive from their hosts are not yet fully known. On occasions, Lepidoptera may even infest or attack caterpillars of their own species. This usually happens under exceptional circumstances such as overcrowding or adverse climatic conditions—for example, excessive dryness. Conditions of this sort usually arise either where they are bred or after the simultaneous emergence of a large number of individuals.

How caterpillars move

Caterpillars are insatiable and indefatigable eaters. They often have to travel long distances to procure food, so they have to be good walkers, too. Nature has endowed them with the necessary means of adhering to a surface under any conditions. The prolegs play an essential role in this. The caterpillars anchor themselves by small hooks and sometimes also by suckers on the prolegs. Besides providing a means of attachment, the silk threads emitted by special glands also serve as a kind of safety line. If a caterpillar loses its balance and

Left: Chrysalis (top) of *Actias selene*. The detail of the chrysalis (bottom) shows the rudiments of the antennae that will appear on the adult

277

falls, it drops gently instead of plummeting to the ground. If then climbs back again to its original position by means of the thread attached there and issuing from its mouth.

Some larvae move exceedingly slowly while others are very fast and can sometimes make sudden, jerky movements. These different characteristics are related to the number and positions of the prolegs. One of the most distinctive types of movement is the 'looping' action of the Geometridae caterpillars which get their name from the way they move along a surface as if they were measuring it inch by inch. In fact, these caterpillars have fewer prolegs than usual, those on the third to fifth segments being absent. In order to move forward, they fix their anal prolegs to the surface and thrust their bodies forward. They then secure themselves to the surface with their thoracic legs in the new position and bring up the abdomen which forms a loop behind them. They then repeat the process. Being fairly fast movers, the Geometridae caterpillars are able to 'measure' sizeable distances in a short time.

Caterpillars which build protective cases around themselves from a variety of materials also move in a curious fashion, using only their thoracic legs to propel themselves forward. The front of the body emerges from the case and stretches forward for some distance. The caterpillar then clings to the surface with its legs and drags the rest of its body, case included, behind it. The case is securely attached to the body by the strong hooks on the prolegs.

Of all Lepidoptera, the Thaumetopoeidae family undoubtedly move in the most striking way. These insects, commonly known as processionary moths, march close together in single file following a trail of silk left by the caterpillar at the head of the column. This runs the entire length of the column and each caterpillar contributes to it. The caterpillars' objective is to reach a place where food supplies are abundant, and since these journeys usually

Right: A newly emerged *Limentis camilla* (White Admiral butterfly). The chrysalis is attached head-downwards to the twig by a band of silk

Left and below: The voracious caterpillars of *Actias selene* (the Luna moth). The caterpillars' irritant hairs protect them from predators

Above: Another *Actias selene* caterpillar after a moult. The discarded larval skin can be seen on the upperside of the branch

take place at night, they have no points of reference in their surroundings to enable them to retrace their steps. But they invariably manage to return to their nests without any difficulty if they wish to do so. J. H. Fabre, an extremely astute observer of insect behaviour, realized that the orientation mechanism of the processionary caterpillars was linked to the silk thread running from the nest to the leading caterpillar. He performed numerous experiments on the larvae of the European processionary moth (*Thaumetopoea pityocampa*) to prove his theories.

Certain caterpillars which inhabit the large seeds of exotic plants have adopted a strange way of moving. When the sun's rays beat down too fiercely on the seed and the temperature inside becomes unbearable, the caterpillar, which has neither the ability nor the desire to leave the seed, gathers itself together and suddenly springs in such a way that the seed is slightly jolted. Nine times out of ten this only has to be repeated a few times for the seed to be once more in shadow; the caterpillar then continues its meal undisturbed.

Although they are tireless workers, caterpillars occasionally take a break from their activities. Some remain quite motionless, often mimicking their surroundings by means of colouring and position. Others fix themselves to a surface with a silk thread and then cling to it using only their prolegs. Others, again, take up a strange position, holding the thorax erect and the head bent down. This position, which has been likened to that of the famous Sphinx found near the pyramids in Egypt, earned them the name of Sphingidae. Most Sphingidae caterpillars also have a short horny outgrowth which adds to their distinctive appearance.

Processionary caterpillars indulge in social behaviour even when at rest. Like certain other Lepidoptera, they build communal nests in the branches of trees out of a huge silk web, the size and shape of which varies from one species to another. This is known as a communal web. Although the processionary caterpillars only leave their nests to go on food-hunting expeditions, other Lepidoptera, such as the Hyponomeutidae (small ermine moths) for example, never abandon the social nest since it is constructed in such a way that the caterpillars find their food inside it.

Like certain butterflies and moths, some caterpillars migrate. It is not unusual, particularly in America and South Africa, to see impressive gatherings of caterpillars slowly wending their way from one place to another. They never travel very far and migration is mainly provoked by over-crowding, resulting from the simultaneous emergence of a large number of caterpillars in a restricted area. Oddly enough, migratory caterpillars generally belong to species which migrate as adults.

Silk production

Caterpillars may seem to be pests to be combated at all costs, but since ancient times man has succeeded in limiting their destructive capacities in some cases and

Right: Comparison of the movement of
Geometridae caterpillars (right) and other
caterpillars (left)

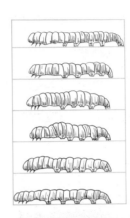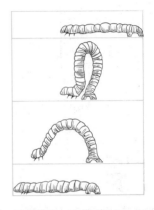

Top left: Caterpillars of *Cerura vinula*
(the Puss moth)
Bottom left: A more normal-shaped caterpillar
in motion
Below: A line of processionary caterpillars

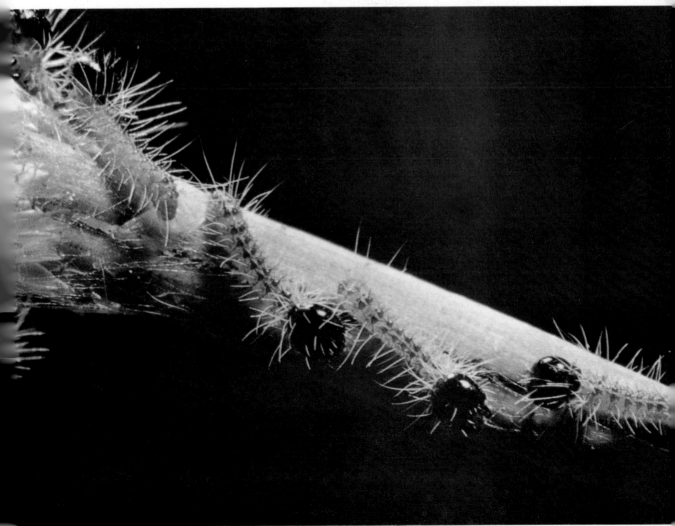

even in deriving considerable economic benefits from them. Nearly 5,000 years ago the Chinese discovered that silk could be used to make a textile fibre. It is said that the silk industry was founded by the Empress Hsi Ling Shi who gave it her patronage about the year 2640 BC. The rulers of the time soon realized that silk from the silkworm (*Bombyx mori*) provided a source of immense wealth and accordingly they passed rigorous laws— disobedience to which could be punishable by death—to prevent the secrets of silkworm breeding spreading abroad. For more than 3,000 years the Chinese were unchallenged producers of silk and sole repositories of a greatly envied skill. Even the Romans imported all their silk from the Orient; and it was only in the sixth century AD that silkworm breeding was introduced to Europe, when two Persian monks, bribed by Emperor Justinian I, brought back a few silkworm eggs from the East concealed in a hollow walking-stick. The silkworm spread quickly thanks to the abundance of mulberry trees, particularly in southern Greece, and silkworm breeding spread to the Arab world, where it expanded to a remarkable degree. Later, the Arabs introduced the silkworm to Sicily. In the 1920s and 1930s there was a boom in silkworm breeding in northern Italy and numerous factories for the industrial production of 'silk seed' (that is, eggs) sprang up there. Silkworm breeding has now become rather neglected owing to the invention of synthetic silk and the gradual disappearance of agricultural craftsmanship. Very few silk factories are left and natural silk has therefore once again become a luxury product.

Silkworm breeding starts with the eggs which are bought from special factories. The eggs are placed on a suitable surface and kept at a temperature of about 22°C (71°F). Shortly afterwards, minute whitish caterpillars begin to hatch. At first they are inactive; in little more than 30 days, after devouring a staggering quantity of mulberry leaves (*Morus alba* or *Morus nigra*)

Right: The genus Zygaena, to which this moth belongs, is represented in Britain by only a few species but more are found in Europe

284

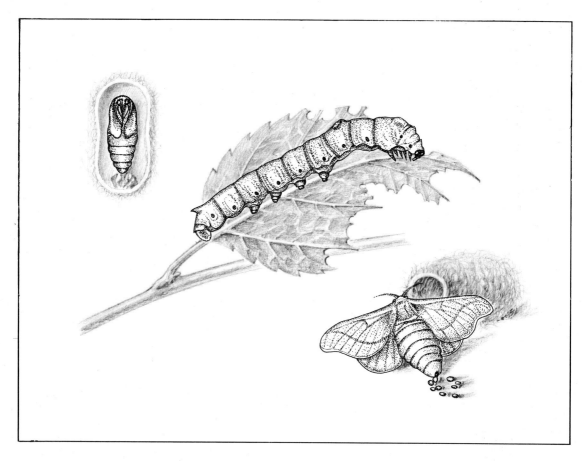

Above and right: The silkworm moth (*Bombyx mori*). The drawing shows, from left to right, the chrysalis, larva, and adult female in the act of laying eggs. The photograph shows an adult that has just emerged from a cocoon

and undergoing four moults, they grow from 3 to about 80 millimetres (0.11 to 3.10 inches) long. It has been estimated that the caterpillars hatched from about 30 grammes (1 ounce) of eggs have to consume more than 1,200 kilos (over 2,600 pounds) of mulberry leaves to attain maturity. Approximately 700 kilos (1,500 pounds) of this is eaten after the last larval moult. The mulberry leaves are spread over the floor of the grids where breeding takes place. At first the leaves are chopped finely, but as the larvae grow, the pieces are bigger and finally the leaves are served whole.

When the silkworms have reached maturity, some 30 days after birth, they grow more active and attempt to climb up anything placed near them. At this stage the breeder plants a large number of upright branches into the floor of the grid so that the silkworms can climb up easily. The silkworm then begins to spin a framework of silk threads on to the branches. This will form the outer layer of the

cocoon within which it will be snugly imprisoned. The thread may be as much as 1,500 metres (almost a mile) long. The cocoon takes a few days to complete. It has a soft, thick appearance with a slight depression in the centre. Depending on the breed, it can be white, yellow or pale green.

In the meantime, the silkworm inside the cocoon has been transformed into a chrysalis. It lies motionless waiting for the moment to emerge as a moth. This is a critical time because the breeder has to prevent the completion of the cycle. The emerging moth would damage the cocoon irreparably by breaking many of the silk threads. He therefore exposes the cocoon to a temperature of 80–85°C (176–185°F) in special ovens. This kills the chrysalis and means that the silk will remain intact. The cocoon is then sent to the silk factory where it undergoes a series of treatments before being used. The outer layer of the cocoon consists of an irregular arrangement of rough silk threads known as 'floss-silk'. This and the inner lining of the cocoon are scrapped and only the middle part or cortex is reeled, with silk from other cocoons, to make the raw silk which will be made up into cloth. One ounce of silkworm 'seed' produces an average of 60–65 kilos (about 130–145 pounds) of cocoons, occasionally peaking to double this figure. The silk derived from them is equal to between one-ninth and one-tenth of the weight.

Scarab beetles

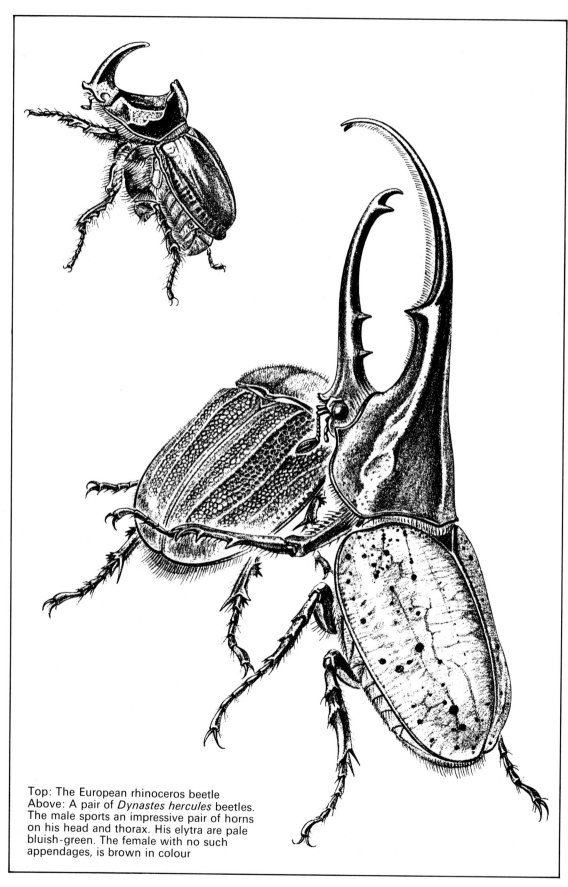

Top: The European rhinoceros beetle
Above: A pair of *Dynastes hercules* beetles.
The male sports an impressive pair of horns
on his head and thorax. His elytra are pale
bluish-green. The female with no such
appendages, is brown in colour

Scarab beetles belong to the order Coleoptera (beetles) and are of the Scarabaeidae family (chafers and dung-beetles) which totals about 20,000 species with almost world-wide distribution. This is one of the largest group of the entire order and includes maybugs and Rose-chafers, as well as dung-beetles whose strange behaviour led the ancient Egyptians to regard them as sacred because they believed them to be connected with the gods, the dung-balls they make representing the earth and the beetle the sun itself.

As with all beetles, their forewings are modified to form elytra. These are stiff wing-cases protecting, when at rest, the second pair of wings which are used for flying. Their mouth parts are adapted for chewing, and reproduction is generally oviparous. After a period of incubation, a cylindrical segmented larva emerges which may be stumpy or flattened and may be devoid of limbs or only have legs on its thorax. The larvae of Scarabaeidae and their allied families are fleshy and curved into the shape of the letter 'c'. After anything up to ten years, the larva turns into a pupa and in due course emerges as an adult insect, capable of reproduction. Scarabs differ from other beetles in that they have squat, oval bodies and clubbed antennae consisting of a series of closely packed blades from which they get the name of 'lamellicorn beetles'. These blades open out at times of activity. Sexual dimorphism is widespread. The males of a great many species have large and impressive skeletal outgrowths on their heads and on their prothoracic shields which are absent in the females. For example, the Rhinoceros beetle has a backward-facing horn on its head and a larger, forward-facing horn on its prothoracic shield.

Similarly, the male Hercules beetle (*Dynastes hercules* of tropical America) has long horns on the front of its head and thorax. In spite of their menacing-looking horns, these beetles are harmless and their long, pincer-shaped appendages are incapable of inflicting wounds. Indeed, all too often, magnificent specimens have been ruthlessly crushed to death through unwarranted fear of their 'bite'. This species is active at night or during hours of twilight. The male grows to a length of 18 centimetres (7 inches), nearly half of which is accounted for by the horn on its back. The larvae, which are also quite large, eat wood and have a mechanism which enables them to produce a characteristic hissing noise.

The Sacred scarab beetles and almost all the dung-beetles, which are well known for their peculiar feeding and reproductive habits, belong to the subfamily Scarabaeinae. The adult Sacred scarab beetles search for relatively fresh manure of a large grazing animal from which they shape hard compressed balls the size of small apples, much larger than the 2.5 centimetre (1 inch) length of the beetle itself. These balls of dung serve solely as food.

First the beetle works on the dung to get

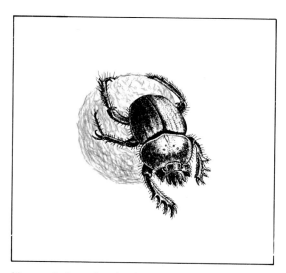

Above: A dung-beetle shown rolling its ball of dung. It does this by pushing it with its hind legs

a manageable lump which it then rolls into a ball by pushing it backwards with its hind legs while supporting itself on its forelegs. During this process, it often happens that another beetle of the same sex helps accumulate the food store. In most cases, an amicable working relationship is established, though there are times when a newcomer's only purpose is to rob the owner of his food supply. When the ball is sufficiently well rounded, the beetle or beetles search for a suitable place to bury themselves and their dung-balls in order to enjoy their meal in peace.

At the start of the mating season, the beetles form pairs. Each couple hunts for fresh dung, makes a ball and rolls it along to a suitable burial place. The beetles use their heads and forelegs to dig a hole into which they push the ball. The female then goes down into the underground chamber and laboriously moulds the dung into a pear shape with a tightly packed base and a soft top; she also makes a cavity inside the upper section with a vertical ventilation shaft leading to the top. When her work is . done she lays an egg in the cavity inside the 'pear' and then goes away to start work on making another. Female Sacred scarab beetles rarely lay more than four eggs in the course of a season. When the egg opens, the new-born larva finds itself surrounded by

food — more than enough for its immediate needs — so it eats and grows until the supply is exhausted and then turns into a pupa, from which it emerges early the following spring as an adult beetle, ready for reproduction. Roughly speaking, these patterns of behaviour are found among all dung-beetles. There are species in Asia which make clay-coated dung-balls of considerable size. Over a period of time, some of these balls grow so hard — possibly due to the premature death of the larva inside — that they have been mistaken for cannon-balls by farm labourers who have unearthed them.

The other species of Scarabaeinae beetles behave like the scarab beetles already described, though there are slight variations from one species to another. Beetles of the genus Onthophagus are found almost all over the world. They live in large colonies in manure and dig holes and tunnels inside it where they lay their eggs.

Dung-beetles of the genus Geotrupes, however, are the most common in Europe. They do not belong to the Scarabaeidae family, although they are near-relatives. They are in fact members of the Geotrupidae family. Their wing-cases are black with iridescent metallic highlights. They use their powerful forelegs to dig holes in the ground for burying the lumps of dung in which they deposit their eggs. This family also includes the genus Typhoeus, which is less common than Geotrupes but still quite widely distributed, and numerous species which lay eggs in goat and rabbit dung after rolling it along specially bored underground passages.

The maybug or Cockchafer (*Melolontha melolontha*) also belongs to the Scarabaeidae family. Maybugs are sometimes extremely common, especially in the southern counties of England; they can be even more abundant on the Continent. They usually appear between the middle of April and the end of May, depending on local climatic conditions and on whether a particular year is warm or cool. The females lay their eggs in underground tunnels and the pale, fleshy

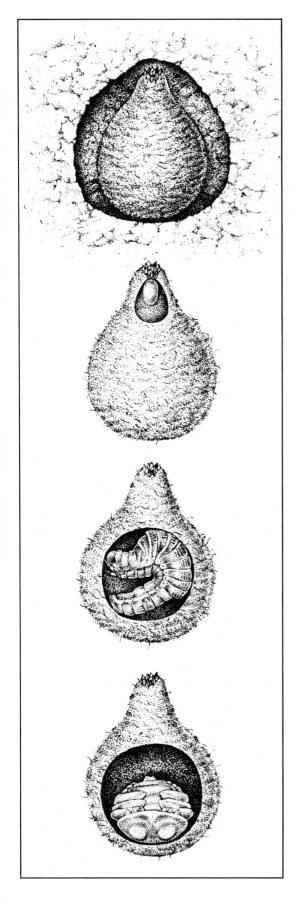

larvae which emerge are equipped with strong chewing mouth parts. They spend the summer feeding on the roots lining the tunnels. With the onset of the first cold spells, they dig down deeper and wait, well sheltered, for the return of warmer weather when they work their way upwards and start feeding on roots again. This cycle is repeated until, at the end of the third summer, they dig down further than usual and pupate. The adult beetle emerges from its pupa late in the autumn but remains under ground until the following spring when it finally surfaces.

The way these larvae develop accounts for the unexpected population explosions among maybugs. These usually occur at three-yearly intervals, but sometimes there may be a gap of four or five years if the weather is particularly cold. More eggs are laid when these insects are very abundant, but a minimum of three years is needed for the larvae hatched from them to emerge as adults and in turn lay the eggs of another generation which will appear three years later. Adult maybugs feed voraciously on plants and consequently cause considerable damage to crops by devouring young buds and shoots, leafy branches and other plants with their powerful jaws.

Beetles of the Polyphylla (*Polyphylla fullo*) and Amphimallon genera are similar to maybugs. The former are the largest scarab beetles in Europe. They are 3 centimetres (just over 1 inch) long and their wing-cases are dark brown marbled with white. They feed mainly on pine needles. Amphimallon beetles, with their distinctive light-brown, hairy backs, are easily found in fields during the summer.

The Cetonia beetles (subfamily Cetoniinae) include the Rose-chafer (*Cetonia aurata*). They belong to the group of vegetarian scarab beetles which feed on

Left, from top: The 'pear' made by the female of the Sacred scarab beetle in her underground cell; the 'pear' with the egg at its upper end; the developing larva living on the walls of the chamber; the chrysalis during its period of quiescence

flowers, fruit and leaves, and lay their eggs in rotten tree-trunks which form the main food for their larvae together with other decaying vegetable matter.

In conclusion, from Rose-chafers, whose wing-cases are beautiful shades of golden green with metallic highlights, it is a short step to the subfamily Rutelinae whose members are best known for the coloration of their backs. The colours range from blues to greens of varying degrees of brilliance, with stripes and highlights from orange to violet and changing according to the beetle's position in relation to the light.

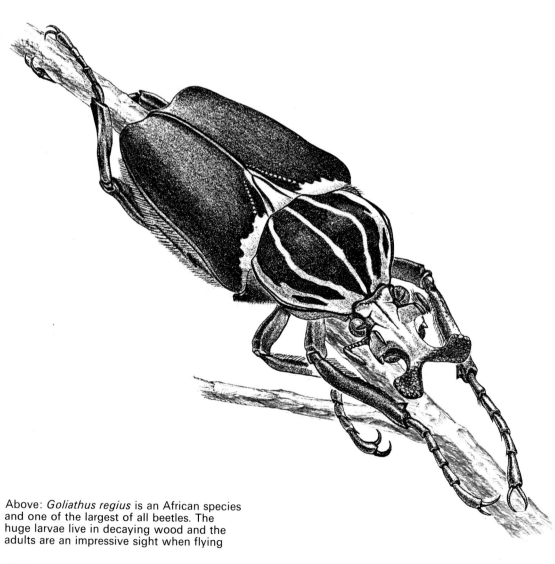

Above: *Goliathus regius* is an African species and one of the largest of all beetles. The huge larvae live in decaying wood and the adults are an impressive sight when flying

Jumping insects

The world high-jump record currently stands at about 2 metres 30 centimetres (7 feet 6.55 inches). The holder will have spent years undergoing hard training, keeping to a carefully calculated diet and helped by all the technical and scientific aids that are employed in present-day athletics. With all this, man has managed to raise himself a distance of his own height plus, say, a quarter above the ground. A flea, a couple of millimetres (a fraction of an inch) long can easily make a leap that carries it to a height of 20 centimetres (7.87 inches); proportionally to this, a man of average height ought to be able to jump about 160 metres (525 feet) above the ground, and land unharmed.

Apart from putting human records to ridicule, this degree of disproportion in physical achievement can be explained by two factors, one biological, the other more purely physical. Firstly, while insect muscle is essentially of the striated type (that is, showing a pattern of transverse stripes when seen under the microscope)—like that of vertebrates, including man—it is not quite the same as vertebrate muscle. The striations of insect muscle fibres can be organized in a number of ways, but they are always considerably denser than those of vertebrates and this indicates that they are functionally more efficient. Furthermore, the system of oxygenating the

internal tissues by means of tracheae is very efficient for small-sized organisms such as insects. Hence the muscles of an insect are capable of greater effort than man's, and they tire less, too. Indeed, when insect muscle is exhausted this is not due to 'fatigue' through the accumulation of waste products because the muscle can manage without oxygen when it is under stress. Instead, an insect muscle that reaches exhaustion is merely temporarily lacking in energy—in sugars and similar substances that constitute its 'fuel'.

There is also a physical factor, however. The larger an animal is, the much greater the muscles it requires in proportion to its size. As body size increases, the ratio of muscle power to weight becomes less, and with it the animal's potential performance. This relationship between muscle power and body size is one of the factors that explains why insects are small creatures.

Jumping insects include nearly 1 million species, and many groups among them have independently developed jumping habits of different kinds. Collembola (commonly known as springtails) are tiny and very primitive insects, invariably wingless, which are commonly found under stones where they form the principal food for many other species, especially pseudoscorpions. Collembola can make leaps of considerable size using a special flicking mechanism. At the tip of the abdomen they carry a furcula, a long, rigid structure jointed at its base. At rest, this is bent

Left: A young grasshopper, newly emerged from the egg, takes a look at the world around it. The wings are not yet developed

forward and lies under the abdomen, where it is hooked in place by another structure called the retinaculum, which restrains it at its tip. When it is disturbed, the springtail uses its powerful abdominal muscles to extend the furcula with lightning speed, and as the furcula unfolds, like a flick-knife blade, the insect is catapulted into the air.

With the exception of this order of insects, click beetles and a few others, almost all jumping insects use their legs for jumping. Some or all of the legs of these insects have undergone modifications of varying degree. Among the Orthoptera, such insects as grasshoppers, locusts and crickets have an extremely long third pair of legs. The femur is equipped with exceptionally powerful muscles, and the tibia, which is long and thin, acts as a lever against the ground. The spectacular leaps of these insects centre mainly on the joint between the femur and the tibia.

Many of the Hemiptera, related to the cicadas, are also good jumpers; the best known in Britain is *Cercopis vulnerata*, an insect less than 1 centimetre (0.39 inches) long, bluish-black in colour, with six symmetrical bright red spots on its front wings. It is extremely common in fields in the late spring and in summer, living on the sap of the meadow grasses which it sucks out with its rostrum or beak, with which all Hemiptera are provided. If you try to catch it, it dodges out of reach with a very agile leap, and then flies off. Insects of this group have a rather different type of jumping limb from the Orthoptera, and the important joint in their case is the one between the two basal segments (those nearest the body) of the insect's leg.

The large order Coleoptera includes such agile jumpers as the Elateridae or click beetles, the Mordellidae or tumbling flower beetles, and the Halticinae or flea beetles of the family Chrysomelidae. Click beetles have elongated bodies, and—at least in Europe—are rather inconspicuous creatures. Some species are very widespread, however, and are well known to country children because of their peculiar jumping habits. They have evolved a unique type of leap, which is performed not by their legs or any other body appendage but by the whole back of the insect. It has only one purpose—to turn the beetle the right way up when it is on its back; the beetle has no other means of righting itself.

If you take a click beetle and place it upside down on your palm, it will 'sham dead' for a minute or two, after which it bends its body at the joint between the prothorax and the mesothorax, so that it is supported only by its head and the tips of its outer wings. In this position, it reveals a long process arising from its prothorax

Top right: Detail of the head and thorax of a nymphal grasshopper
Right: An adult grasshopper well camouflaged among dead vegetation

Left: An Orthopteran of the suborder Ensifera (Ephippiger species). The long ovipositor can be clearly seen

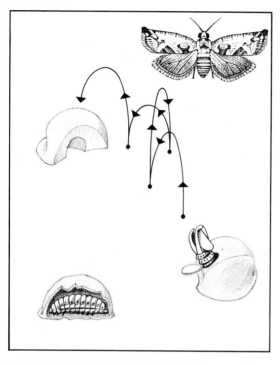

which is normally fitted into a groove on the ventral side of the neighbouring segments at rest. Then, with a sudden jerk, it straightens itself out, thus projecting itself into the air. If it lands on its back once again, it continues the gymnastic exercise until it lands on its feet. As it straightens itself out, a distinct click can be heard, and it is this that has given the beetle its common name.

The Mordellidae are small beetles with bodies that are rather flattened from side to side and a long conical-shaped abdomen. They are very common in summer, particularly on the flowers of umbelliferous plants, and are capable of considerable leaps. The Halticinae are a subfamily of the large and complex family Chrysomelidae. The commonest members of the subfamily in Europe are small, oval-shaped beetles,

often dark green or blue with a fine metallic sheen. They are often seen on all kinds of herbaceous plants, including some cultivated species. If disturbed, they take off with a great leap, using their amazingly powerful hind legs. These are characterized by lobulated or notched expansions of the outer ends of the tibiae, providing increased contact with the surface from which the insect has to jump. But the most interesting features of the hind legs are the tarsi which, instead of appearing as the natural extension of the tibiae, are bent upwards and do not make contact with the ground.

Fleas belong to the order Siphonaptera and also use the hind legs for jumping. The hind legs of fleas are not particularly long, unlike those of Orthoptera, but they have a peculiar mechanism allowing them to leap powerfully. The jumping muscles are the femoral muscles arising in the thorax and they are so arranged as to draw the leg against a pad of a rubber-like protein called 'resilin'. The system is in unstable equilibrium and when the tension is released the femur swings suddenly downwards and throws the insect into the air. The insect can hurl itself to a height of 25 centimetres (9.84 inches), and land 35–40 centimetres (about 15 inches) away from its starting-point.

The most interesting object of all, however, is without doubt the jumping bean, well known in Mexico and in the southwest of the United States. These beans are actually seeds, which are sold as 'magic' objects at village fairs. If they are laid in the sun on a more or less compact surface they almost immediately start

Top left: Adult and larva of *Carpocapsa saltitans*. The larva lives inside the seeds of Sebastiana and makes them perform strange jumping movements, which has given the plant its popular name of Mexican jumping bean
Left and right: Close-ups of the head of a grasshopper, showing details of the compound eye and antennae

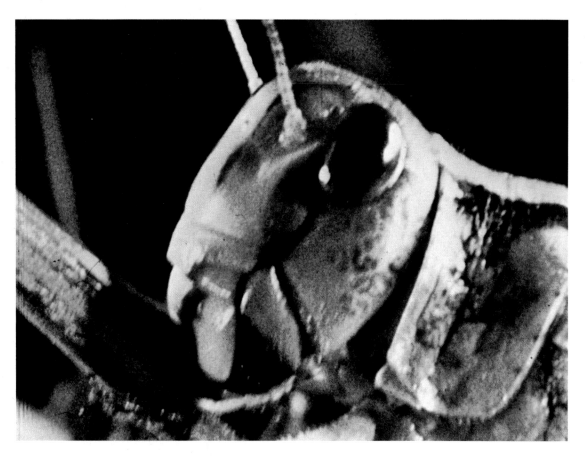

jumping this way and that. The 'magic' really resides in the inhabitants of the seeds as each one contains the larva of a microlepidopterous insect. These larvae, disliking the excessive heat, bend themselves into a V shape in the hollow they have made in the pulp of the seed. Then, by snapping straight again, they succeed in moving themselves, seed and all, until they reach the shade, where they can quietly settle down again to continue feeding.

The best-known jumping insects, however, are the locusts, grasshoppers and crickets, which all belong to the order Orthoptera.

Anatomy of an orthopterous insect

A typical member of Orthoptera is the locust, which is really a large grasshopper belonging to the family Acrididae; locusts are grasshoppers with a swarming type of behaviour. The following description of the morphology of the Orthoptera is based on the structure of the locust.

The head is very solidly built, and bears two large compound eyes at the sides of the front of the head. These eyes are elongated in a vertical direction, sometimes kidney-shaped, and are often curiously striped or brightly coloured in contrasting shades. Even a simple lens will show up the structure of the compound eye, which in the Orthoptera, as in other adult insects, has a surface composed of a very large number of minute hexagonal facets. These are the cornea of the individual visual units or ommatidia, which are arranged together to form the compound eye.

At the front of the head, more or less between the compound eyes, there are generally three tiny, glittering round caps. These are the simple eyes or ocelli, which are not organs of sight but photoreceptors; they inform the insect of the amount of light around it and bring about an appropriate response on the part of the compound eyes.

Above and left: These two pictures of the head of a grasshopper indicate the size and strength of its chewing mouth parts

Locusts have short, many-jointed antennae which are highly mobile because of the fact that their basal segment arises in a hollow of the head capsule, surrounded by an elastic ring. This whole arrangement, known as the torulus, allows the antenna to change direction freely and with great speed. The antennae, it must be remembered, carry large numbers of delicate sense organs, mainly concerned with mechanical stimuli but also with other types of stimulus.

The mouth generally points downwards, at right angles to the long axis of the body. The very powerful mouth parts are of the chewing type and are composed of a single upper labrum, two mandibles each of which is composed of a single segment that is extremely hard, then a first and second pair of maxillae. The great strength of the mandibles, which are capable of chewing up very hard materials such as the leaves of many grasses, has its counterpart in the extremely well-developed muscles that move the mandibles. These occupy a large part of the cranial cavity and are attached to its walls. The head capsule—itself heavily sclerotized (armoured with a protein called sclerotin)—is further protected from the extreme mechanical strains that arise during mastication by a solid internal support, the 'tentorium'. This is essentially a sclerotized bridge, lying in the frontal plane and constructed in the form of a cross with its front arms resting on the middle part of the front of the cranium, while the rear arms are attached to the sides of the 'occipital foramen'—the hole that joins the cranial cavity to the body cavity as a whole.

The first maxillae are paired structures composed of two lobes and a feeler or 'palp'; the second maxillae are fused to form a labium and also carry a pair of palps. They play no part in the actual chewing of food; their chief role is to hold the food in place and to assist in the process of swallowing.

Apart from the muscles of mastication, the cranial capsule contains the front portion of the central nervous system. A few instruments and a good lens are all that is needed to study the syncerebrum or brain, which is formed by the union of three structures—the protocerebrum, deuterocerebrum and tritocerebrum. The brain is connected to the rest of the central nervous system through a ring of nerve tissue surrounding the first part of the alimentary canal; this nerve tissue is known as the perioesophageal ring. The division of the central nervous system into ganglia is more evident in its remaining parts, where it can be seen to be formed of a number of rounded masses of nerve-cells and nerve-fibres, arranged to form a ventral chain subdivided to correspond with the segments of the insect's body. It is worth recalling here that insects are so-called metameric organisms, made up of a series of 20 articulated segments, 6 forming the head, 3 the thorax and the remaining 11 the abdomen.

The perioesophageal ring joins the brain to the suboesophageal ganglion, which is the ventral ganglionic centre of the head and is formed by the fusion of three ganglia; it supplies paired nerves to the mandibles, first maxillae and labium. The ventral nerve-cord arises from the suboesophageal ganglion and consists of a double series of ganglia lying on the floor

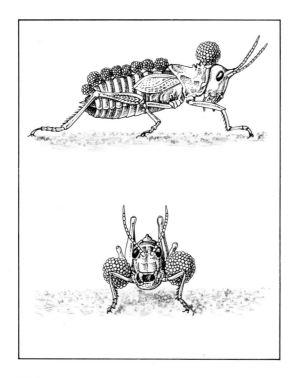

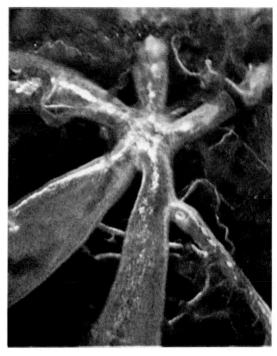

Above: An adult locust showing the typical colouring of the gregarious phase

Far left: Grasshoppers of the genus Dicthyphorus secrete bubbles of a blistering fluid to defend themselves from predators
Left: Detail of the tracheae through which Orthoptera and other insects breathe

of the thorax and abdomen; the first three ganglia are situated one in each of the thoracic segments, while the remainder lie in the abdomen.

Jumping and flying organs

The head is followed by a clearly distinguishable prothorax, which carries the first pair of legs on its lower lateral surface. These legs serve only for locomotion; they clearly show the segmentation typical of the insect limb, with a coxa at the base followed by a short trochanter, a femur, a tibia, a tarsus subdivided into small flattened tarsomeres, and a pretarsus equipped with two curved hooks.

The mesothorax and the metathorax each carry a pair of legs and a pair of wings, but while the mesothoracic legs are more

or less similar to the pair on the prothorax, the hind pair on the metathorax are completely different, being modified to serve as jumping limbs. The coxa and trochanter at the basal end of the leg, and the tarsus and pretarsus at the outer end, have not undergone much modification, but the femur and tibia are enormously increased in length, so that when the leg is fully extended it reaches a long way past the tip of the abdomen. In addition, the femur is markedly thickened, particularly at the base, so that it looks like the drumstick of a chicken. Within this thickened limb is a formidable complex of muscles. The tibia, in contrast, is tough but thin; it is tipped with sharp spurs which stick into the ground and prevent the leg from slipping as it snaps from the closed position, like a pair of compasses, to a position of full extension, catapulting the insect into the air.

Many of the Orthoptera are good flyers, but the order also contains quite a number of short-winged or wingless forms. There is, for example, the genus Eugaster, or the Ephippigera, very common in southern Europe in the late summer; these are plump little insects, poor flyers and not good at jumping either. They are the favourite (and easy) prey of many predatory wasps. Some wingless species, then, have evolved from species—presumably with normal wings—which found their way into subterranean habitats and are among the most interesting cave-dwelling creatures.

In the winged Orthoptera the second pair of wings is used solely for flying, the first pair acting as protective covers when the insect is resting or walking about. The wings of the first pair are often called tegmina (wing-covers) and sometimes, though mistakenly, elytra. They are rigid, sturdy and have conspicuous venation; they are normally held parallel to the lengthwise axis of the body, overlapping considerably on the back, and generally

Left: The joints of
the grasshopper's
middle and hind legs.
The hind pair are
powerful limbs that
enable the insects to
perform its prodigious
leaps. These legs are
equipped with special
muscles and the joint
is constructed in such
a way as to assist the
action of the muscles

Right: Detail of the
claws at the end of a
locust's leg. These
claws enable the insect
to hold securely on to
plant stems
Below: A grasshopper's
prehensile limbs clasp
a few blades of grass

conceal the entire length of the abdomen. Their colouring, brown or grey and sometimes green shades, and in some cases their shape, help to camouflage the insect effectively in its chosen habitat, be it the scorched, reddish earth of semi-arid Mediterranean regions, the yellowish sand of the desert, the luxuriant foliage of a tropical forest, or the undergrowth of a temperate forest, where the floor is covered with dead leaves.

But the outer (or first) pair of wings of the Orthoptera not only serve as a protective covering for the much more delicate inner pair, or as a means of camouflaging the insect and blending with the environment. They also carry part or all of the sound-producing apparatus, more properly called the stridulatory organs.

Singing to the sun and moon

The fact that the Orthoptera can produce sounds, commonly described as their 'song', is well known. Leave the city in high summer and you will hear, in the sunny meadows and on uncultivated land, a chorus that can drown even the loud song of the cicadas. This is produced by the males of grasshoppers and bush-crickets (family Tettigoniidae), the species of which are usually found in small colonies in grass and rough vegetation. Most Orthoptera are sun-worshippers, although a number of crickets sing towards evening and into the night in warm weather; the house cricket is almost entirely nocturnal.

The sound itself is generally produced by special structures, located on the first pair of wings, when they rub against each other or against modified parts of the legs. The common green bush-cricket, *Tettigonia viridissima,* is a handsome member of the Orthoptera approximately 7–8 centimetres (about 3 inches) long, with lengthy, thread-like antennae. It is commonly seen in coastal districts of southern and western England and less commonly inland in late summer. The males carry a structure

Right: Grasshoppers are not generally considered as flying insects. Nevertheless they possess two pairs of wings, the first of which are hardened and reinforced with tough wing veins, as shown in these photographs, and the second membraneous. The large, migratory species, known as locusts, are accomplished flyers

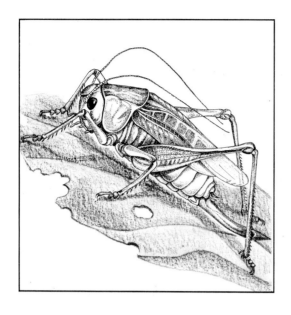

Bush-crickets (Tettigoniidae, above) and true crickets (Gryllidae, below) differ from grasshoppers by having very long antennae, and the ovipositor of the female is shaped like a sword or needle

Below: A dead cricket is attacked by ants. Below right: A grasshopper, its wings outspread, is photographed in the middle of a leap

known as the 'file' on the lower surface of the left wing, near the root. This feature is, anatomically speaking, a very much thickened segment of the wing vein with a large number of minute transverse ridges on its surface. Its counterpart, on the upper surface of the right wing, is a smooth area enclosed in a sort of rigid frame. This, too, is a modified wing vein and is known as the 'scraper'. When at rest, the parts of the wings that bear these structures lie one on top of the other with the left wing uppermost. Short, rapid opening and closing movements of the wings cause the file to rub against the scraper, giving rise to stridulation. The volume of sound is increased by the presence of air-filled cavities of varying sizes in the thorax and more particularly in the abdomen and which, as a result, function as sounding-boxes.

The grasshoppers (family Acrididae), marked with patches of contrasting colours and having short antennae, also possess stridulatory organs located (but only in

part) on their wings. The outer edge of the wing carries projections of various shapes which are played on by files located on the inner part of the femur of the last pair of legs. When a grasshopper is engaged in stridulation, the rhythmic rise and fall of its long hind legs is easy to see; if the movement is slow, the note is a low one, becoming progressively higher in pitch as the movement speeds up.

True crickets (family Gryllidae) use their front wings for stridulation in a similar fashion to bush-crickets, but they differ in that the file is on the right wing and the wings always lie with the right wing uppermost. The resulting sound produced by the complex structure of the stridulatory organs gives rise to a delicate song that can be pleasant to the human ear. Men of various historical periods and various civilizations have often kept crickets and other members of the Orthoptera in captivity in order to hear them sing. The classical Athenians were very fond of the song of crickets and grasshoppers. In

China, too, until recent times, musical crickets were carefully bred, fed on fresh leaves and treated when they fell sick. (Indeed, the Chinese have long and detailed treatises on the subject of 'cricket medicine'.) These Chinese musical crickets were reared in tiny cages, often of precious materials and exquisite workmanship, some of which were veritable masterpieces of their craft.

But perhaps this is not really so surprising. Moreover, although Chinese civilization is totally different from that of the West, cages for musical crickets have been made in Europe even in this century in Provence in southern France; and in Italy, especially in Tuscany, the custom of 'raising the cricket' on Ascension Day was still quite widespread until only a few decades ago. It probably derived from distant memories of pagan festivals to celebrate the return of spring.

At all events, the production of sounds by the Orthoptera is certainly not intended to delight the human ear. The stridulatory organs, which are generally confined to male insects, seem to have an important function in locating and recognizing members of the opposite sex in the breeding season, although the biological significance of stridulation in the Orthoptera is not yet fully known and is certainly not exclusively that of a mating call. In order to hear the call, the females are equipped (as, indeed, are the males) with highly sophisticated acoustic organs. These consist primarily of a tympanic membrane or 'eardrum', a thin membrane derived from the cuticle and kept in a state of tension by appropriate hard structures, which starts to vibrate in response to sound-waves of the precise frequency emitted by the male. These membranes may lie on the insect's outer surface, while in more advanced groups they are protected with voluminous folds of skin. They are connected to sensory cells which transmit the signal along the acoustic nerves to the central nervous system. However, the female does not merely need to become aware of the presence of a male: she has to find him, and therefore must be able to locate the source of the sound. Mammals manage to do this by making use of the fact that the sound-wave does not reach both ears at the same instant, because of their anatomical position and the position of the hearer in his surroundings. The central nervous system then uses this discrepancy in timing to identify the source of a sound. Crickets and bush-crickets, however, carry their tympanic membranes on their front tibiae, close to the joint between tibia and femur. The insect 'scans' the surroundings by swinging its legs as it walks, and recent research has demonstrated that in the species studied they will orientate themselves by 'listening' with one leg at a time. The 'listening' leg on its own is capable of using complex mechanisms to supply the insect with adequate information to guide it. In grasshoppers the tympanic membranes are at the base of the abdomen.

The mechanism of flight

As pointed out earlier, the function of the first pair of wings goes far beyond merely covering and protecting the second pair. As for the second pair themselves, they are finer and more membraneous, much larger in area than the first pair. They are occasionally coloured bright red and black, or red and blue, and at rest they are folded up in the form of a fan along the insect's back with the first pair above them giving protection.

In the Orthoptera, only the second pair of wings is used for flying. The flight is a rather ponderous movement in a straight line, unlike, say, the graceful aerobatics of butterflies or the lightning soaring and diving of the dragonfly. Even so, the Orthoptera are capable of flying great distances, and this is especially true of those species that gather together in swarms and set off on long migratory journeys, often devastating large areas in the process.

The wings of insects, unlike those of all other flying creatures such as birds and bats,

are not modified limbs but organs intended from the very beginning as instruments of flight. The wing-beat is produced by a set of muscles whose organization and mode of action is unique to insects and is particularly well shown in the Orthoptera. The wings themselves have no muscles, and the few muscle bundles that have an insertion into the wing, the so-called direct wing muscles, do not move the wing but alter its angle. The mechanism for moving the wings is powered by a large number of strong muscle bundles, the so-called indirect wing muscles. These are not inserted into the wing itself, but join together various parts of the thorax. The muscles running in a vertical direction join the tergum (the hardened outer part of the insect's upper surface) with the corresponding sternum on its belly. Contraction of these muscles causes a flattening of the thorax so that the tergum and sternum are brought closer together and this results in elevation of the wings, which are mounted flexibly between the pleura and the tergum. The opposing muscles run longitudinally. When these contract, they

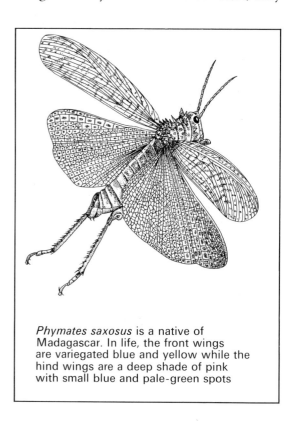

Phymates saxosus is a native of Madagascar. In life, the front wings are variegated blue and yellow while the hind wings are a deep shade of pink with small blue and pale-green spots

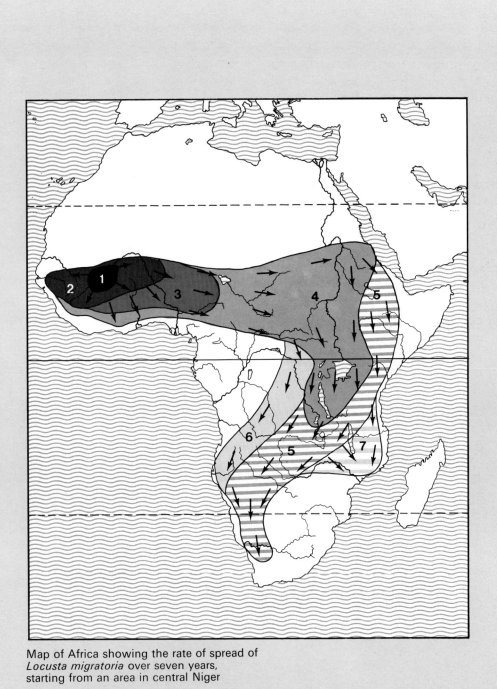

Map of Africa showing the rate of spread of
Locusta migratoria over seven years,
starting from an area in central Niger

restore the original relationship between the two diameters of the thorax, and lower the wings. The alternation of these two movements gives rise to the beating of the wings in flight.

For most species of Orthoptera, however, flight is not normally the most important means of locomotion. Orthoptera are essentially terrestrial creatures that normally move around on foot, interrupting this with short flights when they are disturbed or threatened. But flight becomes very important in mass migration of the large grasshoppers called locusts, known and feared since ancient times.

Insects that cross the desert

With vivid imagery and stately prose, the Bible describes the eighth plague that struck Egypt. For the agnostic it is a legend, for the believer the literal truth, but in any case it is entirely true to life. Even in recent times, no more than 20 years ago, there

were reports of massive invasions of locusts in North Africa and in the central parts of southern Africa. These swarms were estimated to number billions of individuals, and for all that modern chemical insecticides could do, they left few living green plants behind.

The abundant supply of locusts is no doubt the reason why the African desert tribes have made them one of their staple articles of diet. Even the Greek historian Herodotus described this fact, in the fifth century BC. And today, a flour prepared from sun-dried and ground locusts still accounts for a fair proportion of the food supply of the Touaregs of the Sahara. This flour, although it has a nauseating smell, is rich in fats and also in vitamins, derived principally from the vegetables that fill the alimentary canal of these insects. Furthermore, if it is mixed with goat or dromedary milk and cooked, it loses its unpleasant smell and becomes, if not actually a delicacy, at least a food that can be eaten

without qualms, even by a European. It is also the custom, in the same areas, to eat crisp savoury fried locusts in the way that we eat shrimps.

However, mass migrations are not a constant feature of the life cycle of locusts. Indeed, of the several thousand species of grasshoppers known to science only a few are migratory, while the remainder are practically sedentary and generally solitary insects, which only come together in the mating season. Furthermore, even the migratory species such as *Schistocerca peregrina*, *Nomadacris septemfasciata*, *Dociostaurus maroccanus* or *Calliptamus italicus* (the last two being found in southern Europe) normally behave like other Orthoptera. They go through a 'solitary phase', during which they feel no urge to live a social life, and this phase contrasts with the 'gregarious phase', during which they gather together in huge numbers in one area, and then take off on a migration covering many thousands of

kilometres or miles in a vast swarm that darkens the sky as it passes, with a rushing noise that some have compared with the sound of a violent downpour of rain.

The mechanism that gives rise to this impressive mass phenomenon and the causes of it are among one of the most fascinating and complex topics of insect biology. They have not been fully elucidated even to this day and there are still many mysteries to be solved. According to the latest theories, however, the process takes place as follows. After one or more generations of normal development in the solitary phase, a generation appears in a particular area with a strong tendency—long before adult life—to group together. The gregarious generation is almost always preceded by a generation which, while it is still solitary or at least not overtly gregarious, shows a more rapid development than normal. The members of the gregarious generation may also appear conspicuously different from those

Far left: Locusts mating
Above left: Locust eggs are stuck together with a secretion, produced by special glands in the female, which solidifies on exposure to air
Above: A young nymph emerges from its egg by tearing open the cover
Left: The moment it is born, the young locust must moult in order to free its legs which are enclosed in a membrane

315

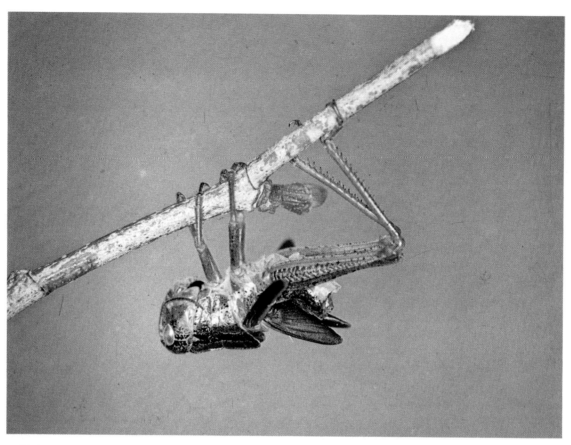

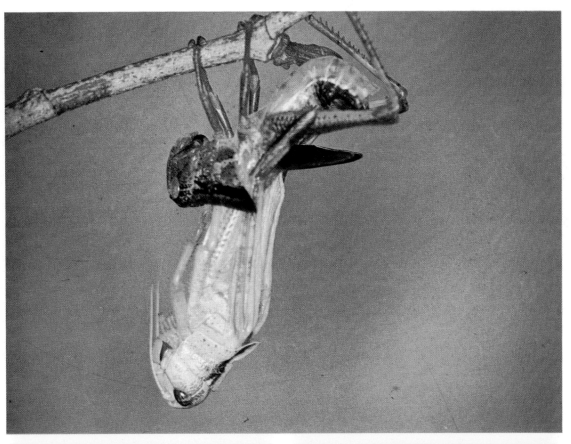

Previous two pages: Successive stages in the
moult of a locust. From four to ten months
are normally required for a new-born nymph
to transform itself into a reproductive adult

The photographs on this page show how, after
its final moult, the insect expands its wings
and dries them in the air. The discarded
skin is shown hanging on a twig (above)
Opposite left: The head and pronotum or
first thoracic segment of an adult locust,
seen from above
Opposite right: Detail of a moulting nymphal
locust. The head is to the bottom of the
photograph; the pronotum has split and the
nymph is dragging itself out of its old skin

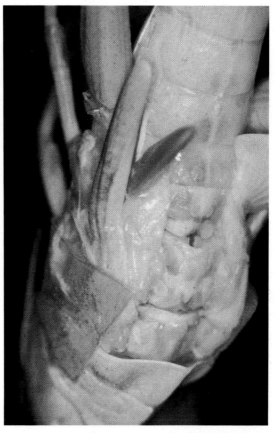

of the solitary phase, particularly in their colouring.

The appearance of the gregarious generation, which does not follow a regular pattern, is attributed by most recent theories to overcrowding in a particular area. The result is not so much food shortage as such, but overcrowding stress or neurophysiological distress and this is thought to be the true cause of transition from the solitary to the gregarious phase. As already mentioned, the transition is not a sudden event, but takes place over the course of an 'intermediate' generation, in which the life cycle is speeded up. The eggs laid by the females of the intermediate generation give rise to nymphs (they are not called larvae, because metamorphosis in the Orthoptera is of the simple type), and these already have a marked tendency to gather in large groups. Apart from their size, the nymphs bear a close resemblance to the adults but are wingless and, of course, sexually immature. Very soon, vast

hordes of locust nymphs numbering millions of individuals set off, marching in close formation and following a precise direction. Nothing will stop them now, save perhaps an enormous fire. Not a plant can survive their passage.

The proverbial voracity of the locusts has recently been explained (at least in regard to some species of the hot and dry regions of Africa) as more than a purely food-related phenomenon. Some German researchers have demonstrated that these insects do not need to drink water or eat fleshy plants in order to provide themselves with water. They obtain all the water required for their metabolism from plants—even perfectly dry plants—by special processes of digestion.

The insects reach adulthood, and with it the full and functional development of their wings, by a gradual process, as do all insects with the so-called simple type of metamorphosis. They pass through a number of moults, each of which involves a short period of inactivity, followed by the splitting of the old shell and the emergence of the insect in the next stage, soft and depigmented. In the course of a few hours it rapidly increases in size, and its new skin, now exposed to the air, undergoes oxidation which gives it its final colours and renders it as tough as its predecessor.

The final moult takes a little longer than the others. The mature nymph attaches itself firmly to a support (usually the branch of a bush) and remains quiescent for some time. Eventually it splits its skin and the adult insect emerges. From the wiry sheaths of the nymph emerge the adult wings, still moist and limp. Very soon they stretch open under the pressure of internal fluids that fill up the system of vessels and spaces which form the wing veins. After this, the locust takes to the air, but it will be some weeks before its sexual organs are able to function.

In the first few days of its adult life, the locust makes only short flights and does not leave the area of its final moult. After some time, however, the entire community takes wing and leaves the area, often migrating a distance of thousands of kilometres or miles. Some species fly from Morocco as far as Niger, crossing the entire Sahara in the process, and others go from the East African grasslands to the Cape of Good Hope. Throughout their journey, they continue to eat at a phenomenal rate, and every now and then the females lay clutches of eggs from 30 to 100 at a time in small holes that they dig in the ground with the tip of their abdomen. These eggs produce nymphs that may give rise to the solitary or the gregarious forms according to the local conditions, or they may be less gregarious than their parents—that is, they become a transitional phase. After a variable number of solitary generations, overcrowding and other conditions will once again call forth the appearance of a new gregarious generation, and a new migration will start.

The marauding locusts

The Bible relates how, during their exile in Egypt, the children of Israel had become resigned to their servitude but that one of them, Moses, having been saved from the waters of the Nile to which he had been committed, was entrusted by God with the mission of freeing the Israelites and guiding them to the Promised Land. As the Pharaoh of the day was unwilling to lose such a large number of slaves, he repeatedly refused Moses permission to leave. After a series of entreaties and threats, Moses called upon God's help. The land of Egypt was thereupon struck by a series of calamities, each more terrible than the last, and all aimed at softening the Pharaoh's heart. After seven of these had failed to produce the desired effect, there occurred events more appalling than any that had gone before: the locusts, the darkness and the death of the Egyptian firstborn.

'And the Lord said unto Moses, Stretch out thine hand over the land of Egypt for the locusts, that they may come up upon the land of Egypt, and eat every herb of the land, even all that the hail hath left. And Moses stretched forth his rod over the land of Egypt, and the Lord brought an east wind upon the land all that day, and all the night; and when it was morning, the east wind brought the locusts. And the locusts went up over all the land of Egypt, and rested in all the coasts of Egypt; very

Left: Nymph of an African locust on a tuft of wheat leaves. Its wings are not yet fully developed

grievous were they; before them there were no such locusts as they, neither after them shall be such. For they covered the face of the whole earth, so that the land was darkened; and they did eat every herb of the land, and all the fruit of the trees which the hail had left: and there remained not any green thing in the trees, or in the herbs of the field, through all the land of Egypt.'

This passage from Exodus, terrifying and concise, vividly describes an invasion of migratory locusts. Even in biblical times, locusts were considered as a plague only slightly less intolerable than total darkness or the death of all the firstborn. In more recent times, too, locusts have continued to be the most harmful and the most feared of all insects in the warmer parts of the world.

The countries of North Africa have perhaps suffered more from them than any other region; and important scientific institutes have been founded there to study and control their migration and to perfect the most efficient chemical and biological counter-measures. Other areas are also subjected more or less regularly to the onslaught of locusts, and the list grows longer every year.

In 1873, 1874 and again in 1875 hordes of migratory locusts even travelled as far as central Germany. These swarms originated in the East, in the regions round the Black Sea and the Caspian Sea, and it did not take them long to cover the distance to Silesia and Brandenburg. Their path was marked

by the destruction of agricultural areas and by severe damage to forests. Some cities, such as Wroclaw in Poland, even struck commemorative coins to mark this unprecedented and disastrous invasion.

Around 1880, swarms of many millions of locusts appeared, as if from nowhere, in southern Russia and spread over an enormous area, covering several regions. On this occasion, many people died as a result of the famine which followed the destruction of almost all cattle fodder and the consequent death of animals from hunger within a few days. The water, too, was made undrinkable by the quantities of drowned locusts. Even bread was scarce because the locusts gathered in swarms inside bread-ovens, totally obstructing them.

Devastation on a massive scale

In 1908, a report told of a great invasion of locusts in the Canaries, an agricultural region where African and American fruits ripen together. Repelling the invasion was therefore of crucial importance for the inhabitants, the great majority of whom lived only by their crops. 'The proximity of Africa', said the report, 'a day and a half distant by sea, exposes the Canaries to two sorts of pestilence: in summer it is the sands of the Sahara that are carried here by tornadoes, rendering the air unbreathable; while in this season it is the locusts, which often devastate the countryside. The present invasion seems more dangerous than earlier ones, since the insects form thick clouds; and these, when they come to earth, are up to nine or ten centimetres [almost 4 inches] thick! The insects can quickly fly across the island, but on this occasion their winged battalions have covered the countryside on the island of

Left: Nymph of a locust, a term used for those large grasshoppers that alternate between solitary and gregarious phases
Right: A group of nymphs migratory locusts in the gregarious phase. In breeding stations their habits are studied to find means of preventing the damage such insects cause

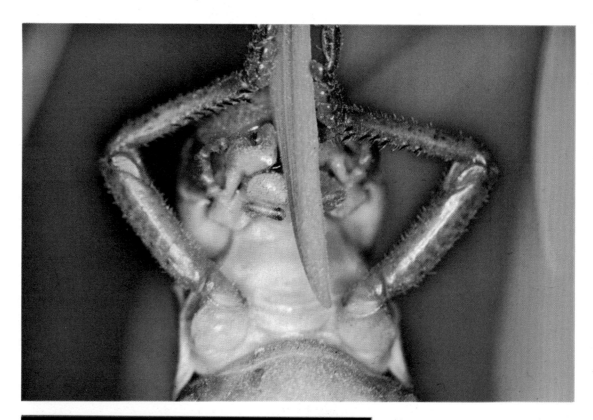

Above and left: The locusts'
voracious and destructive
appetite for grass and
cereals is legendary—
but all too true. For
thousands of years, numerous
attempts have been made to
fight the insects and halt
their migrations

Right: Even the dreaded
locust has enemies in nature.
The spider's web, for
instance, provides an
effective snare

Grand Canary, which lives mainly by the cultivation of tomatoes and other vegetables. Energetic measures have been taken, under the direction of engineers and agronomists. Hundreds of peasants armed with sticks are driving the invading insects towards the sea, and in order to prevent them from returning a number of tugs and steam fishing-boats from the ports of Lux and Tenerife are also following and sounding their sirens to scare them since this is a sound that the insects appear to find particularly unpleasant. The tactic seems to be successful. In the meantime, the brunt of the invasion has been borne by the plantains, the orange plantations, the sugarcane, peaches and almonds.'

Even in more recent times, despite new methods for combating them, locusts continue their ceaseless onslaughts. We are fortunate in that we no longer experience such episodes as the invasion of Cyrenaica and Numidia in 125 BC which caused the death of 800,000 people, or the invasion of Algeria in 1867 which killed more than 500,000. Locust migrations nevertheless continue to be an object of fear and sorrow. In 1955, a vast swarm of these insects descended on southern Morocco. According to reliable calculations, the insect cloud was 250 kilometres (155 miles) long and 20 kilometres (12 miles) wide, and caused more than £80 million worth of damage.

Locusts are also at home in South Africa. The most recent report of their depredations dates from 1966 when the railway system was first subjected to incredible delays and finally seized up altogether due to the number of live and dead locusts lying in thick layers on railway lines. Trains were no longer able to make normal journeys, since their wheels would sink into the mass of locusts and could not get a grip on the track.

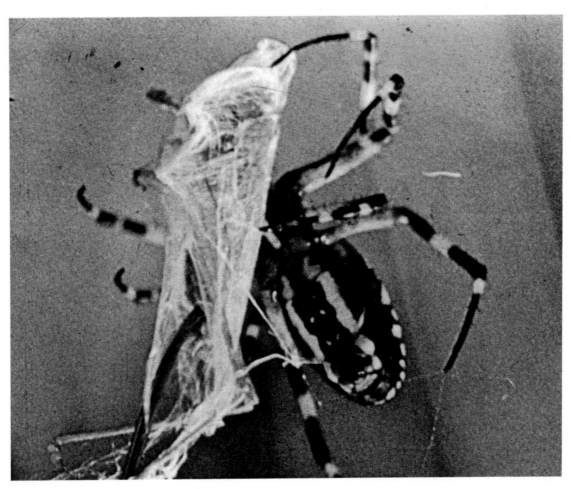

Responsibility for the world-wide calamities described does not lie with one species alone. *Dociostaurus maroccanus* migrates through Spain, Asia Minor, the Caucasus and Turkestan; *Locusta migratoria* extends to Russia and to tropical regions throughout the Old World; Africa (except for South Africa) and parts of Asia are visited by *Schistocerca gregaria*, while Central and South America receive the attentions of *Schistocerca paranensis*.

Italy has always been liable to the visits of migratory locusts. Sicily and Sardinia are periodically affected, and on several occasions even the northern regions, particularly Lombardy, have suffered. Invasions of huge proportions were recorded in 873 BC, 1364, 1542, and most recently in 1946 and 1947, although on these last occasions the invasion was not as great as earlier ones.

The greatest damage is caused by *Dociostaurus maroccanus,* a species from Africa,

Above: A migratory locust in the gregarious phase. The two phases are distinguished by differences in behaviour and variation in colour. Individuals in the solitary phase are predominantly green while those in the gregarious phase show deeper shades of brown

Right: Many grasshoppers show considerable variation in their colour. Much of this variation may be genetic, but some species are able to respond to their background by increasing or decreasing their black pigment. The nymph in this photograph is effectively camouflaged

and also by *Calliptamus italicus,* a typical Italian species which sometimes spreads to France, Switzerland and central Europe as far as Russia. All locust invasions are extremely difficult to combat, due to the enormous number of individuals in a swarm and therefore the innumerable eggs that they lay when they land. During an invasion by locusts in Algeria in 1890, over 500,000,000,000 eggs and over twice this number of nymphs were collected and destroyed.

A new generation

The female lays her eggs immediately after copulation, burying them in special holes that she digs in the ground to protect them. Each female can lay from 30 to 100 eggs at a time, and may lay ten such clutches; hence she produces up to 1,000 eggs each season. Mohammed, wishing to show in practical terms the reproductive powers of locusts, wrote in the Koran that every female lays 99 eggs, and that if she were to lay 100 the world would be buried in locusts.

To lay her eggs, the female digs a hole in the ground using the movable short, curved structures at the tip of the abdomen. Extending her abdomen into the hole, she lays her eggs, enclosed in an oötheca or tube made of material secreted by glands connected to her reproductive apparatus. In view of the large number of eggs and their relatively large size, the pit that the female digs must be quite deep. In order to make this deep pit, the female's abdomen must be considerably lengthened, and to do this she literally inflates herself with air which she pumps into special abdominal sacs derived from the tracheae. In this way the abdomen can grow to four times its length, thanks to the extensible articular membranes that join its segments together.

The nymphs hatch out after a period of two to four weeks or more, depending on local factors, and immediately begin to gnaw leaves and to march forward as a horde with ever-growing appetites. Various writers have produced numerous lists of the plants that locusts like to eat, whether in the nymphal or adult stage. In

practice, however, it is true to say that both
cultivated and wild plants, grasses and the
leaves of shrubs and trees will all be eaten.
In an area where many types of plants are
found growing together, it may happen
that the locusts prefer one type and ignore
another, but this normally only happens
where they have a choice. Where they do
not, it is a rare plant that is spared. For
example, during a notable invasion of
Somalia in 1928 the locusts mainly attacked
sunflowers, vegetables, cotton plants,
couch-grass and other wild grasses, leaving
the maize and other cultivated crops almost
intact, although in previous invasions these
had been completely destroyed.

In 1961–62, locusts descended on
southern Morocco and settled on the
orange groves of the Sous Valley. Over a
short period—about five days—they destroyed more than 7,000 tonnes (in excess
of 6,800 tons) of fruit at a rate of around 60
tonnes (58 tons) an hour. This is a prime
example of the way in which a locust

Three examples of South African migratory
locusts
Below: Immature insect in the solitary phase;
bottom: immature insect in the gregarious
phase; below right: a female laying eggs
in the ground

invasion can jeopardize the economy of an agricultural country, particularly if it is remembered that it takes several years to repair the damage and make plantations productive again.

Combating locust attacks

Various means have been used to combat locusts and these can be divided into mechanical, chemical and biological methods. The system adopted by the Canary islanders in 1908, as quoted earlier, was certainly imaginative, but even today there is no single, reliable method for coping with a mass attack. The main difficulty is that of predicting both the year and the region that will be affected, making it impossible to take precautionary measures. At the same time, the vast number of insects and their extreme fertility make them hard to control. In an attempt to overcome this difficulty, countries at risk have set up laboratories with the most advanced equipment, some of them mobile, ready to sample invading populations and to institute control measures. These laboratories keep in close touch with each other providing useful information and warning some of the regions lying in the line of attack.

Among mechanical control measures, one of the oldest that is still in use is that of deploying beaters armed with sticks and shovels to kill the adult locusts. But even more important is the massive hunt for eggs. If these have been recently laid and are not yet embryonated, shallow hoeing of the ground is sufficient. This is because the eggs, unless they are on the point of hatching, dry out quickly once they are brought to the surface. They are then also an easy prey for birds and other insectivorous creatures.

Even today, primitive peoples try to combat migratory locusts by using instruments that produce an intolerable noise. They arm themselves with empty tin cans,

which they beat with sticks and clubs to make a terrible din. Although this drives the locusts away it does not provide a complete remedy since they merely move on to a neighbouring area where they will reproduce and give birth to a new generation of pests. After chemical and biological methods, mechanical ones provide the next best means of control.

Zinc barriers and flame-throwers

As early as last century, mobile barriers were used against locust invasions in Algeria and Morocco. These were special constructions of cloth or zinc, a few tens of centimetres or several inches high, which were laid along a line several hundred metres or yards long in affected areas. Beyond the barrier, a trench was dug, quite deep, as long as the barrier itself and more than 1 metre (about 3 feet) wide. Young nymphs, which cannot fly, are known to become very active and mobile after their first moult. At this time they gather together and march off, driven by an irresistible urge, crossing hills and even wide watercourses in their path. When they meet the artificial barriers, they attempt to climb over them, but not many succeed—particularly if the barriers are of zinc—and most of them gather in a mass at the base of the barrier. Meanwhile, those that succeed in crossing the barriers fall into the trench on the other side and are crushed and suffocated by the vast numbers of other nymphs that land on top of them. At this point, the beaters come into action and soon destroy any survivors.

In some cases, when crops have been ruined, flame-throwers can also be used to good effect. Here, too, it is the nymphs that are killed, while the adults can fly away to safety. Extensive smoke-screens in strategic

Below left: Two researchers engaged in a 'mark and recapture' experiment in Australia
Below: Captured specimens in Africa are transferred to special jars before being sent to research laboratories

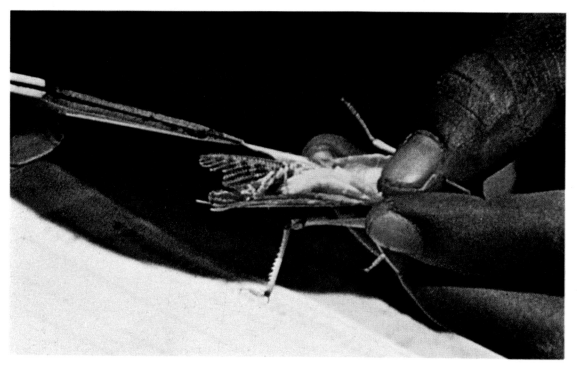

areas will also keep away the swarm, but this method can only be used when the wind is favourable and atmospheric pressure is high.

Chemical and biological methods

Chemical methods are generally more effective and give better results. They mainly involve powerful contact-acting insecticides, or poisons spread over the plants on which the locusts normally feed, or poisoned bait that will begin to take effect once it has been eaten. Insecticides are spread from aircraft, helicopters and motor-boats equipped with powerful hoses. But since most insecticides are non-selective, they carry the grave disadvantage of killing off a large number of useful insects and of being poisonous for birds, fish, and insectivorous creatures in general.

Poisons are generally better and more reliable. These are usually mixed with bran or sawdust and scattered over a wide area. Poisoned bait is often laid down together with food of which locusts are particularly fond, and this combination has proved effective. Indeed, if this approach is followed in regions where locusts are believed

Above: Captured locusts are first examined and then, later, are reared in the laboratory
Right: A nymph (top) and an adult (bottom) being bred in cages in order to discover the reasons for the change from the solitary to the much more dangerous gregarious phase

to develop and eventually give rise to migratory swarms, it is even more successful. The great majority of the chemicals used are compounds of arsenic and have to be handled with great care, using masks and gloves for protection. This is, however, standard practice in treating fruit trees with antifungal agents.

Yet another weapon—though not the most modern—is the use of biological methods, and this involves exploiting the locusts' natural enemies. During the last century, scientists (particularly in Russia) were interested in the potential usefulness of certain parasites in the control of locusts. Some of the Hymenoptera, for instance, are keen locust-hunters. They immobilize their prey with a poison secreted by glands situated close to the sting, and carry them, still living, to their nests, where they feed them to their young. *Sphex luteipennis* has turned out to be a particularly active and skilful hunter.

In Argentina, certain larviparous flies

334

Above: Scene in a locust breeding station, where the insects are allowed to reproduce in order that the nymphs can be studied

have also been used, but the method is difficult to put into practice and a principal disadvantage is that it can only, at best, be a preventive measure. It would be of no use at all for dealing with an attack. Another difficulty is that certain regions have no effective parasites on locusts, and their mass introduction could throw the local ecology seriously out of balance.

Insectivorous birds particularly active against Orthoptera have also been used on locusts. This method again has important drawbacks. First of all, it involves the mass breeding of the birds and their introduction into the infested areas— a very time-consuming operation. In addition, once the region is free of locusts, it will not be visited by another migration for some time. There will therefore be a vast number of birds free to prey on any and every insect, with grave consequences for the local insect population.

Other biological methods that have been used in certain areas with varying success include the identification of fungi and bacteria that cause serious epidemics among locusts and kill them off in large numbers. This last approach is still in the experimental stage, though it has already been successfully used in the United States and South Africa.

Insect against insect

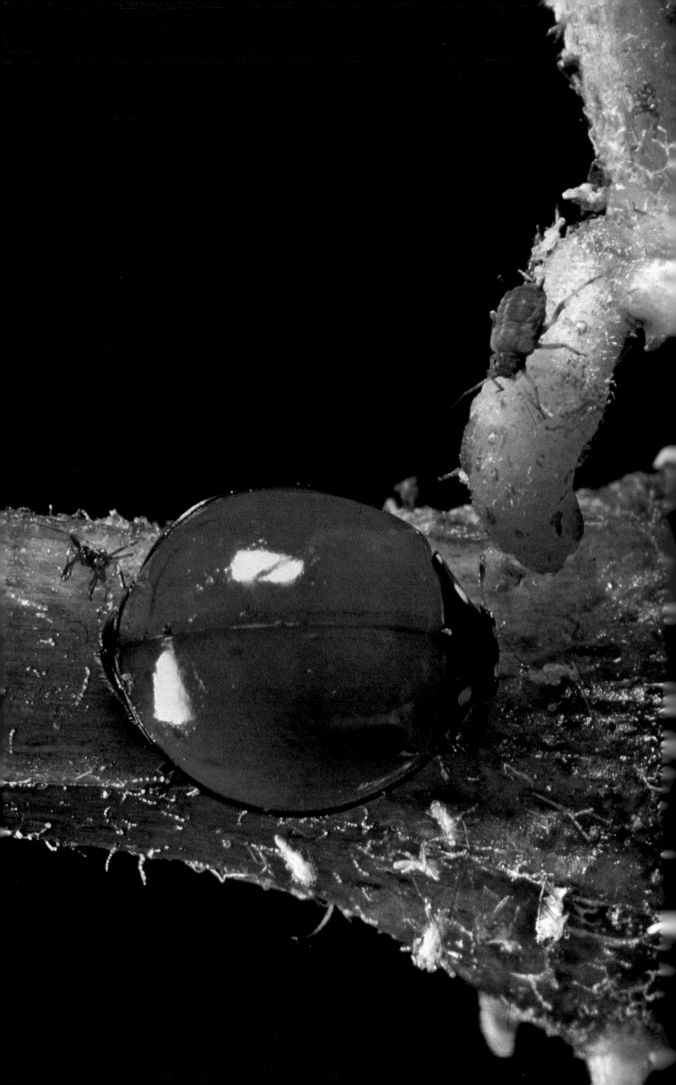

Since the appearance of insects on earth at least 250 million years ago, their advance has continued without a break; and of all the creatures on the earth, they are probably the only ones that are really capable of exerting a decisive influence on human life. The insect species discovered so far number almost 1 million, but there may well be as many more that have not yet been observed. From broad plains to the highest mountains, from tropical forests to deserts, they have colonized every sort of environment with amazing success, often adapting to seemingly intolerable conditions. There are certain dipterous larvae that live in oil wells; others live in hot springs at temperatures of 49–51°C (122°F); some small beetles survive in water that is subject to continuous changes in salt concentration and temperature. It seems that little can stand in the way of these creatures, with their extraordinary capacity to hold their ground in the struggle for survival—a capacity that they have acquired through complex evolutionary mechanisms. Many factors play a part here. Among the most important are their possession of wings, a most efficient means of spreading abroad, and their fertility, which is always remarkable and sometimes astounding.

It has often been stated that if every

insect could grow to reach reproductive life, and if every egg or larva gave rise to an adult, then long ago the world would have been submerged in a thick layer of insects. Fortunately for man, however, insects are the staple diet of a vast number of other animals which live on eggs, larvae and adults and so keep the various insect species down to reasonable numbers. One need only consider the slaughter perpetrated on insects by birds, amphibians, reptiles, mammals and fish to realize just how many insects must be eliminated at some stage of their development. But for this, they would certainly be the absolute and undisputed masters not only of all dry land on the earth's surface, but of the waters, too. In addition to the depredations carried out by other members of the animal kingdom, insects are also subject to the often relentless attacks of other insects; and this war is carried on in the most varied ways and with most surprising results.

Relations between men and insects are somewhat complex to define and to analyse. In general, these small winged creatures are regarded not with hate but with instinctive dislike, and the logical consequence is that many of us try to kill any insect—not with our hands, which might be harmed in the process, but with any object that is considered suitable. In this way, harmless or even useful species regularly encounter the same sort of treatment as harmful ones. All this may be due to the fact that, whereas there are just a

Left: Apart from being among the most beautiful of insects, ladybird beetles are also some of the most useful for they attack pest species

few insect species that are useful to humans, there are an enormous number that directly or indirectly cause us harm; it leads us to react to insects in general in a hostile way. Among the insects that have earned themselves a high place on the black list must be numbered the aphids, the scale-insects, certain Lepidoptera and, above all, mosquitoes and other biting flies.

Aphids will be discussed later in connection with some of the insects that prey on them, but as regards the scale-insects, it is worth noting that they do in fact belong to the same suborder as the aphids, namely the Homoptera. Scale-insects, Coccidae, include a very large number of species showing marked sexual dimorphism, the males being winged and the females wingless. During the course of their development, the females may even lose their legs, becoming fixed to a plant from which they draw nourishment and on which they will spend the rest of their lives. In this situation, they often look like tiny, flattened shells.

Right: A ladybird beetle and a group of scale-insect larvae on which it preys
Bottom right: Female scale-insects are always stationary. They produce an abundant secretion of wax or lac which covers their bodies

Below: The hunter and the hunted. A spider is shown with its prey, a fly that mimics a wasp. The wasp-like markings of the fly will deter a vertebrate predator such as a bird but a spider is not duped

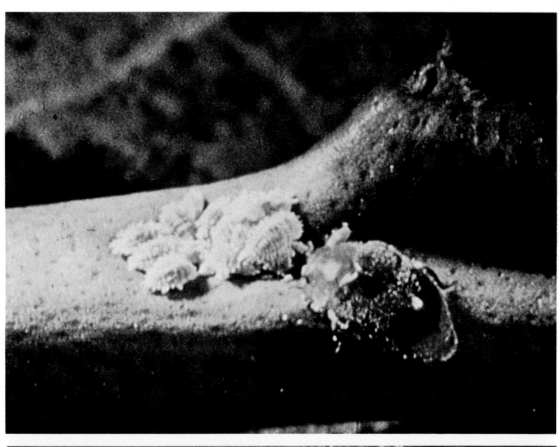

Top: A male scale-insect. The males have two wings and quite large eyes
Above: Larvae and females of various species of scale-insect

Left: Two more female scale-insects, motionless on the plant from which they derive all their food. The white material is a mass of waxen filaments that may have a protective function

Male coccids have vestigial mouth parts, while those of the females are very well developed. They are of the piercing and sucking type, with tough stylets enabling the insect to bore through plant tissues in search of sap.

The females either lay their eggs inside wax egg-sacs, which are very conspicuous objects, or else under the shell-like scale that covers their bodies. Some aspects of the life of certain scale species are still shrouded in mystery. It has not yet been possible, for instance, to identify the males of these species, and it appears that they may reproduce parthenogenetically with the eggs eventually giving rise to new individuals, invariably females, without male sperms playing any part. Scale-insects carry out their depredations on all parts of the plant, and if conditions are favourable for reproduction they may very quickly wipe out a fertile plantation.

Among the better-known scale-insects is the white mulberry scale, *Diaspis*

Top left: Eggs of the pine processionary moth clustered around a pine-needle
Centre row: Larvae begin to emerge from the eggs
Far left: A parasitic chalcid wasp lays its own eggs inside the eggs of a processionary moth
Left: A single processionary larva
Top: An adult processionary
Above: A wasp has killed an adult moth and after removing the wings and legs will carry it off to its nest to feed the wasp larvae
Above right: When the abdomen of a female moth is opened, it is seen to be filled with eggs
Right: The chrysalis made by a processionary larva in which an ichneumon-fly laid its egg has produced an ichneumon larva instead of an adult moth

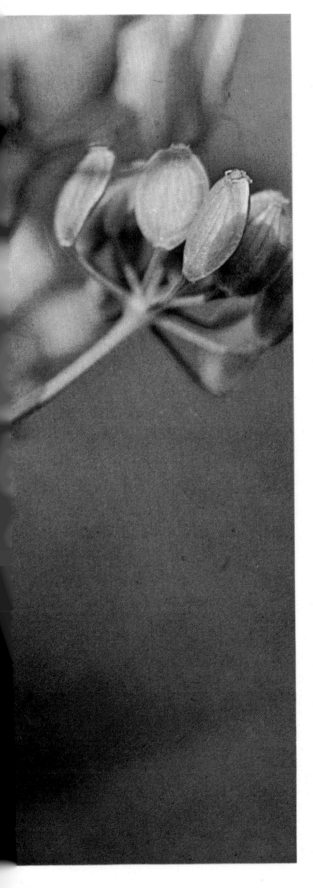

pentagona, which spread through Italy at the end of the nineteenth century, having been accidentally imported from its original home, the Far East. In a very short time, it threatened to destroy all mulberry plantations in the country, and attempts to control it were unsuccessful until the great Italian entomologist, Antonio Berlese, introduced a small species of wasp into Italy. This wasp was a parasite of Diaspis in its original home, and kept its numbers down very effectively in Italy, too. Mulberry trees were thus saved through a war of insect against insect. This was one of the earliest campaigns in the biological war that began with the battle against the cottony cushion scale, *Icerya purchasi*, a native of Australia, which was a major pest of citrus trees in California. A beetle, a species of ladybird, was introduced to control the pest, and it very quickly succeeded in the task.

These are two instances of successful biological warfare. Often, however, it is less successful, because the insect that is imported to keep the pest at bay finds the conditions in its new home unfavourable for reproduction. Such is the case with another scale-insect, the San José scale (*Quadraspidiotus perniciosus*), which has spread unopposed through the United States, inflicting incalculable damage on fruit trees. Over the last 30 years, this species has unfortunately also spread in southern Europe but the damage it has caused has so far been much less severe than in America.

Even among scale-insects, however, not every species merits extermination. Some are highly cherished, useful creatures. The Indian lac insect, for instance, is used in the production of shellac and varnishes. Its body becomes covered with a waxy substance known as lac, which is the raw material used. Another scale-insect, *Ker-*

Left: A colourful plant-sucking bug, *Graphosoma italicum* is a member of the family Pentatomidae. This family includes a number of species that are crop pests in countries with warm climates

mococcus vermilio, which is native to the whole of the Mediterranean basin, was once used in medicine and in the dyeing trade; at present it is used as the source of a substance employed in the preparation of a well-known liqueur, alkermes.

Insects in procession

Some of the Lepidoptera are bitter enemies of man, who will fight them with every available weapon. One of these is the pine processionary moth *Thaumetopoea pityocampa*; another is the oak processionary *Thaumetopoea processionea*. The first of these infests pine trees and its caterpillars build conical nests for themselves, from which they come out to feed on the leaves of the pine tree. This species may defoliate whole plantations of pines. The oak processionary attacks both the common oak and Turkey oak trees, laying its eggs in groups of a hundred or two on the trunk and branches. The caterpillars devour the

Below: A Cotton Stainer (Dysdercus species), a tropical Hemipteran belonging to the family Pyrrhocoridae that causes severe damage to cotton crops

leaves and buds, stripping entire woods of their leaves and spoiling the acorns, arresting the growth of the trees and sometimes killing them outright.

Thaumetopoea caterpillars live as a large group inside their spacious nests and travel as a body in search of food, especially during the hours of darkness. The epithet 'processionary' is applied to these moths because of the caterpillars' curious habit of moving in procession. They may form a column 2 metres (6.56 feet) in length, with the foremost member acting as guide while the remainder follow in one or more files. Many entomologists have tried to explain this pattern of behaviour. Some have suggested that it is produced by stimulation provided by the rear bristles of one caterpillar to the head of the one behind, and vice versa. This is not a completely adequate explanation, however, since if the leading caterpillar is removed, his place is immediately taken by the one behind and the procession will continue. It is possible

that the silk threads secreted by individuals on the march help to maintain the cohesion of the procession.

The damage they do to vegetation is not the only reason for the hostility with which the processionary moths are regarded, however. More important still are the unpleasant effects of coming into contact with these insects in person. The caterpillars are covered in highly irritant bristles, which give rise to intense itching when brought into contact with skin. If they come into contact with the eyes, or reach the respiratory tract, or are swallowed, they can cause severe inflammation and even death to both men and animals. Furthermore, it is not only the caterpillars that possess this feature: the discarded skins that they leave in the nest also have hairs that retain their irritant, blistering properties for a long time.

Over the years, man has devised many different ways of attacking the Thaumetopoeids. Almost invariably these have been

Larva and adult of the antlion (*Myrmelon formicarius*). The drawing shows the ingenious ant-trap that the larva makes in the sand

Left: Two adults of
Chrysopa (lacewings)

inadequate, and in any case enormously expensive. The only way to put a partial curb on the development of the moths would be to collect all their nests and to destroy them. Fortunately, as we shall see, various insects live on the eggs, caterpillars and adults of processionary moths, and these predators alone are capable of containing this harmful and dangerous pest within reasonable bounds.

Among the medium-sized Hemiptera that harm both man and his crops are those bugs that suck the sap from plants with their pointed rostrum or beak. Some, like the species that lives on cotton plants, can destroy an entire harvest by inflicting irreparable damage on the flowers. The bed-bug, which used to be an unwelcome but very common inhabitant of human settlements, has now become much rarer as a result of greater hygiene. It can only multiply to a serious extent if conditions once more become favourable to it; luckily it is only a blood-sucker and is not known to carry human diseases.

In fact, there are a great many insects that interfere with man's health or his activities—far more than can be described here—and man himself cannot do much to curb them. This is left to other insects, which take up the role of faithful, and essential, allies. A very brief list of the most important ones will be given, passing rapidly through the various insect orders. The title of this chapter takes on added meaning when one reflects on the absurdity

of man's indiscriminate use of insecticides, ridding himself for a short while of particular parasites (or cutting down their numbers) at the cost of destroying other, useful creatures at the same time, and introducing insecticides into the food chain, possibly with serious and as yet unseen consequences.

Above: The eggs of Chrysopa are attached to a plant stem by long stalks. The larvae of lacewings are natural enemies of aphids

Winged and sedentary predators

The order Mantoidea includes a species that is common in southern Europe, the Praying Mantis (*Mantis religiosa*), whose name is ill suited to its predatory habits for it is in fact a real scourge of the insect world. The Praying Mantis is a green or brown insect with a long body and a small triangular head with prominent eyes. Its two hind pairs of legs are used for walking, while the front legs serve for catching prey. They are described as raptorial limbs, since the tibia and femur are armed with spines and articulate with one another like the blade of a penknife, thus effectively blocking the escape of the victim, which is instantly torn to pieces by the mandibles. These insects have such a strong carnivorous instinct that occasionally, for instance when food is scarce, they may show cannibalistic behaviour, the stronger larvae eating the weaker ones and even the females regularly devouring the males during mating. Another characteristic feature of the mantis is the oötheca, a spongy case that may contain hundreds of eggs.

The most aggressive insect-eating insects, without a shadow of doubt, are those of the order Odonata, and among these the prize must go to their champion performers, the dragonflies. Everyone knows these insects, with their long, thin bodies. Their heads have enormous eyes, capable not only of looking in all directions but of distinguishing shapes up to 5 or 6 metres (about 16 or 19 feet) away, and movement up to 15 or 20 metres (50 or 65 feet). They have extremely short antennae, while their mouth parts are characterized by the tough-toothed mandibles which give the order its name—Odonata meaning 'toothed'.

The wings of these insects are those of excellent, fast flyers. They are long and rather narrow, and are kept firm by a number of principal veins and a dense network of secondary veins. The legs are normally not used for walking, but only for clinging while the insect is at rest and for capturing prey in flight. Adult dragonflies spend all their time hunting, inflicting slaughter on smaller insects, particularly mosquitoes and gnats. They catch them with their legs, then crush them and chew them up with their tough jaws.

The larvae are no less useful than their parents. They are equipped with legs, large eyes and very powerful jaws. They live under water, and can often be found in large numbers in ditches, canals and streams, but they prefer the calm waters of ponds and marshes. They are dull in colour, and live half-submerged in the mud or hidden among water-plants, lying in wait for the insect larvae that make up their prey.

The organ they use for taking their prey is an unusual one, known as a mask. Actually an altered and extended labrum or lower lip, this raptorial organ at rest is folded up against the underside of the head. As the larva lies in wait, it seizes a suitable moment to shoot out its mask in the direction of its victim. The mask carries a sharp, pincer-like structure at its tip and acts just like an arm bearing a claw. As it folds back towards the head after seizing the prey, it brings the victim within reach of the mandibles; the larva can then settle down to its meal.

The order Hemiptera includes a great many species that do harm to man and his crops. Reference has already been made to the bugs that damage harvests and to the bed-bug as well as the scale-insects and the aphids. Fortunately, though, the order also contains insects that perform a useful function in preying on other insects and keeping their numbers down.

Important predators among aquatic Hemiptera are the water-scorpions, such as the Nepa, and the back-swimmers, for example, Notonecta. Water-scorpions, like Praying Mantises, are armed with raptorial front legs for catching hold of any suitable prey that comes within range. Among the terrestrial Hemiptera is the 'masked hunter' (*Reduvius personatus*), an inhabitant of old houses which gets its name from the habit of covering its head with dust, thus becoming practically invisible. All reduviids are predacious, feeding on other insects by piercing them with their sharp snouts and sucking out their juices. The masked hunter may unfortunately also attack humans, and when it does so it invariably causes small but extremely painful bites.

Allies of man

The order Neuroptera consists of insects that may reach a considerable size. They are generally active at dusk or at night and have two pairs of membraneous wings, approximately equal in size and covered with a dense network of veins. At rest, the wings are generally held over the abdomen.

Neuroptera is divided into two sub-orders, Megaloptera and Planipennia, which are now regarded as separate orders. This latter group includes some species that do man a service by ruthlessly preying on a large number of crop-damaging insect species. Adult Neuroptera have chewing mouth parts, with tough, well-developed jaws. Two types of mouth parts are found in the larvae: the chewing type, similar to that of the adult, and the piercing and sucking type, shaped like a pair of surgical forceps. The blades of the forceps are made up of the mandibles that are traversed by a hollow channel which is used to suck out the body fluids of the victim.

Below: A lacewing larva. These larvae often camouflage themselves with the remains of their past victims

Some typical Neuroptera are the antlion, the beautiful lacewing, and the strange owlfly. Only the lacewing is found in Britain. The common European antlion is best known for the ingenious traps that the larvae set in soft, sandy or dusty terrains. Where the ground is soft enough, the larva begins to move backwards and trace out a circular ditch. Starting on the inside of this ditch, it moves in an ever-decreasing spiral, throwing sand out of the ditch with rapid movements of its head. In this way, it can quickly construct a perfect conical-shaped trap, at the bottom of which it lies in wait for its prey. Only its head and its powerful, wide-open jaws can be seen above the surface of the sand. If an insect, a spider or some other small creature

Below: Winged forms of aphids among a mass of young nymphs

is unfortunate enough to fall into the pit, it tries in vain to climb up the side and reach safety. Continuously showered with falling sand, and sliding helplessly about on the shifting sand under its feet, it slips ever further from safety and closer to the terrible, gaping jaws below which are ready to snap shut savagely on their victim. Once the victim has been carefully sucked dry, the husk is thrown out of the trap so that it is not clogged up with debris. The predator gets its name of antlion from the fact that it feeds mainly on ants; but it will tackle much bigger prey too, such as large spiders and insects. These larger creatures will put up more of a fight, but it is always the antlion that wins.

Lacewings of the species Chrysopa are common, beautiful Neuroptera. Typical features are their transparent wings and their iridescent green bodies. These delicate insects are frequently seen indoors, attracted either by the light, or else in autumn searching for a place to hibernate. With their frail, elegant, slender appearance, no one would imagine them to be the savage hunters they really are, both in the larval stage and as adults. Their preferred prey are aphids or plant-lice, insects which may look innocuous but are actually a serious pest that cause immense damage to cultivated plants, both directly and indirectly.

Aphids belong to the order Hemiptera and the suborder Homoptera, since both pairs of wings are of similar composition, unlike the other suborder, Heteroptera.

Above left: Aphids cover herbaceous plant stems in their hundreds to suck out the sap
Left: The sugary secretion produced by aphids is highly prized by ants, which establish a symbiotic relationship with aphids in order to ensure a supply of the liquid

Aphids have the piercing and sucking type of mouth parts in the form of a tough snout. Their bodies are always small, and a characteristic feature is the pair of so-called cornicles on the abdomen. These tubular structures excrete a waxy liquid which can be projected in the direction of an attacker so as to clog its mouth parts; they form, in effect, a wax gun and a very effective defensive weapon.

Aphids feed on the sap of the plant on which they live, and in order to get it they plunge their snouts into the plant tissue. When you see a rose-twig completely covered by hundreds or thousands of aphids, it would be wrong to imagine that they are simply sitting idly at rest. They are literally stabbing the plant to death, sucking out its vital fluids without which it cannot live; what is more, their beaks are constantly making new wounds on the plant's surface. Although these wounds may be very small, they provide a way in for microscopic bacteria and fungi which can cause the plant grave harm. Aphids are in fact among some of the most important carriers of viruses causing severe diseases in plants.

Aphids may be detested by humans, who will seek to destroy them by every means possible, but they are loved and cherished by ants, which thereby do the farmer an ill service. Ants are extremely fond of the aphids' sugary excretion known as honeydew, and in order to get it they lovingly look after them, even carrying them from one plant to another when the first is sucked dry. This habit increases the damage done by aphids, for as they are continually stimulated by the ants to secrete more honeydew, they consume far more sap than they really need. Such overfeeding also speeds up their development and their reproductive rate—a very serious matter, for even in normal circumstances they have an astonishingly high reproductive rate, partly caused by the large number of descendants an individual insect produces and partly by the very short generation time. If every aphid managed to reproduce itself, and if every egg produced a new individual, the aphids' destructive potential would make that of the locusts seem nothing but an unimportant trifle in comparison. Fortunately, the thousands of species of aphids are kept down not only by man's puny efforts, but by a large number of natural enemies, including ladybird

Left: The remains of this aphid colony show cast skins and dark, hard, parasitized ones each containing a parasitic wasp larva

Right: A Cicindela larva hidden in its burrow, and a female Methoca, its natural enemy, which has just detected its presence and will paralyse it with its sting before laying an egg on it

beetles, syrphids, Hymenoptera and birds, as well as the lacewing larvae and adults.

The female lacewing lays her eggs in large numbers on aphid-infested plants, so that as soon as the larvae hatch out they can find food in plenty. Lacewing eggs can be easily found in the fields or in most gardens. They have an unusual and very characteristic appearance, each egg being borne on a long, thin stalk. For a long time, it was not realized that these strange objects were eggs at all: they were thought to be fungi, even being given a proper scientific name. The larva that hatches out of this strange egg immediately starts hunting for aphids, which it captures with its powerful jaws and sucks dry. These larvae have the characteristic habit of covering their bodies with all kinds of matter—bits of moss and bark, grains of sand, and often the empty shells of their victims. Although its victims are mostly aphids, the lacewing will also eat other insects which makes it an invaluable ally of man in his battle with insect pests.

The owlflies are the most beautiful of all Neuroptera, and on account of their colouring and certain body details they are often mistaken at first glance for butterflies.

Their larvae, like those of the antlion, live in the earth, among mosses and plant debris, under stones, or less often under tree bark or on leaves. Some, like lacewing larvae, cover their upper surfaces with debris. They live on other insects, and when hungry will sometimes attack each other.

Among the Lepidoptera, there are few species that can be regarded as man's friends. Very many inflict severe damage on crops and on various types of stores. Many other species live on plants that are of no use to humans, so that their presence passes unnoticed. Man has a few allies among the butterflies and these include some species of Lycaenidae (Hairstreak and Blue butterflies) which are small, often light or dark blue in colour and are found in flowery meadows. The chrysalids of some species, instead of being plant-eaters like most of their brethren, are carnivores, feeding on aphids and scale-insects.

Useful species of Diptera

Among the Diptera, too, there are many species that are agricultural pests or parasites. Some species, however, help man to control insect pests. The Asilidae or robber flies are a family of Diptera that behave as predators. They will attack any insect, even those larger than themselves, and first paralyse it before drinking its body fluids. The larvae may also be carnivorous, though they normally live on rotting vegetable matter.

The Bombyliidae or bee-flies hide their predatory habits under an elegant exterior. Bombylius has a body covered with long, thick fur. It flies very quickly, darting from one spot to another and often hovering motionless in the air. The eggs are laid in flight, the female flying lower and lower till the tip of her abdomen just touches the spot she has chosen. Bombyliid larvae live on the eggs and larvae of various other insects. Some of their common victims are, fortunately, the pine processionaries. Unfortunately, however, the bee-flies have

Above: The bee-fly is an ally of man, the larvae being parasitic upon processionary caterpillars, which they also kill

their own redoubtable enemies, and the worst of these are spiders, which slaughter them in large numbers.

A family of flies of great economic importance are the Syrphidae, which as adults visit flowers and play an important part in cross-pollination. In addition, many of their larvae are predacious on other insects, particularly aphids, and perform a useful service in this way.

Aphid-eating syrphid larvae are brightly coloured, green or yellow, and they move over infested twigs rather like leeches. They do not usually have far to go to find the aphids, since the mother syrphid will have taken care to lay her eggs close to an aphid colony. The nursery is thus next door to the larder. The larva approaches a victim and stabs it, with lightning speed, with its mouth parts. The aphid is then lifted up, and the larva withdraws its head into the upper part of its body, forming a sort of sack in which the helpless victim is imprisoned and sucked dry by the syrphid larva. As soon as it has finished, it attacks another victim, which meets the same fate. The mass slaughter thus inflicted on aphid colonies does something towards keeping their numbers within reasonable bounds.

Another family of Diptera that are of some importance in the context of this chapter is that of the Conopidae or thick-headed flies. These bear a resemblance to certain Hymenoptera. The adults visit flowers and help in cross-pollination, while the larvae are endoparasites of other insects, particularly Hymenoptera and Orthoptera, inhabiting the bodies of these insects and feeding on them.

The Tachinidae are another family that performs a service for man, since a great many tachinid larvae are endoparasites of other insects and destroy vast numbers of them. The flies of the genus Phryxe are among the most active enemies of the pine processionary moth. They lay their eggs on the processionary caterpillars, and the larvae that hatch from these eggs kill the caterpillars at metamorphosis.

Beneficial beetles

The Coleoptera (beetles) include approximately 300,000 species and are found throughout the world. A good many of these are harmful to mankind, but some others—not many—are useful.

The family Cicindelidae or tiger beetles, for example, are predacious, and will attack even fast-moving and toughly built insects. They are found on beaches, country tracks, or the dry beds of mountain streams. Here the larvae, which are also predacious, dig deep vertical tunnels in the ground and sit at the entrance, which they block, cork-like, with their heads. As soon as some unwary insect passes within range of their trap-like jaws, they seize it and will drag it into the burrow. The remains are then

Below: A fly of the family Tachinidae, the larvae of which are parasitic on processionary caterpillars. These flies are so useful that they are bred expressly for this purpose

thrown far away from the burrow with a sharp jerk of the head.

The family Carabidae or ground beetles include some of the most beautiful beetles, with handsome shapes and fine colouring. Some are predacious on lepidopterous larvae, and thus perform a useful service to man. One example is the genus Calosoma, often known as caterpillar-hunters. The adults of this species frequent tree-trunks in search of the caterpillars, chrysalids and adults of other insect species, showing a marked preference for the various stages of the processionary moth. They destroy large numbers of these insects, proving themselves to be true friends of man.

No less useful are the Staphylinidae or rove beetles, which again perform a useful service, of some economic importance, by destroying large numbers of other insects. Ladybird beetles, too, deserve our gratitude for the large numbers of aphids and scale-insects that they destroy. Some species of ladybirds, such as *Rodolia cardinalis*, have even been expressly imported from their homelands to control particularly harmful scale-insects.

Two other highly beneficial families, the Dytiscidae (predacious diving beetles) and the Hydrophilidae (water scavenger beetles) should also be mentioned. Dytiscids, both larvae and adults, move rapidly in the water and are indefatigable predators. They will attack any water creature that is not too big for them. They are especially fond of insects, and kill large numbers of them; but they will also take crustaceans, small frogs and young fish fry. When it captures a victim, the diving beetle larva immediately injects it with a paralysing secretion to immobilize it and also with an enzyme-rich liquid that breaks down the constituents of the body and reduces it to predigested pulp. At this point the meal is ready, and a few minutes later nothing is left of the victim save an empty husk.

The usefulness of the diving beetle as a predator on other insects is obvious, considering the vast numbers of larvae and pupae of mosquitoes and other blood-sucking Diptera destroyed by it. The damage that the beetle does in attacking young fish, for instance, is a small price to pay for this useful service. Equally useful, and in much the same way, is the water scavenger beetle, the giant among water beetles. Only the larvae of this family are carnivorous; the adults live mainly on plants.

Allies among the Hymenoptera

Another group that must not be forgotten in this respect is the Hymenoptera Parasitica whose females, armed with a long ovipositor, lay their eggs within the bodies of larvae or chrysalids of other insect species. As the larvae develop, they consume the body of their hosts from within.

Right: Bembix wasps (top and bottom) camouflage the entrances to their burrows with soil and twigs. These wasps prey on various flies which they take to their burrows for their larvae to feed on. Their prey include flies that attack enemies of the processionary caterpillars, and as a result they may be regarded as beneficial insects

By the time their unique food-store is used up, they have completed their development. The largest European species include *Rhyssa persuasoria*, which may reach 4 centimetres (1.57 inches) in length. This species parasitizes the wood-eating larvae of the Siricidae or horntails. In order to lay her eggs within such larvae, the female may have to penetrate wood up to 6 centimetres (2.36 inches) thick.

Another equally well-known European species is *Pimpla instigator*, a parasite of many lepidopterous larvae that do great damage to forests, such as the genera Limantria and Bombyx. Pimpla is not the only ichneumon that is useful to man. Most of the other members of the family Ichneumonidae are in fact parasitic on insect pests, as are many other related families. Another example from the family Platygasteridae, *Platygaster herrickii*, parasitizes the eggs of the hessian fly, *Phytophaga destructor*, which has caused incalculable damage to wheat in North America. Biological control of the hessian fly by Platygaster is in every way preferable to the use of insecticides.

The Hymenoptera Aculeata contains many species that are natural antagonists of insect pests, among them members of the genus Bembix, family Sphecidae. These nest in the ground, and when they

Above: The ichneumon fly (*Rhyssa persuasoria*) can penetrate a thick layer of wood with its ovipositor in order to reach the larvae of wood-wasps in whose bodies it lays eggs

have captured their prey, they paralyse it and fly with it to their nest where they feed it to their larvae which are kept in unsealed cells and fed daily. Their prey consists of dipterous flies, many being of the family Tachinidae—species of which parasitize other insects including the larvae of processionary moths.

The biological struggle

Ever since the dawn of agriculture, when man first scattered some of his store of seeds over the soil instead of eating them, hoping to reproduce the parent stock, he has been aware that his crops depended not only on physical and climatic considerations, such as rain, wind and temperature, but also on biological factors—the presence of other plants and of animals. Such factors fell into one of two categories: beneficial ones which had to be encouraged, and harmful ones to be avoided or destroyed.

Although this simplistic view originally provided a valuable impetus to the development of agricultural skills, and therefore of civilization, it has by now lost much of its validity. Indeed, it underlies many of the great stresses and strains of our complex technological civilization, threatening the very survival of man and his environment. The issue is long and complicated but is also of extreme and universal relevance, for there are certain problems, such as the conservation of the environment or the conditions of human life, which must be tackled without further delay.

Until quite recently—about a century ago—while it was true that man's agricultural activities had transformed the environment in many parts of the earth, this transformation had not noticeably altered

Left: *Graphosoma italicum* is a common shield-bug which causes crop damage. Most shield-bugs feed mainly on plants, but some are carnivorous and are of interest to research workers, who prefer to use natural enemies rather than insecticides against plant pests

the general biological equilibrium. It is a well-known fact that in any natural environment no living organism is actually independent of the others. The survival and development of all populations and all species, both fauna and flora, depend directly or indirectly on all the other forms of life in the area; and all are in harmony with their physical and geographical environment. Thus, a prairie contains a number of species of grasses which coexist, each having its own requirements in the way of light, water and soil; and between them they support a certain number of species of herbivorous animals. These, in their turn, live on the grasses, each in its own way; and thus they harmoniously regulate the growth of the prairie grasses, taking part in a system of mutual control. The herbivores in their turn support a number of species of carnivorous predators, which eliminate the superfluous members of the herbivore population, mainly of course the weaker members, and thus control their multiplication. The chain of interdependence—enormously complex in real life—ends with those organisms, mainly fungi and bacteria, that break down all the organic residues, fallen dead plants, animal carcasses, and excrement, and put essential growth factors back into the earth for the plants.

This harmonious equilibrium of interdependent living organisms gives a certain stability to all natural systems. Up to a point, man also fitted into this system,

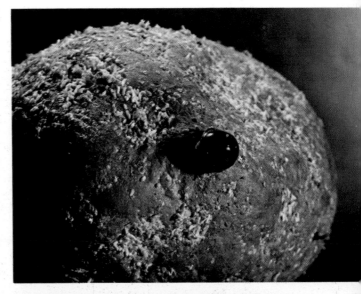

The photographs on these two pages show
some of the protagonists in the biological
control campaign
Far left: Two species of ladybird beetle
Left from top: Eggs, larva and pupa of a
ladybird
Top: A ladybird, bred to combat the
mulberry scale, is reared by being fed on
scale-insects (the whitish parts) which
in their turn are feeding on a potato
Above: The larva of a particular species
of ladybird which bears a strong
resemblance, in appearance and colouring, to
the scale-insects on which it lives

which is capable of accommodating considerable changes. Thus, as long as he confined his agricultural activities to encouraging cereals rather than other grasses, say, or fruit trees rather than other types of tree, the changes that he wrought did not lead to any great ecological imbalance.

But the introduction of intensive farming methods, with the consequent need for more radical exploitation of the earth's resources, coupled with the rise in the human population and its increased demand for food, have crystallized the problem of controlling the natural enemies of the farmer's crops—that is, those organisms, mainly insects, which in one way or another interfere with agricultural productivity. There are vast numbers of such enemies, and there is practically no fruit, cereal or vegetable that is safe, in normal circumstances, from attack by a whole host of insect species. Some attack the leaves, others the wood, others the fruits or the seeds, others the roots, and together they cut production down to a fraction of what it might have been.

It is worth stressing, moreover, that it is precisely the practice of intensive farming (an essential method in today's world) that favours the multiplication of harmful species. Obviously, a species that lives on a particular plant will be able to multiply at a tremendous rate when it is presented with a copious supply of food; and if the food in question is a crop of agricultural importance undergoing intensive cultivation, then the insect has all the requirements for its 'population explosion'.

With the rise of modern technology, agricultural pest control has been approached in a radical manner, initially almost exclusively by chemical means. This involves the synthesis of compounds, some more potent than others, but all toxic, aimed at controlling and if possible destroying the pest populations, particularly insect pests.

The intention has been to prepare compounds that act selectively against one or a limited number of species, without endangering other creatures, but it has become increasingly apparent that the use of insecticides in agriculture is fraught with great dangers. First of all, many substances hitherto considered harmless to man have turned out to be dangerous, mainly because their massive use over a number of years has led to their accumulation in our environment and foods in dangerous concentrations. Secondly, and more disturbingly in the long term, they have caused (and continue to cause) alterations in the biological equilibrium of such magnitude that they will be extremely difficult to correct.

Up until a few years ago, for example, Italy's rice-growing regions were infested with mosquitoes. To get rid of them, insecticides were used on a massive scale. They initially succeeded in drastically reducing the mosquito population, but at the same time destroyed vast numbers of other aquatic invertebrates. This led to a fall in the animal population and almost to the disappearance of animals such as frogs and certain fish species which lived on water insects. Not only were they now short of food, but they were also progressively poisoned by the insecticides that had been regarded as 'harmless to higher animals'. Once the frogs and the fish disappeared, so did the herons and other water-fowl, as a more or less direct consequence.

At the present time, the commonest bird species in the Italian ricefields is the rook, a very hardy, omnivorous bird. No longer hampered in its expansion by other 'competing' species, it invades the ricefields in swarms at sowing-time and devours the seed as soon as it is sown. At the same time, new strains of mosquitoes have appeared, ever more resistant to insecticides even in huge doses; and so the original problem is

Right: Near Antibes in France, parasitic and other useful insects are bred for use in biological control. To produce large numbers of parasitic insects for release, they must be bred on pest species that are artificially reared on specially maintained crops

back once again. This brief outline is only one of a great many examples that could be quoted, in which chemical warfare against insects has led in the long run to undesirable and harmful effects that are then difficult to correct.

Manipulating nature

Such considerations have resulted, particularly in the postwar period, in an increasing awareness among scientists of the need to find new means of control aimed at limiting as far as possible the expansion of insect pest species without doing any further harm to the overall ecological balance. The most increasingly favoured approach today is that of biological control, though it is beset with con-

siderable difficulties, not all of them scientific in nature.

What, then, is meant by biological control? It is a term that implies the use of living creatures to eliminate harmful animal species, or at least to reduce drastically the damage they do both to man and his products. It involves altering an existing biological equilibrium in a natural environment (or more often, in this context, an environment that has already been more or less radically upset by man's farming activities) in such a way as to discourage an unwanted species. The strategy is based on the general observation that there are few species, and particularly few insect species, that are not attacked by other insect predators or parasites at some stage of their life cycle—egg, larva, pupa or adult. This

may not be a natural law, but it is very generally true; and any strategy of biological control therefore depends on an accurate study of the life cycle of the insect in question, and then a search for its insect enemies. In practice, however, as will be shown, it is not strictly necessary to adopt this approach; in some cases, biological control of insect pests is possible using other methods.

The aim of biological control (in contrast to the unattainable aim of chemical control) is not the total extermination of even the most harmful species, for it is now accepted by scientists that the complete elimination of a species is likely to result in a state of imbalance, the consequences of which cannot yet be foreseen although they are almost certain to prove very grave. The aim, therefore, is the reduction of a species to a level where the damage it can do is minimal and economically acceptable.

Once the natural enemies of the insect in question have been identified, the project will pass to the laboratory phase. The life cycle and the ecological requirements of the natural enemies are then studied, so that they can be reared in large numbers and as cheaply as possible. When this has been achieved, the battle is almost over. Large quantities of these laboratory-reared insects are taken into the field, to a site where crops are known to be infested. Some of the results obtained by this technique are highly encouraging. The following are just a few examples of biological control which will clearly show its potential for the future.

Fighting harmful species

Aphids, small insects belonging to the order Hemiptera, are therefore related to the bugs and the cicadas. They feed exclusively on plant sap, and are commonly known as plant-lice. They are often seen, particularly in springtime, sitting motionless in enormous numbers on the tender young shoots of all kinds of plants,

Left: Beneficial and harmful insects that are reared in the laboratory are bred from specimens caught in the wild
Below: Captured specimens are sorted into species and according to sex before being taken to the laboratory

and close inspection with a magnifying glass will disclose their beak-like mouth parts plunged deeply into the plant tissues. Through this beak they suck the descending plant sap, rich in sugars and in nitrogenous compounds synthesized by the leaves of the plant.

The damage they do is caused not only by the withdrawal of large amounts of essential substances from the plant—since a single plant is usually parasitized by large numbers of aphids—but also by the fact that they inject a salivary secretion into the plant tissues, which in some species may cause rapid degeneration. This results first in local necrosis (death of surrounding cells) and then the formation of reactive tissue, which is more or less deformed and functions poorly. Another important way in which aphids do harm, in common with all sap-sucking insects, is by spreading a variety of virus infections from plant to plant. The aphid sucks up the virus in the sap of an infected plant and then transmits it to healthy plants when it moves to them for food.

Many aphid species live on plants cultivated by man, and it is therefore desirable that they should be controlled. Fortunately they have many natural enemies, including the syrphids—dipterous flies rather like the house fly, brightly striped in black and yellow across their bodies—which are commonly seen in summer, especially in the heat of the day. The larvae of many species of syrphids are flat, brightly coloured, and very agile, although they have no legs. They live on aphids, impaling them with their stiletto-like mouth parts and sucking out their juices. A German entomologist has reported that a single larva of *Metasyrphus corollae* (one of the commonest European species) can devour more than 400 bean aphids (*Aphis fabae*) in the course of its development, lasting about ten days. In spite of this, the attempt to use syrphid flies for biological control of aphids has not been successful for the moment, due to certain peculiarities in the life cycle of these flies.

A more fruitful approach has been the use of ladybird beetles to control both

aphids and some species of scale-insects; these are related to aphids, are similarly equipped with sucking mouth parts and also feed on sap. Everyone is familiar with the ladybird, a small, oval-shaped beetle, with a convex and often shiny body, generally bright red with black spots on the back. It is not commonly known, however, that most of the more than 3,000 known species of ladybird live mainly on aphids and scale-insects, both as larvae and as adults. This fact, allied to the ease with which ladybirds can be reared in the laboratory, has enabled some French scientists to achieve brilliant success in the control of scale-insects in North Africa, where they constitute a serious threat to the date-palm plantations that are one of the region's chief agricultural resources.

Despite this, problems may sometimes be encountered in breeding insects for widespread use in biological control campaigns. For instance, during a study of the use of certain species which feed on the mulberry scale-insect in their natural environment, these species turned out

Above: Jumping Ceratitis larvae. These are bred as food for the larvae of *Opius concolor,* a beneficial hymenopteran which lays its eggs within the larvae of the olive fruit fly *Dacus oleae,* preventing their development and limiting the damage they can do to olive crops
Above left: A syrphid larva. These larvae feed on aphids and are thus one of man's allies in biological control

initially to be rather hard to rear because it was impractical to breed their preferred prey, the mulberry scale, in captivity on mulberry trees in sufficient numbers to feed them. The possibility of using a substitute food was therefore investigated: some other species of plant, one that it would also be prepared to eat if mulberry were not available. The best substitute food turned out to be the potato, on which it was possible to breed large numbers of mulberry scales, and thus, in turn, to breed the ladybirds that fed on them.

The pine processionary moth (*Thaumetopoea pityocampa*) is a medium-sized moth whose larvae live on pine trees and feed on the pine-needles. All the members of a brood live together in a single silken nest, about the size of a large apple, and at dusk they leave it and move in single file, as though in procession, making for the branches on which they will feed. A heavy infestation by this species can wreak havoc with a pine forest, and successful attempts have been made to control it by introducing ants of the species *Formica rufa* into infested areas. Worker ants of this species are avid hunters of processionary caterpillars and will pursue them into the topmost branches of the trees.

Although rearing these insects is a complicated and difficult task, the problem can be solved. It is quite an easy matter to take one of their large nests, which may be as big as a barrel, and to transport it from the ants' home territory, with a few elementary precautions, to wherever it is needed. The ants stand up well to quite long journeys in the back of a lorry, but it is necessary to ensure that the container, normally made out of metal, is well sealed.

Parasites and their parasites

So far, consideration has been given to those insect species that control other species regarded as pests by feeding on them either only in the larval stage, as the syrphids do, or in all phases of the life cycle, as the ladybird does, or only in adult life, as is the case with ants. In every case, however, these are predacious insects, hunting their prey in order to feed on them directly. But there are other species, of far greater importance in biological control, which spend the larval stage of their development as parasites of other insects, often agricultural pests. The vast majority of these parasites are Hymenoptera.

A particularly interesting example is that of *Opius concolor*, a member of the hymenopterous family Braconidae. These insects are small, the adults being barely 1 millimetre (0.03 inches) long. Originally from northern Africa, they look at first glance like extremely small wasps. The female of the species has a slender but tough ovipositor and through it she can inject her eggs into the creature within which the larvae will then develop as endoparasites. Her choice of host is the larva of a dipterous fly, the notorious olive fruit fly (*Dacus oleae*) which lives in the pulp of the olive fruit, irreparably damaging it and often threatening the entire year's harvest. In some years the loss caused by these flies throughout the Mediterranean basin has been calculated at more than 800,000 tonnes (785,000 tons) of olives.

European biological control programmes therefore had great hopes of the introduction of *Opius concolor* into Europe. The scientists came up against a difficulty, however. Winter conditions, in the south of France in particular, did not permit this insect to complete the whole of its annual life cycle there. A substitute host was therefore sought to enable the parasite to be raised easily and cheaply in the laboratory and to be available in large numbers at just the right time to be released in the olive plantations.

Such a substitute host was in fact found—the larva of another dipterous fly, the Mediterranean fruit fly (*Ceratitis capitata*). This fly can be raised in captivity and is fed on a carrot-based gruel. The adult female flies, however, would not lay their eggs on this artificial food, and

374

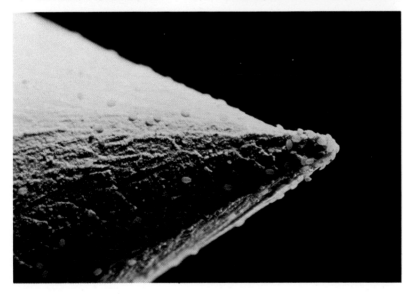

Top: These watermelons
are being used to breed
the fruit pest known
as the San José scale
(Quadraspidiotus
perniciosus)
Above left and left:
Attracted by the light,
the larvae gather at
the tip of the clay
cone that has been
stuck on to the fruit.
They are taken from
here to serve as food
for *Prospaltella*
perniciosi, their
natural enemy. This
process enables large-
scale breeding of
Prospaltella to be
carried on, and the
insects are then sent
to areas where crops are
infested with the San
José scale

various tricks had to be devised to persuade them to lay on special pieces of equipment from which the eggs could then be collected. These were then 'seeded' into the gruel, where they quickly developed and hatched. One last problem still remained, however: finding some way to persuade the female Opius, whose instincts tell her to pierce her ovipositor through the pulp of the olive fruit in search of Dacus larvae, to inoculate her eggs into Ceratitis larvae instead, as they wriggle about in the carrot gruel. The inventiveness of the entomologists was equal to the task. At this stage, the Ceratitis cultures are covered with a thin layer of plastic, similar in appearance and consistency to the pulp of an olive, and Opius was duly taken in. Before long, the cultures gave rise to a swarm of Opius, ready to be released in the olive-groves where their preferred hosts, *Dacus oleae,* could be found.

Below: Incubators in which Prospaltella are reared on an industrial scale. Each incubator has a batch number and the doors carry circular apertures to which tubes can be fitted. The adult Prospaltella are attracted into these tubes which can then be removed and capped and the parasites transported to infested crops

The San José scale

The scientific name *Quadraspidiotus perniciosus* is given to a scale-insect which does a great deal of damage to many types of fruit tree and which is commonly known as the San José scale. In its natural environment, its numbers are controlled by a hymenopterous insect belonging to the family Chalcididae and known as *Prospaltella perniciosi*. This looks like a tiny wasp, less than 1 millimetre (0.03 inches) long. The female uses her ovipositor to place her eggs within the bodies of scale-insects, which are sluggish in their youth and move about scarcely at all once they become adults. The eggs hatch out into small whitish grubs which lack legs but have enormous appetites. The grubs feed on the internal organs of their host, without doing them much harm initially; but when the Prospaltella larva is ready to transform into an adult it will attack its host's vital organs and kill it.

Prospaltella has been successfully introduced into territories that were previously foreign to it and in which the San José scale was found; the results have been very satisfactory, since Prospaltella is easy to breed. The first step is to fit out the nurseries for the scale insects which are reared on near-ripe watermelons. The surface of a watermelon is enormous in relation to the size of the insect, and a few fruits will be sufficient to breed large stocks of scales. New fruits are 'seeded' with young scales at a stage when the insects are still relatively mobile. In order to transfer some of the stock to a new watermelon, all that is needed is a well-colonized fruit to which a conical cap of clay or some other material is fitted at one end and then brightly illuminated. Like many other insects, young scales are attracted to light, and when they reach the tip of the cap they lose their footing and fall off. They can thus be collected almost automatically in special containers, from which they will then be transferred to a fresh watermelon.

This explains why it is not difficult to raise Prospaltella in captivity on its natural host. It is also very easy to transfer Prospaltella larvae to the orchard or market garden where they are needed. It simply involves hanging a watermelon covered with parasitized San José scales on a branch of a fruit tree. In just a few days the Prospaltella adults will emerge and then set about laying their eggs on the scales that are infesting the surrounding plants.

A tiny insect, less than 1 millimetre (0.03 inches) long and belonging to the Hymenoptera, the chalcid *Aphelinus asychis* is, in its larval stage, a parasite of certain aphid species that do particular harm to plants such as tomatoes and aubergines, in which the fruit is relatively large compared to the plant that bears it. A heavily infested crop produces little fruit, and what there is will be so small and withered that it is often unsaleable. The chalcid in question has also proved quite easy to breed, and although its use in aphid control is still experimental, the results have been so good that it merits a large-scale trial.

The use of bacteria and viruses

Not all research in the field of biological control involves the use of insects. There have also been many studies of the use of disease-causing microbes—bacteria and viruses—which have the advantage of being selective in their action. For instance, a bacterium called *Bacillus thuringensis* produces a toxin that is very effective against lepidopterous larvae (caterpillars) in general, without being in the least harmful to vertebrates or other insects (which would have made its use highly dangerous, in view of the ecological imbalance it might have caused). Not even the larvae of hymenopterous parasites, that might be present in the bodies of infected caterpillars, suffer the slightest harm from the bacterium infecting their host. These factors have led to the preparation and marketing of cultures of *B. thuringensis*, which protects many types of cultivated plants, especially garden produce.

As for viruses, perhaps the most famous relevant example is that of myxomatosis. This fatal disease, confined to rabbits, was artificially spread in Australia in order to achieve a drastic reduction in the rabbit population. The rabbit is not native to Australia but was introduced by settlers from Europe. Having no serious competitors for its food supply, and above all no natural predators such as regulate its numbers in Europe, the rabbit species multiplied to an incredible extent and endangered crops as well as native vegetation, threatening to turn woods and scrubland into deserts. The introduction of myxomatosis, which is spread from infected rabbits to healthy ones mainly by the bites of blood-sucking insects such as mosquitoes, quickly reduced the Australian rabbit population.

Viruses can also perform valuable service in the fight against insects. The *Smithiavirus pityocampae* infects processionary caterpillars, causing disease in the larvae, and it has been successfully used on a large scale. The best-known example of its use was in a vast pine forest in the south of France, where the trees were being devastated by myriads of processionary caterpillars and the very survival of the forest seemed in jeopardy. A large number of processionary caterpillars were therefore bred in the laboratory and infected with the virus. An imposing mass of infected caterpillars was then desiccated—viruses being known to withstand such treatment—and ground to powder. This was diluted in water and sprayed over the forest with the help of specially equipped helicopters. The disease became widespread, and the processionary population was cut down to an acceptable level.

A biologically soluble problem

So far, biological control has been discussed in terms of campaigns against harmful creatures, involving the more or less massive slaughter of members of the offending population. But this particular approach is only one of the many facets of the biological struggle, albeit the most conspicuous and the most widely known. An example can be cited from Australia where scientists are trying out various solutions to a particular problem.

Before the arrival of European colonists, Australia was populated by a unique type of fauna, among which the larger herbivorous mammals were not represented at all. When the colonists introduced sheep, and more particularly cattle, into the continent, they disturbed the delicate ecological balance of the countryside, especially in the broad tracts of land that were suitable for pasture. Because of the peculiar nature of the Australian herbivore population, the local dung-beetles did not include the large and numerous species that function as 'scavengers', particularly in Africa, where they quickly clean mammalian excrement off the soil and bury it.

This meant that large amounts of cow-dung remained on the surface of the soil in the pasturelands, which led to undesirable consequences. For one thing, many species of flies multiplied unchecked. Their maggots were capable of developing successfully in excrement so long as it remained in the open air; they could not have done so if it had been buried. Furthermore, as the cow-pats dried out on the grassland, they altered the plant population, discouraging the growth of ordinary grass, which the cattle ate, and favouring the growth of other grasses that cattle would not eat. Last but not least, all the waste products that would have served as a valuable fertilizer for the pasture-grass if they had only been buried, were instead exposed to the elements, and above all to the hot, dry air of the region. Precious substances were thus broken down and lost into the atmosphere.

In view of all this, a group of Australian research scientists has spent years studying the possibility of introducing species of dung-beetles that could improve the situation without causing undesirable side-effects. Some species have already been successfully introduced and others are still being carefully studied in their natural habitats before being transferred to Australia. It is obviously of paramount importance to make a thorough study of these beetle species in order to be sure that the remedy is not worse than the disease. This is why the research is being carried out mainly in southern Africa which is the region that most resembles Australia, both in its natural features and climate.

The attractions of an integrated approach

For all its experimental and practical successes, biological methods on their own clearly cannot solve every problem, and chemical methods on their own do more harm than good in the long run. Of the two, biological methods are generally free from the gravest dangers, but they have the disadvantage that they often tend to be very complicated and take a long time.

In the past few years, scientists have increasingly been coming round to the idea of what is called 'integrated control'—the combination of various control methods, for example, biological and chemical, in order to achieve the best possible results without incurring the drawbacks of either method when used on its own. Thus, for example, Soviet scientists have shown that the use of *Bacillus thuringensis* to combat caterpillars of a diminutive lepidopterous genus, Yponomeuta, which attacks fruit trees, is much more effective if it is combined with very small doses of DDT. This insecticide, which is powerless on its own against Yponomeuta, even in huge doses, and which is being used less and less because of its well-attested dangers, can be used in minute quantities to render the caterpillars far more sensitive to the pathological effects of *B. thuringensis*. It therefore takes considerably less time to rid an orchard of infestation by these caterpillars. This example, together with many others, clearly demonstrates that the future of pest control almost certainly lies in an integrated approach in which the use of chemical methods is so restricted that no danger is posed by pollution.

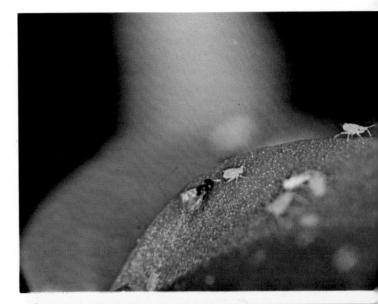

Top: The small wasp *Aphelinus asychis* chooses a suitable aphid to receive its egg, which will be laid within the victim's body
Above: Close-up of the wasp introducing an egg into a living aphid through its long ovipositor

Bibliography

Andrewes, C., *The Lives of Wasps and Bees,* Chatto & Windus, London 1969.
Burr, M., *The Insect Legion,* Nisbet, London 2nd edn. 1954.
Butler, C. G., *The World of the Honeybee,* Collins, London 1954.
Chauvin, R., *The World of an Insect,* Weidenfeld & Nicolson, London 1967.
Chinery, M., *A Field Guide to the Insects of Britain and Northern Europe,* Collins, London 1973.
Clausen, L. W., *Insect Fact and Folklore,* Macmillan, New York 1954.
Farb, P., *The Insects,* Time-Life, Amsterdam, 1964.
Harris, W. V., *Termites: Their Recognition and Control,* Longman, London 1961.
Higgins, L. G. and Riley, N. D., *A Field Guide to the Butterflies of Britain and Europe,* Collins, London 1970.
Howse, P. E., *Termites,* Hutchinson, London 1970.
Imms, A. D., *Insect Natural History,* Collins, London 3rd edn. 1971.
Klots, A. B. and Klots, E. B., *Living Insects of the World,* Hamish Hamilton, London 1959.
Oldroyd, H., *The Natural History of Flies,* Weidenfeld & Nicolson, London 1964.
Oldroyd, H., *Collecting, Preserving and Studying Insects,* Hutchinson, London 2nd edn. 1970.
Oldroyd, H., *Insects and their World,* British Museum (Natural History), London 3rd edn. 1973.
Watson, A. and Whalley, P. E. S., *Dictionary of Butterflies and Moths,* McGraw-Hill, New York 1975.
Wigglesworth, V. B., *The Life of Insects,* Weidenfeld & Nicolson, London 1966.

Glossary

Abdomen   The hindmost of the three major divisions of the body, made at the most of 11 segments and without either legs or wings

Antennae   Segmented appendages on the head, carrying sense organs and acting as feelers

Brachypterism   The occurrence of shortened wings

Cerci   Paired, usually short, sensory appendages at the hind end of the abdomen

Chitin   The basis of insect cuticle; it is tough, flexible and fibrous

Cornea   The transparent thickening of the cuticle over a single facet of the compound eye

Corneola   A term sometimes applied to the cornea

Coxa   The first segment of the leg, attached to the thorax

Crop   A dilation of the end of the oesophagus

Cuticle   The outer, non-cellular layer of the body, overlying the epidermis

Ecdysis   *see* Moult

Elytra   Modified front wings of beetles which form protective sheaths for the membraneous hind wings which are used in flying

Epidermis   Single layer of cells which makes the cuticle. It is sometimes called the hypodermis

Exuvia   *see* Moult

Femur   The long, strong 'thigh' segment of the legs

Ganglion   A mass of nerve cells that give out and receive nerves

Gaster   Part of the abdomen behind the 'waist' of bees, wasps, ants and other Hymenoptera

Haemolymph   Insect blood. It is not contained in veins and arteries but freely bathes the internal organs

Halteres   Modified hind wings of true flies (Diptera) which are converted into small stalked knobs and stabilize flight

Hormones   Internally secreted chemical messengers that convey information from one part of the body to another

Hypodermis   *see* Epidermis

Imago   An adult insect

Instar   *see* Moult

Integument   The main body-wall consisting largely of the cuticle and the epidermis

Labium   The lower lip, composed of the pair of second maxillae joined together

Labrum   The upper lip, a simple flap hinged above the mouth

Larva   The active feeding and growing stages of one of the higher insects. It precedes the pupal or resting stage

Ligula   The tip of the labium; it carries sensory lobes

Mandibles   The strong, chewing pair of mouth parts

Maxillae   The accessory jaws lying behind the mandibles. The first pair are separate but the second pair are joined together to form the labium

Mesenteron   The mid-intestine, sometimes called the stomach or mid-gut, where most digestion takes place. It is not lined by cuticle

Mesothorax   *see* Thorax

Metamorphosis   The changes through which an insect passes from the young form to the adult

Metathorax   *see* Thorax

Moult   The shedding of the skin during growth. The cast skin is called the exuvia; the intervals between moults are called stages or stadia; the form assumed during a particular stage is known as an instar

Mycoses   Diseases caused by parasitic fungi

Nymph   The active feeding and growing young stage of one of the less highly evolved insects. Insects with nymphs do not have a resting or pupal stage

Ocelli   Simple eyes as distinct from the compound eyes which are made up of numerous elements. Ocelli are the only eyes present in larvae and are found on many adult insects

Oesophagus   The simple tube leading from the mouth cavity or pharynx to the crop and gizzard

Olfactory organs   The organs for detecting smells or scents

Ommatidium   An individual element of the compound eye complete with lens and light-sensitive cells

Oötheca   A special case for holding eggs that is usually hardened from a secretion produced by the female

Osmeterium   A defensive organ of Swallowtail butterfly caterpillars consisting of a soft forked structure behind the head that can be protruded and produces an unpleasant smell

Oviparous   Reproduction by egg-laying

Ovipositor   The organ at the end of the abdomen of the female through which the eggs are laid

Palpi   Sensory organs or appendages forming part of the maxillae and labium

Parasitism   When one organism lives entirely at the expense of another. Ectoparasites (e.g. fleas) live on the outside of their hosts; endoparasites (e.g. larvae of ichneumon-flies) live inside their host, which is often a caterpillar; cleptoparasites is a term applied especially to those dung-beetles that steal the dung collected by other beetles

Parthenogenesis   Reproduction by females that have not been fertilized by males

Petiole   A stalk

Pheromones   Secretions that convey various types of information to other individuals. They are essentially external secretions, unlike hormones

Prementum   Part of the end of the labium from which appendages known as the ligular arise

Pretarsus   *see* Tarsus
Proboscis   The elongated mouth parts of insects such as mosquitoes or bees
Proctodaeum   The hind part of the intestine that is lined with cuticle
Pronotum   *see* Thorax
Prolegs   False legs on the abdomen of a caterpillar
Prothorax   *see* Thorax
Pupa   The resting stage between larva and adult of the more advanced insects
Retinula   Basal portion of an ommatidium composed of light-sensitive cells
Sclerotized   Cuticle that has been hardened and made dark by impregnation with a horny substance
Sexual dimorphism   Differences in appearance between the two sexes
Spiracles   Holes along the sides of the body through which the tracheae communicate with the air
Stomodaeum   The fore-intestine from mouth to gizzard, lined with cuticle
Stylets   Needle-like mandibles and maxillae of insects that have piercing and sucking mouth parts
Symbiosis   The living together of different organisms for mutual benefit
Tarsus   The last part of an insect leg composed of individual

segments or tarsomeres and ending in a pair of claws. The structures at the tip are called the pretarsus and include the claws and various lobes that enable the insect to climb smooth or steep surfaces
Tarsomeres   *see* Tarsus
Thorax   Group of three segments behind the head and in front of the abdomen and known, respectively, as the prothorax, mesothorax and metathorax. Each segment has one pair of legs; in addition the mesothorax and metathorax each carry one pair of wings. The large shield-like top side of the prothorax is known as the pronotum. The thorax is largely filled with the powerful flight muscles
Tibia   The long, thinner part of the leg between the femur and the tarsus
Tracheae   The tubes that carry air from the spiracles to the tissues
Trochanter   The small segment of the leg following the coxa and usually fixed rigidly to the femur
Trophallaxis   Mutual exchange of food between adults and larvae of social insects, especially ants. In return for food, the larvae produce a secretion that the adults enjoy
Venation   The pattern on the wing of the veins or nervures which are fine tubes providing a supporting framework and contain tracheae and blood
Viviparous   Giving birth to young without first laying eggs

Index   *Page numbers in italics refer to illustrations.*